GCSE Chemistry

Eileen Ramsden

with Tony Buzan

Hodder & Stoughton

A MEMBER OF THE HODDER HEADLINE GROUP

Key to symbols

As you read through this book you will notice the following symbols. They will help you find your way around the book more quickly.

shows a handy hint to help you remember something

shows you a short list of key facts

means remember!!!

gives worked examples to help you with calculations and equations

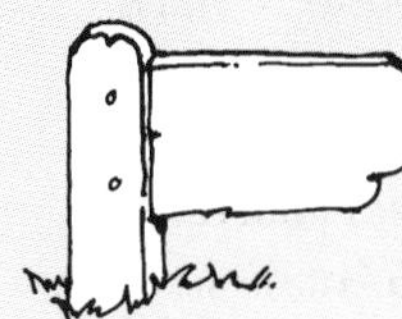
points you to other parts of the book where related topics are explained

ISBN 0 340 66392 8

First published 1997
Impression number 10 9 8 7 6 5 4 3 2 1
Year 2001 2000 1999 1998 1997

Designed and produced by Gecko Ltd, Bicester, Oxon
Printed in Great Britain for Hodder & Stoughton Educational, a division of Hodder Headline Plc, 338 Euston Road, London NW1 3BH by Scotprint Ltd, Musselburgh, Scotland.

Mind Maps: Patrick Mayfield, Gareth Morris, Graham Wheeler
Illustrations: Peter Bull, Simon Cooke, Chris Etheridge, Ian Law, Joe Little, Andrea Norton, Mike Parsons, John Plumb, Dave Poole, Chris Rothero, Anthony Warne
Cover design: Amanda Hawkes
Cover illustration: Paul Bateman

GCSE *Chemistry* and this Revision Guide

This Revision Guide is not intended to replace your textbooks. As tests and examinations approach, however, many students feel the need to revise from something a good deal shorter than their usual textbook. This Revision Guide is intended to fill that need.

Each revision topic begins with a set of Test Yourself questions to give an idea of how well you have already grasped that topic. You could work through the questions again after you have revised the topic. The improvement should be encouraging! There is a set of Round-up questions at the end of each topic. Work out your Improvement Index from your score on the Round-up questions compared with your first score on the Test Yourself questions.

Organising your time

Make a timetable for homework and revision, and keep to it. You have a lot of subjects to cope with. Leave space in your timetable for your leisure activities. Planned use of time and concentrated study will give you time for your other activities and interests as well as work.

When the exam arrives

The night before the exam make sure that you have everything you will need: your pen and spare cartridge, pencils, rubber, calculator, etc. Decide what you are going to wear and get everything ready. You want to avoid any last minute dithering.

Be optimistic. You have done your revision and can have confidence that it will stand you in good stead. Do not sit up late at night trying to cram. A last-minute glance through the Mind Maps you have made yourself is as much as your brain can take in at the last minute.

In the examination room, read the instructions on the front of the paper before you set pen to paper. Do not spend more time than you should on any one question. If you can't answer a question, move on to the next question and return to the unanswered question later. Attempt all the questions you are supposed to answer. Make sure you turn over every page! Many marks have been lost in exams as a result of turning over two pages at once. If you suffer a panic attack, breathe deeply and slowly to get lots of oxygen into your system and clear your thoughts. Above all, keep your examination in perspective; it is important but not a matter of life or death!

A note on content

Part of the content of GCSE Science: Chemistry is specified by the National Curriculum. This part of the content is required by all the Examining Groups. The rest of the content is chosen by the Examining Groups and there are differences between their syllabuses. The topics which are required by some but not all of the Examining Groups are listed below, along with those Examining Groups that require them.

Topic	Examining Groups	Location in Revision Guide
Activation energy	MEG(S), SEG	Topic 15.6
Bond energies	MEG, MEG(N)	Topic 15.7
Bromine, from sea water	MEG	Topic 7.3
Chemical cells	MEG(N), MEG(S)	Topic 12.10
Colloids	MEG(N)	Topic 10.11
Dyes	MEG(N)	Topic 21
Enzymes, mode of action	L, MEG, MEG(S), SEG	Topic 13.8
Food	MEG(N), MEG(S)	Topic 20
Materials compared	NI	Topic 16.4
Tests for gases	W, NI	Topic 19.3
Tests for ions	L, MEG, W, NI	Topic 19.2
Titanium, extraction of	L	Topic 12.5

L = University of London Examinations and Assessment Council
MEG = Midland Examining Group
MEG(N) = Midland Examining Group (Nuffield)
MEG(S) = Midland Examining Group (Salters)
NEAB = Northern Examinations and Assessment Board
NI = Northern Ireland Council for the Curriculum, Examinations and Assessment
SEG = Southern Examining Group
W = Welsh Joint Education Committee

I wish you success.

Eileen Ramsden

Contents

Revision made easy

The four pages that follow contain a gold mine of information on how you can achieve success both at school and in your exams. Read them and apply the information, and you will be able to spend less, but more efficient, time studying, with better results. If you already have another *Hodder & Stoughton Revision Guide*, skim-read these pages to remind yourself about the exciting new techniques the books use, then move ahead to page 10.

This section gives you vital information on how to remember more *while* you are learning and how to remember more *after* you have finished studying. It explains

- **how to use special techniques to improve your memory**
- **how to use a revolutionary note-taking technique called Mind Maps that will double your memory and help you to write essays and answer exam questions**
- **how to read everything faster while at the same time improving your comprehension and concentration**

All this information is packed into the next four pages, so make sure you read them!

Your *amazing* memory

There are five important things you must know about your brain and memory to revolutionise your school life.

1. **how your memory ('recall') works *while* you are learning**
2. **how your memory works *after* you have finished learning**
3. **how to use Mind Maps – a special technique for helping you with all aspects of your studies**
4. **how to increase your reading speed**
5. **how to zap your revision**

1 Recall during learning – the need for breaks

When you are studying, your memory can concentrate, understand and remember well for between 20 and 45 minutes at a time. Then it *needs* a break. If you carry on for longer than this without one, your memory starts to break down! If you study for hours non-stop, you will remember only a fraction of what you have been trying to learn, and you will have wasted valuable revision time.

So, ideally, *study for less than an hour*, then take a five- to ten-minute break. During the break listen to music, go for a walk, do some exercise, or just daydream. (Daydreaming is a necessary brain-power booster – geniuses do it regularly.) During the break your brain will be sorting out what it has been learning, and you will go back to your books with the new information safely stored and organised in your memory banks. We recommend breaks at regular intervals as you work through the *Revision Guides*. Make sure you take them!

2 Recall after learning – the waves of your memory

What do you think begins to happen to your memory straight *after* you have finished learning something? Does it immediately start forgetting? No! Your brain actually *increases* its power and carries on remembering. For a short time after your study session, your brain integrates the information, making a more complete picture of everything it has just learnt. Only then does the rapid decline in memory begin, and as much as 80 per cent of what you have learnt can be forgotten in a day.

However, if you catch the top of the wave of your memory, and briefly review (look back over) what you have been revising at the correct time, the memory is stamped in far more strongly, and stays at the crest of the wave for a much longer time. To maximise your brain's power to remember, take a few minutes and use a Mind Map to review what you have learnt at the end of a day. Then review it at the end of a week, again at the end of a month, and finally a week before the exams. That way you'll ride your memory wave all the way to your exam – and beyond!

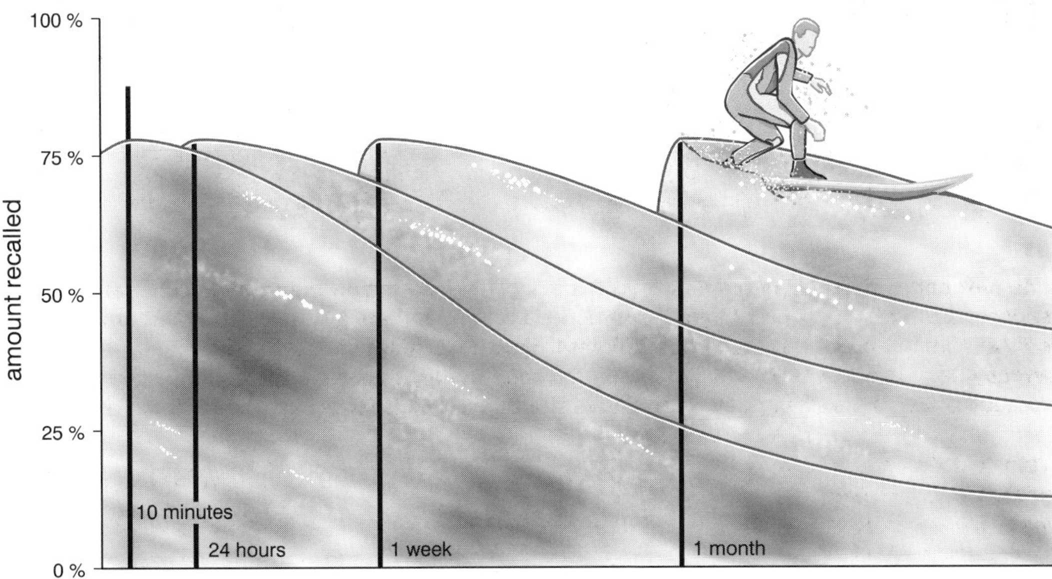

Amazing as your memory is (think of everything you actually do have stored in your brain at this moment) the principles on which it operates are very simple: your brain will remember if it (a) has an image (a picture or a symbol); (b) has that image fixed and (c) can link that image to something else.

3 The Mind Map® – a picture of the way you think

Do you *like* taking notes? More importantly, do you like having to go back over and learn them before exams? Most students I know certainly do not! And how do you take your notes? Most people take notes on lined paper, using blue or black ink. The result, visually, is *boring*! And what does your brain do when it is bored? It turns off, tunes out, and goes to sleep! Add a dash of colour, rhythm, imagination, and the whole note-taking process becomes much more fun, uses more of your brain's abilities, *and* improves your recall and understanding.

A Mind Map mirrors the way your brain works. It can be used for note-taking from books or in class, for reviewing what you have just studied, for revising, and for essay planning for coursework and in exams. It uses all your memory's natural techniques to build up your rapidly growing 'memory muscle'.

You will find Mind Maps throughout this book. Study them, add some colour, personalise them, and then have a go at drawing your own – you'll remember them far better! Put them on your walls and in your files for a quick-and-easy review of the topic.

How to draw a Mind Map

1. Start in the middle of the page with the page turned sideways. This gives your brain the maximum room for its thoughts.
2. Always start by drawing a small picture or symbol. Why? Because a picture is worth a thousand words to your brain. And try to use at least three colours, as colour helps your memory even more.
3. Let your thoughts flow, and write or draw your ideas on coloured branching lines connected to your central image. These key symbols and words are the headings for your topic. The Mind Map at the top of the next page shows you how to start.
4. Then add facts and ideas by drawing more, smaller, branches on to the appropriate main branches, just like a tree.
5. Always print your word clearly on its line. Use only one word per line. The Mind Map at the foot of the next page shows you how to do this.
6. To link ideas and thoughts on different branches, use arrows, colours, underlining, and boxes.

How to read a Mind Map

1. Begin in the centre, the focus of your topic.
2. The words/images attached to the centre are like chapter headings, read them next.
3. Always read out from the centre, in every direction (even on the left-hand side, where you will have to read from right to left, instead of the usual left to right).

Using Mind Maps

Mind Maps are a versatile tool – use them for taking notes in class or from books, for solving problems, for brainstorming with friends, and for reviewing and revising for exams – their uses are endless! You will find them invaluable for planning essays for coursework and exams. Number your main branches in the order in which you want to use them and off you go – the main headings for your essay are done and all your ideas are logically organised!

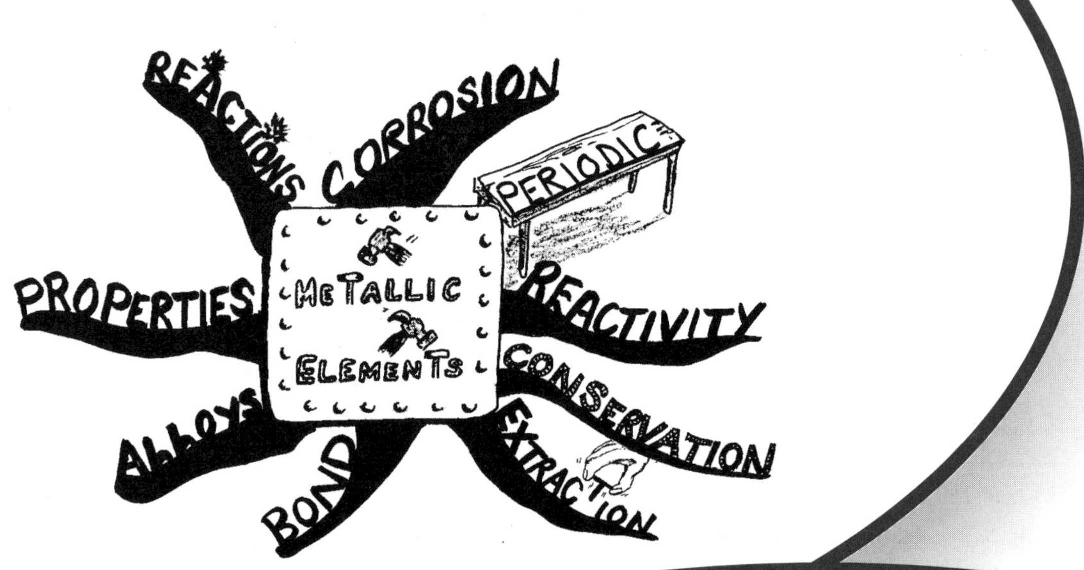
REACTIONS
CORROSION
PERIODIC
PROPERTIES
METALLIC ELEMENTS
REACTIVITY
CONSERVATION
ALLOYS
BOND
EXTRACTION

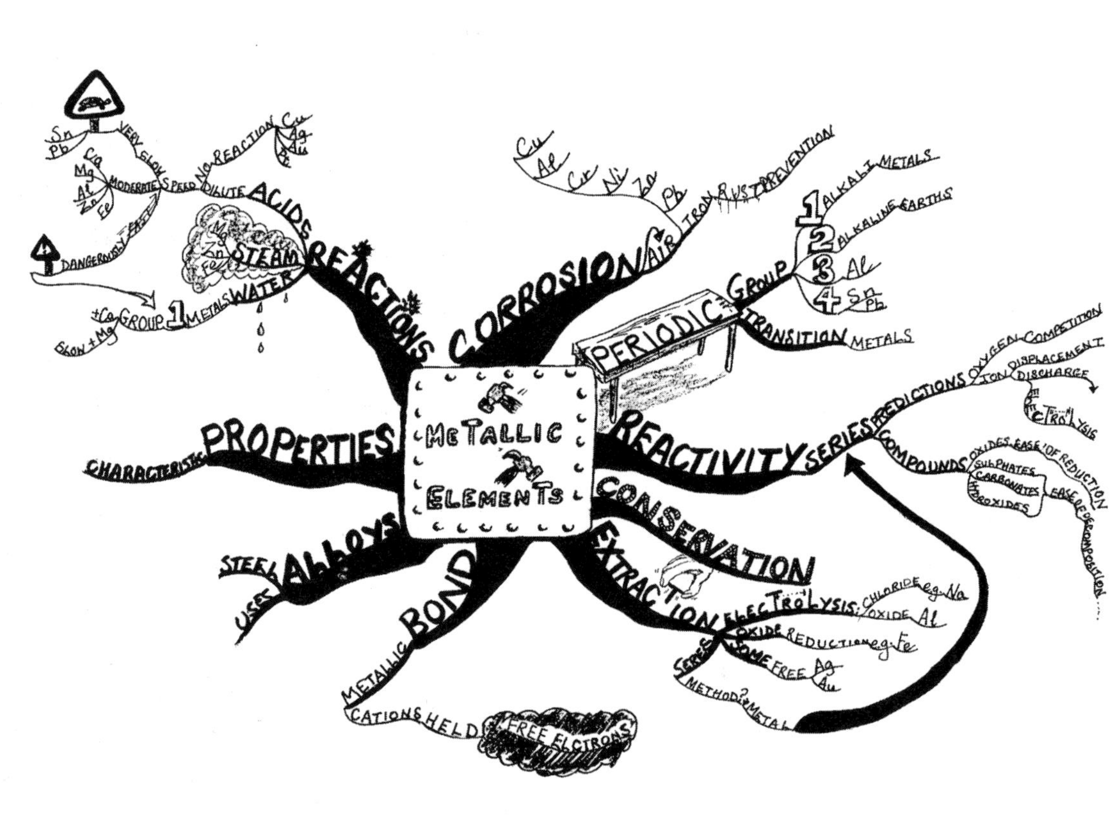
VERY SLOW
NO REACTION
MODERATE SPEED
DILUTE ACIDS
DANGEROUSLY FAST
STEAM
WATER
GROUP 1 METALS
REACTIONS
Cu Al Cr Ni Zn Pb
RUST PREVENTION
IRON
AIR
CORROSION
GROUP
1 ALKALI METALS
2 ALKALINE EARTHS
3 Al
4 Sn Pb
PERIODIC
TRANSITION METALS
PREDICTIONS
OXYGEN COMPETITION
ION DISPLACEMENT
DISCHARGE
ELECTROLYSIS
REACTIVITY SERIES
COMPOUNDS
OXIDES
SULPHATES
CARBONATES
HYDROXIDES
EASE OF REDUCTION
EASE OF DECOMPOSITION
CHARACTERISTIC
PROPERTIES
METALLIC ELEMENTS
CONSERVATION
STEEL
USES
ALLOYS
EXTRACTION
ELECTROLYSIS
CHLORIDE eg. Na
OXIDE Al
OXIDE REDUCTION eg. Fe
SOME FREE Ag Au
SERIES
METHOD ? METAL
BOND
METALLIC
CATIONS HELD
FREE ELECTRONS

4 Super speed reading

It seems incredible, but it's been proved – the faster you read, the more you understand and remember! So here are some tips to help you to practise reading faster – you'll cover the ground more quickly, remember more, *and* have more time for revision!

- **First read the whole text (whether it's a lengthy book or an exam paper) very quickly, to give your brain an overall idea of what's ahead and get it working. (It's like sending out a scout to look at the territory you have to cover – it's much easier when you know what to expect!) Then read the text again for more detailed information.**
- **Have the text a reasonable distance away from your eyes. In this way your eye/brain system will be able to see more at a glance, and will naturally begin to read faster.**
- **Take in groups of words at a time. Rather than reading 'slowly and carefully' read faster, more enthusiastically. Your comprehension will rocket!**
- **Take in phrases rather than single words while you read.**
- **Use a guide. Your eyes are designed to follow movement, so a thin pencil underneath the lines you are reading, moved smoothly along, will 'pull' your eyes to faster speeds.**

5 Helpful hints for exam revision

Start to revise at the beginning of the course. Cram at the start, not the end and avoid 'exam panic'!

Use Mind Maps throughout your course, and build a Master Mind Map for each subject – a giant Mind Map that summarises everything you know about the subject.

Use memory techniques such as mnemonics (verses or systems for remembering things like dates and events, or lists).

Get together with one or two friends to revise, compare Mind Maps, and discuss topics.

And finally...

- *Have fun while you learn* – studies show that those people who enjoy what they are doing understand and remember it more, and generally do it better.
- *Use your teachers* as resource centres. Ask them for help with specific topics and with more general advice on how you can improve your all-round performance.
- *Personalise your* ***Revision Guide*** by underlining and highlighting, by adding notes and pictures. Allow your brain to have a conversation with it!

Your brain is an amazing piece of equipment – learn to use it, and you, like thousands of students before you will be able to master 'B's and 'A's with ease. The more you understand and use your brain, the more it will repay you!

Matter and the kinetic theory

1

preview

At the end of this topic you will be able to:

- **describe the states of matter and changes of state**
- **apply the kinetic theory of matter to solids, liquids, gases, changes of state, dissolving, diffusion and Brownian motion.**

How much do you already know? Work out your score on page 127.

Test yourself

1 Name the three chief states of matter. [3]

2 What can you tell about the purity of a solid from its melting point? [2]

3 What is the difference between evaporation and boiling? [2]

4 How can you tell when a liquid is boiling? [1]

5 Why do vegetables cook faster in a pressure cooker? [2]

6 Why does it take a long time to boil potatoes on a high mountain? [2]

7 What is **a)** the resemblance **b)** the difference between a plastic material and an elastic material? [3]

8 Why are crystals shiny? [3]

9 What happens to the heat energy that is supplied to a solid to make it melt? [2]

10 One litre of water forms 1333 litres of steam. Explain the big difference in volume. [2]

11 Explain why a spoonful of salt can flavour a whole pan of soup. [3]

1.1 States of matter

Everything in the Universe is composed of matter. Matter exists in three chief states: the solid, liquid and gaseous states. Their characteristics are shown in the table.

	volume	shape	effect of rise in temperature
solid	fixed	definite	expands slightly
liquid	fixed	flows – changes shape to fit the shape of the container	expands
gas	changes to fit the container	changes to fit the container	expands greatly (gases have much lower densities than solids and liquids)

Characteristics of the solid, liquid and gaseous states

1.2 Change of state

Matter can change from one state into another, as shown in the diagram.

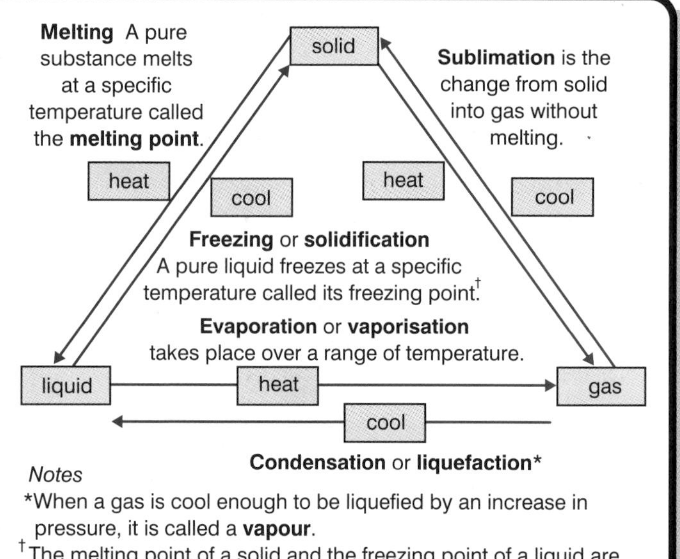
Melting A pure substance melts at a specific temperature called the **melting point**.
solid
Sublimation is the change from solid into gas without melting.
heat
cool
heat
cool
Freezing or **solidification**
A pure liquid freezes at a specific temperature called its freezing point.†
Evaporation or **vaporisation**
takes place over a range of temperature.
liquid
heat
gas
cool
Condensation or **liquefaction***
Notes
*When a gas is cool enough to be liquefied by an increase in pressure, it is called a **vapour**.
†The melting point of a solid and the freezing point of a liquid are the same temperature.

1.3 Some properties of materials

★ **Density:** density $= \dfrac{\text{mass}}{\text{volume}}$.

★ **Melting point:** while a pure solid melts, the temperature remains constant at the melting point of the solid.

★ **Boiling point:** while a pure liquid boils, the temperature remains constant at the boiling point of the liquid.

★ **Conductivity** (thermal and electrical): the ability to conduct heat and electricity is a characteristic of metals and alloys.

★ **Solubility:** a solution consists of a **solute** dissolved in a **solvent**. A concentrated solution contains a high proportion of solute; a dilute solution contains a low proportion of solute. A saturated solution contains as much solute as it is possible to dissolve at the stated temperature.

Solubility is the mass of solute that will dissolve in 100 g of solvent at the stated temperature.

Two ways of expressing concentration are:

$$\text{concentration} = \frac{\text{mass of solute}}{\text{volume of solution}}$$

$$\text{concentration} = \frac{\text{amount (moles) of solute}}{\text{volume of solution}}$$

(see page 88)

1.4 Composite materials

A **composite material** is a mixture of two or more materials which combines their properties. Here are some examples.

- Reinforced concrete combines the compressive (crushing) strength of concrete with the tensile (stretching) strength of the reinforcing steel rods.
- Glass-fibre-reinforced plastic combines plasticity with the strength of fibres, which prevent cracking.
- Plasterboard combines plaster, a brittle material, with paper fibres that prevent cracking.

1.5 The kinetic theory

According to the **kinetic theory of matter**, all forms of matter are made up of small particles which are in constant motion. The theory explains the states of matter and changes of state.

In a solid, the particles are close together and attract one another strongly. They are arranged in a regular three-dimensional structure. The particles can vibrate, but they cannot move out of their positions in the structure.

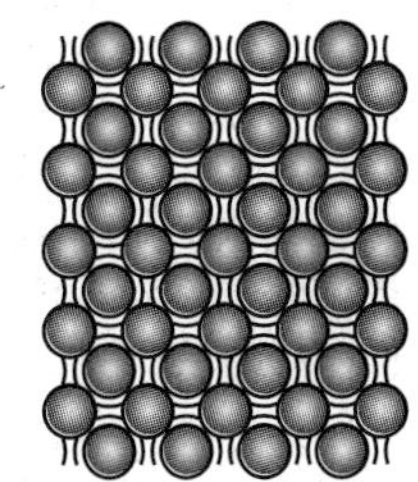
The arrangement of particles in a solid

When the solid is heated, the particles vibrate more energetically. If they gain enough energy, they may break away from the structure and become free to move independently. When this happens, the solid has melted.

In a liquid, the particles are further apart than in a solid. They are free to move about. This is why a liquid flows easily and has no fixed shape. There are forces of attraction between particles. When a liquid is heated, some particles gain enough energy to break away from the other particles and become a gas.

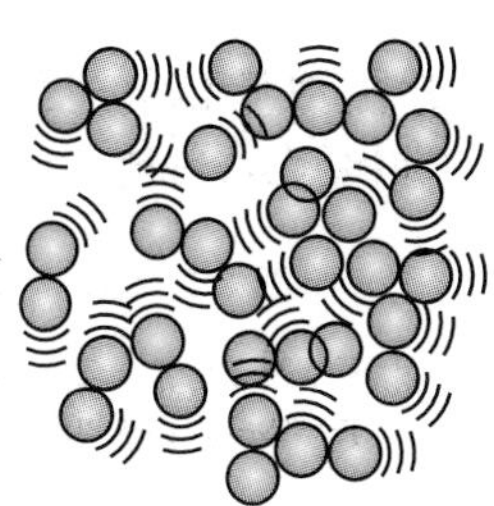
The arrangement of particles in a liquid

Most of a gas is space, through which the particles move at high speed. There are only very small forces of attraction between the particles. When a mass of liquid vaporises, it forms a very much larger volume of gas because the particles are so much further apart in a gas.

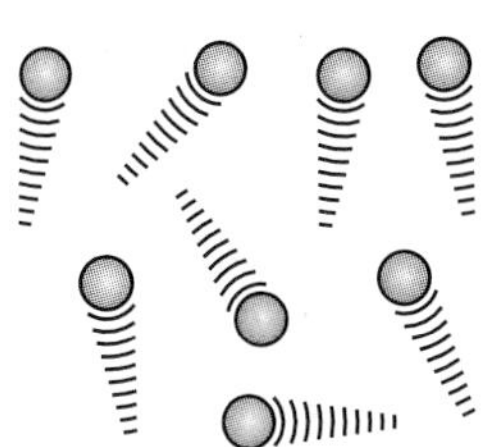
The arrangement of particles in a gas

Collisions between the gas particles and the container create pressure on the container.

Crystals

A crystal is a piece of matter with a regular shape and smooth surfaces which reflect light. Viewed through an electron microscope, crystals can be seen to consist of a regular arrangement of particles. The regular arrangement of particles gives the crystal its regular shape.

A beam of X-rays passed through a crystal onto a photographic plate produces a regular pattern of dots called an **X-ray diffraction photograph**. From the pattern of dots, a crystallographer can work out the arrangement of particles in the crystal.

1.6 What does the kinetic theory explain?

Dissolving of a solid

When a solid dissolves, particles of solid separate from the crystal and spread out through the solvent to form a solution.

Diffusion of a gas

When a gas is released into a container, particles of gas move through the container until the gas has spread evenly through all the space available.

Evaporation or vaporisation

Attractive forces exist between the particles in a liquid. Some particles with more energy than the average break away from the attraction of other particles and escape into the vapour phase. The average energy of the particles that remain is lower than before – the liquid has cooled.

Brownian motion

The botanist William Brown used his microscope a century ago to observe grains of pollen suspended in water. He saw that the grains were in constant motion. The explanation is that water molecules collide with a pollen grain and give it a push. The direction of the push changes as different numbers of molecules strike the pollen grain from different sides.

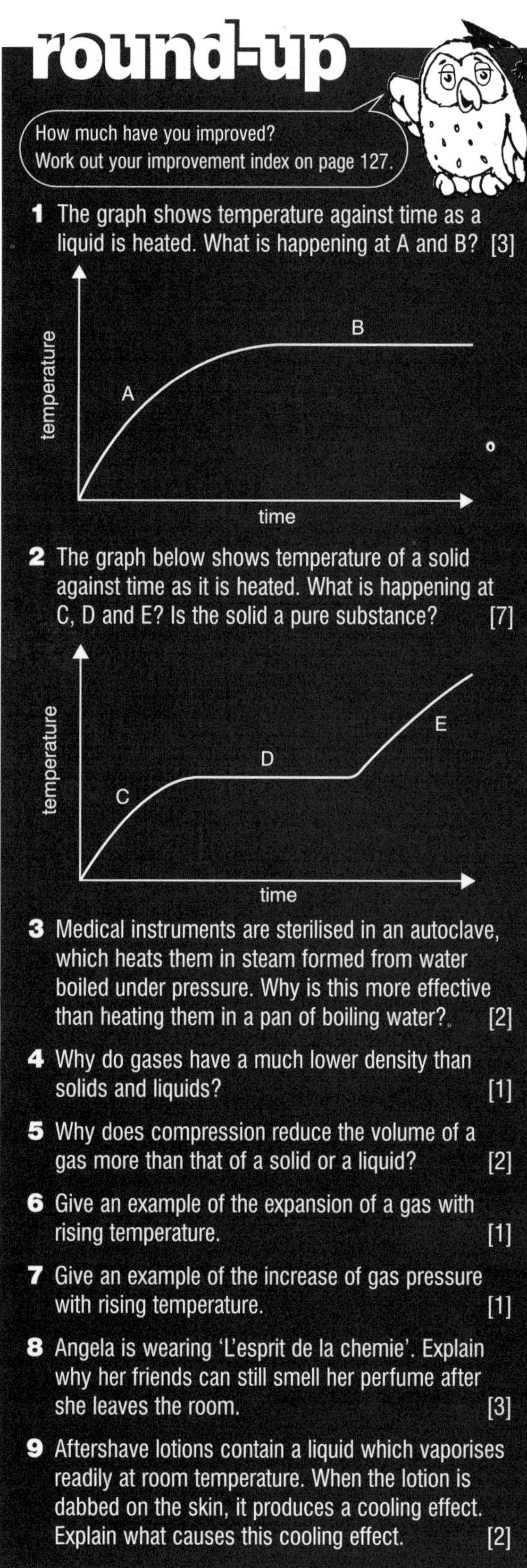

round-up
How much have you improved?
Work out your improvement index on page 127.
1 The graph shows temperature against time as a liquid is heated. What is happening at A and B? [3]
temperature
time
A
B
2 The graph below shows temperature of a solid against time as it is heated. What is happening at C, D and E? Is the solid a pure substance? [7]
temperature
time
C
D
E
3 Medical instruments are sterilised in an autoclave, which heats them in steam formed from water boiled under pressure. Why is this more effective than heating them in a pan of boiling water? [2]
4 Why do gases have a much lower density than solids and liquids? [1]
5 Why does compression reduce the volume of a gas more than that of a solid or a liquid? [2]
6 Give an example of the expansion of a gas with rising temperature. [1]
7 Give an example of the increase of gas pressure with rising temperature. [1]
8 Angela is wearing 'L'esprit de la chemie'. Explain why her friends can still smell her perfume after she leaves the room. [3]
9 Aftershave lotions contain a liquid which vaporises readily at room temperature. When the lotion is dabbed on the skin, it produces a cooling effect. Explain what causes this cooling effect. [2]

Elements, compounds and equations

preview

At the end of this topic you will be able to:

- **list the differences between metallic and non-metallic elements**
- **describe the structures of some elements**
- **distinguish between an element, a compound and a mixture**
- **write an equation for a chemical reaction.**

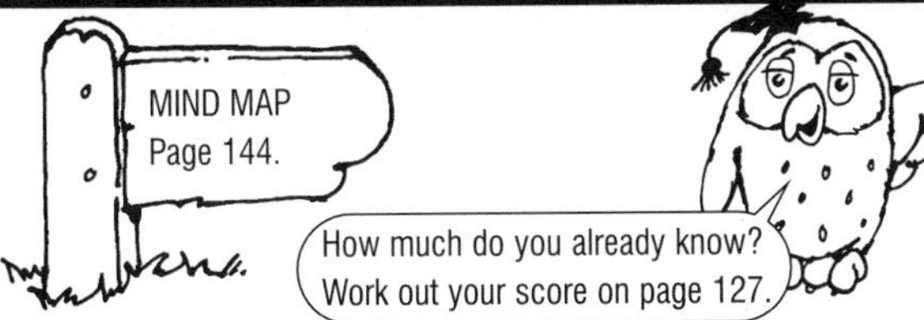

MIND MAP
Page 144.
How much do you already know?
Work out your score on page 127.

Test yourself

1 Explain what is meant by an element. [3]

2 What chemical properties of zinc classify it as a metallic element? [7]

3 Explain why diamond is hard while graphite is soft. [4]

4 Name two methods that can be used to split a compound into elements. [2]

5 How many atoms are there in $2Al(OH)_3$? [1]

6 Balance the equation and insert state symbols. [8]

$$Na + H_2O \rightarrow NaOH + H_2$$

2.1 Metallic and non-metallic elements

Elements are pure substances that cannot be split up into simpler substances. Some elements exist as **allotropes** – forms of the same element which have different crystalline structures. Allotropes of carbon are shown on page 15. Elements are classified as metallic and non-metallic, as shown in the table overleaf.

2.2 Structures of elements

Individual molecules

Some elements consist of small individual molecules with negligible forces of attraction between them, e.g. oxygen O_2 and chlorine Cl_2.

Molecular structures

Some elements consist of molecules held in a crystal structure by weak intermolecular forces. Solid iodine is a structure composed of I_2 molecules; iodine vapour consists of individual I_2 molecules.

Giant molecules

Some elements consist of giant molecules or macromolecules, which are composed of millions of atoms bonded together in a three-dimensional structure, e.g. the allotropes of carbon – diamond, graphite and fullerenes – shown on page 15.

2.3 Compounds

A **compound** is a pure substance that consists of two or more elements which are chemically combined in fixed proportions by mass. Some compounds can be **synthesised** from their elements, e.g. calcium burns in oxygen to form calcium oxide; hot copper combines with chlorine to form copper chloride.

It may be possible to split up a compound into its elements

- by **thermal decomposition**, e.g. silver oxide splits up into silver and oxygen when heated
- by **electrolysis**, e.g. water is electrolysed to hydrogen and oxygen.

metallic elements	non-metallic elements
physical properties	*physical properties*
solids except for mercury	solids and gases, except for bromine (which is a liquid)
dense, hard	Most of the solid elements are softer than metals (diamond is exceptional).
A smooth metallic surface is shiny; many metals tarnish in air.	Most non-metallic elements are dull (diamond is exceptional).
The shape can be changed without breaking by the application of force – either compression, as in hammering, or tension, as in stretching, e.g. drawing out into a wire.	Many non-metallic elements are brittle – they break when a force is applied.
conduct heat (although highly polished surfaces reflect heat)	are poor thermal conductors
are good electrical conductors	are poor electrical conductors, except for graphite; some, e.g. silicon, are semiconductors
are sonorous – make a pleasing sound when struck	are not sonorous
The properties of metals derive from the metallic bond – see pages 179–80.	
chemical properties	*chemical properties*
electropositive – able to donate electrons	electronegative – able to accept electrons
many displace hydrogen from dilute acids to form salts	do not react with acids, except for oxidising acids, e.g. concentrated sulphuric acid
The metal is the cation (positive ion) in the salts, e.g. Na^+, Ca^{2+}; some metals also form oxoanions, e.g. ZnO_2^{2-}, AlO_3^-.	form anions (negative ions), e.g. S^{2-}, and oxoanions, e.g. SO_4^{2-}
form basic oxides and hydroxides, e.g. Na_2O, NaOH, CaO, $Ca(OH)_2$	form acidic oxides, e.g. CO_2, SO_2, or neutral oxides, e.g. CO, NO
The chlorides are ionic solids, e.g. $MgCl_2$, $AlCl_3$.	The chlorides are covalent volatile liquids, e.g. SCl_2, PCl_3.
Hydrides are formed only by the metals in Groups 1 and 2, and these hydrides are unstable, e.g. NaH.	form stable hydrides, e.g. HBr, H_2S

Characteristics of metallic and non-metallic elements

A compound differs from a mixture of elements as shown in the table on the opposite page.

2.4 Symbols

Every element has its own **symbol**. The symbol is a letter or two letters which stand for one atom of the element, e.g. aluminium Al, iron Fe. See the table on page 23.

2.5 Formulas

Every compound has a **formula**. This is composed of the symbols of the elements present along with numbers which give the ratio in which the atoms are present.

A molecule of sulphuric acid (see below) contains 2 hydrogen atoms, 1 sulphur atom and 4 oxygen atoms, giving the formula H_2SO_4.

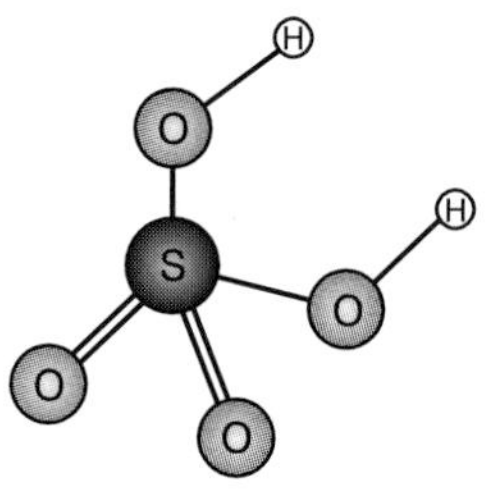

H_2SO_4 – a single molecule

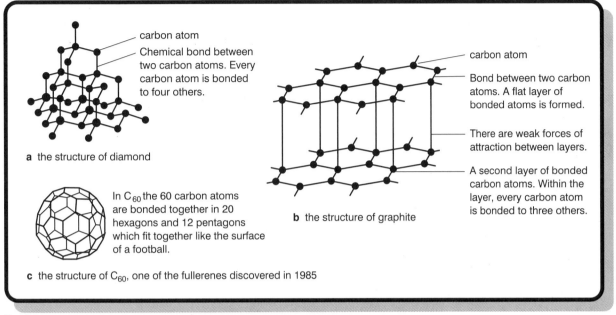

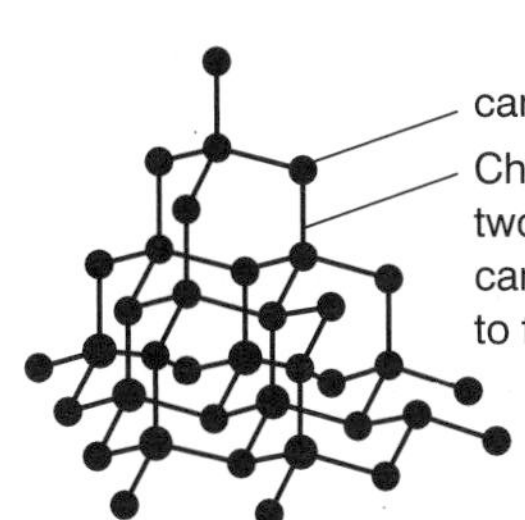
carbon atom
Chemical bond between two carbon atoms. Every carbon atom is bonded to four others.

a the structure of diamond

carbon atom

Bond between two carbon atoms. A flat layer of bonded atoms is formed.

There are weak forces of attraction between layers.

A second layer of bonded carbon atoms. Within the layer, every carbon atom is bonded to three others.

b the structure of graphite

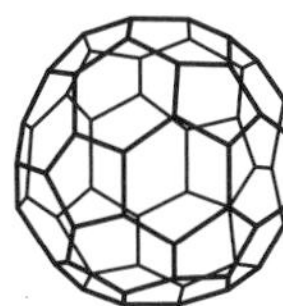
In C_{60} the 60 carbon atoms are bonded together in 20 hexagons and 12 pentagons which fit together like the surface of a football.

c the structure of C_{60}, one of the fullerenes discovered in 1985

The allotropes of carbon

mixtures	**compounds**
No chemical change takes place when a mixture is made.	When a compound is made, a chemical reaction takes place, and heat is often taken in or given out.
A mixture has the same properties as its components.	A compound has a new set of properties; it does not behave in the same way as the components.
A mixture can be separated into its parts by methods such as distillation (see pages 17–19).	A compound can be split into its elements or into simpler compounds only by a chemical reaction.
A mixture can contain its components in any proportions.	A compound contains its elements in fixed proportions by mass, e.g. magnesium oxide always contains 60% by mass of magnesium.

Differences between mixtures and compounds

Silicon(IV) oxide, shown here, consists of macromolecules which contain twice as many oxygen atoms as silicon atoms, giving the formula SiO_2.

The formula of ammonium sulphate is $(NH_4)_2SO_4$. The '2' multiplies the symbols in brackets: there are 2 nitrogen, 8 hydrogen, 1 sulphur and 4 oxygen atoms.

Writing $2Al_2O_3$ means that the numbers below the line each multiply the symbols in front of them, and the 2 on the line multiplies everything that comes after it, giving a total of 4 aluminium and 6 oxygen atoms.

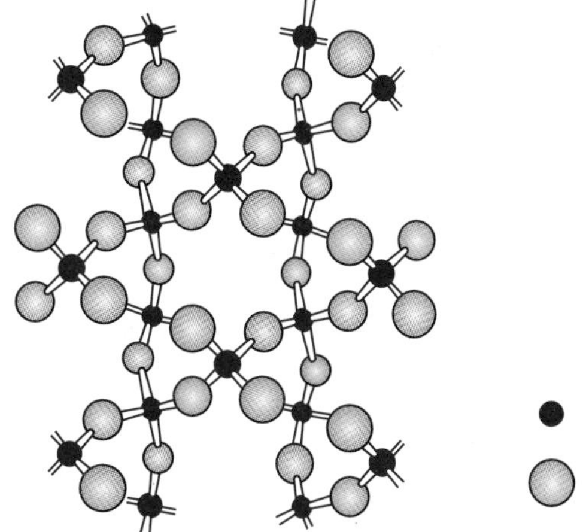
silicon
oxygen

SiO_2 – a macromolecule

2.6 Equations

To write an equation for a chemical reaction:

1 Write a word equation for the reaction.

2 Put in the symbols for the elements and the formulas for the compounds.

3 Put in the **state symbols** (s) for solid, (l) for liquid, (g) for gas, (aq) for in aqueous solution (in water).

4 **Balance** the equation. This means making the number of atoms of each element on the left-hand side (LHS) equal the number on the right-hand side (RHS). Do this by writing a 2, 3 or other numeral in front of a symbol or a formula to multiply that symbol or formula. **Never try to balance an equation by altering a formula**.

Example

1 calcium + water → hydrogen + calcium hydroxide solution

2 $Ca + H_2O \rightarrow H_2 + Ca(OH)_2$

3 $Ca(s) + H_2O(l) \rightarrow H_2(g) + Ca(OH)_2(aq)$

4 There are 2 hydrogen atoms on the LHS and 4 hydrogen atoms on the RHS. There is 1 oxygen atom on the LHS and 2 oxygen atoms on the RHS. Multiply H_2O by 2:

$Ca(s) + 2H_2O(l) \rightarrow H_2(g) + Ca(OH)_2(aq)$

The equation is now balanced.

Ionic equations

In **ionic equations**, only the ions that take part in the reaction are shown. Here are some examples.

★ **Neutralisation**

acid + alkali → salt + water

$H^+(aq) + OH^-(aq) \rightarrow H_2O(l)$

★ **Displacement**

zinc + copper(II) sulphate solution → zinc sulphate solution + copper

$Zn(s) + Cu^{2+}(aq) \rightarrow Zn^{2+}(aq) + Cu(s)$

★ **Precipitation**

barium chloride solution + sodium sulphate solution → barium sulphate precipitate + sodium chloride solution

$Ba^{2+}(aq) + SO_4^{2-}(aq) \rightarrow BaSO_4(s)$

round-up

How much have you improved?
Work out your improvement index on pages 127–8.

1 The element Q forms ions Q^{2+}. Is Q metallic or non-metallic? [1]

2 The element R forms an acidic oxide RO_2. Is R metallic or non-metallic? [1]

3 The element E forms a crystalline chloride ECl_2. Is E metallic or non-metallic? [1]

4 The element G forms a stable hydride HG. Is G metallic or non-metallic? [1]

5 Contrast four physical properties for sulphur and copper (a non-metallic element and a metallic element). [4]

6 How would you distinguish between a mixture of powdered sulphur and iron filings and a compound of iron and sulphur? [4]

7 How many atoms are present in $3(NH_4)_2SO_4$? [1]

8 Balance the equation and insert state symbols: [4]

$CaCO_3 + HCl \rightarrow CaCl_2 + CO_2 + H_2O$

9 Write an ionic equation for the reaction: [3]

iron(II) sulphate + sodium hydroxide → iron(II) hydroxide + sodium sulphate

Well done if you've improved. Don't worry if you haven't. Take a break and try again.

Separating substances

preview

At the end of this topic you will be able to:

- **describe methods for separating the components of mixtures.**

How much do you already know? Work out your score on page 128.

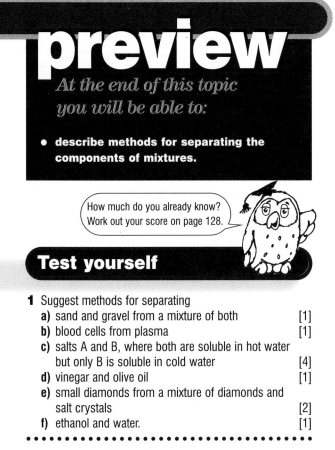

Test yourself

1 Suggest methods for separating
  a) sand and gravel from a mixture of both [1]
  b) blood cells from plasma [1]
  c) salts A and B, where both are soluble in hot water but only B is soluble in cold water [4]
  d) vinegar and olive oil [1]
  e) small diamonds from a mixture of diamonds and salt crystals [2]
  f) ethanol and water. [1]

3.1 Mixtures from the Earth

All the materials we use must come from the Earth's crust and atmosphere. Few of the raw materials we use are found in a pure state in the Earth's crust, and we have to separate the substances we want from a mixture of substances. The table shows some separation methods.

3.2 Soluble solid from insoluble solid

To separate a soluble solid from a mixture with an insoluble solid, add a solvent, e.g. water, and stir to dissolve the soluble solid. Filter as shown in the diagram. The insoluble solid is left on the filter paper. Evaporate the filtrate to obtain the soluble solid.

A faster method of filtration is filtration under reduced pressure.

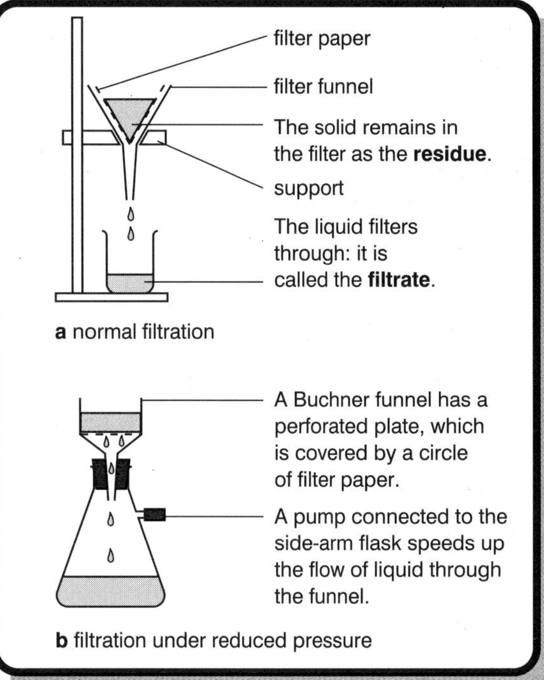

filter funnel
The solid remains in the filter as the **residue**.
support
The liquid filters through: it is called the **filtrate**.
a normal filtration
A Buchner funnel has a perforated plate, which is covered by a circle of filter paper.
A pump connected to the side-arm flask speeds up the flow of liquid through the funnel.
b filtration under reduced pressure

Filtration

mixture	type	method
solid + solid	solid mixture	Utilise a difference in properties, e.g. solubility or magnetic properties.
	in a solution	Use chromatography.
solid + liquid	mixture	Filter or centrifuge.
	solution	Crystallise to obtain the solid; distil to obtain the liquid.
liquid + liquid	miscible (form one layer)	Use fractional distillation.
	immiscible (form two layers)	Use a separating funnel.

Methods of separating pure substances from mixtures

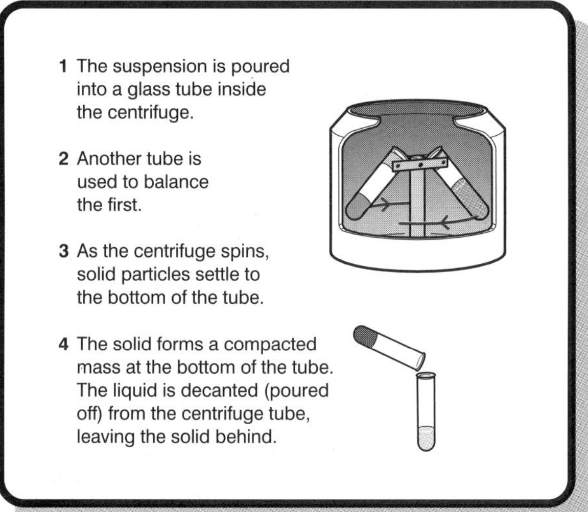

1 The suspension is poured into a glass tube inside the centrifuge.
2 Another tube is used to balance the first.
3 As the centrifuge spins, solid particles settle to the bottom of the tube.
4 The solid forms a compacted mass at the bottom of the tube. The liquid is decanted (poured off) from the centrifuge tube, leaving the solid behind.

Centrifuging a suspension

Filtration cannot separate particles which are so small that they pass through the pores in filter paper. An example is bacteria, which form a **suspension** in water. When a suspension of bacteria in liquid is spun at high speed, bacteria settle to the bottom. This method of separation is called **centrifuging** or **centrifugation**.

3.3 Soluble solids by chromatography

The following diagram shows chromatography on a solution of the pigments in green leaves. The solvent, ethanol, carries the pigments through a strip of **chromatography paper**. The pigments separate because they travel at different speeds.

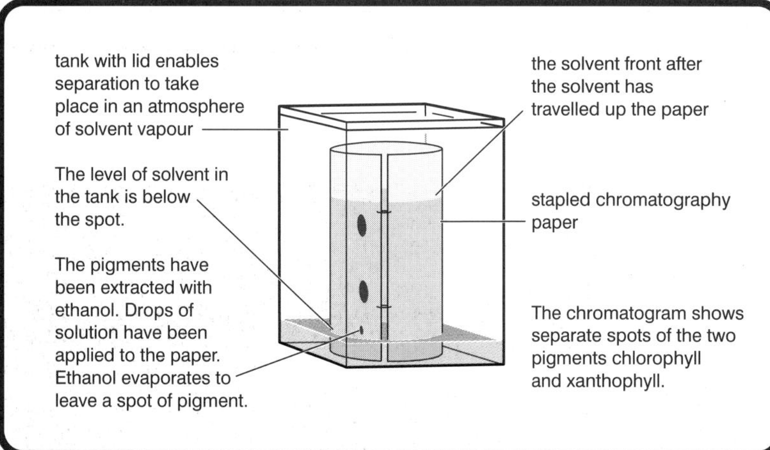

tank with lid enables separation to take place in an atmosphere of solvent vapour
The level of solvent in the tank is below the spot.
The pigments have been extracted with ethanol. Drops of solution have been applied to the paper. Ethanol evaporates to leave a spot of pigment.
the solvent front after the solvent has travelled up the paper

The chromatogram shows separate spots of the two pigments chlorophyll and xanthophyll.

Chromatography on an extract from green leaves

3.4 Immiscible liquids

The mixture of immiscible liquids, e.g. oil and water, is poured into a **separating funnel**. The mixture settles into two layers. The tap is opened to allow the bottom layer to run into a receiver. Then the tap is closed and the receiver is changed. The top layer is run into the second receiver.

3.5 Solvent from solute

To separate the solvent and solute in a solution, heat the solution in the **distillation** apparatus shown here. The solvent distils over and condenses into the receiver, leaving the solute behind in the distillation flask.

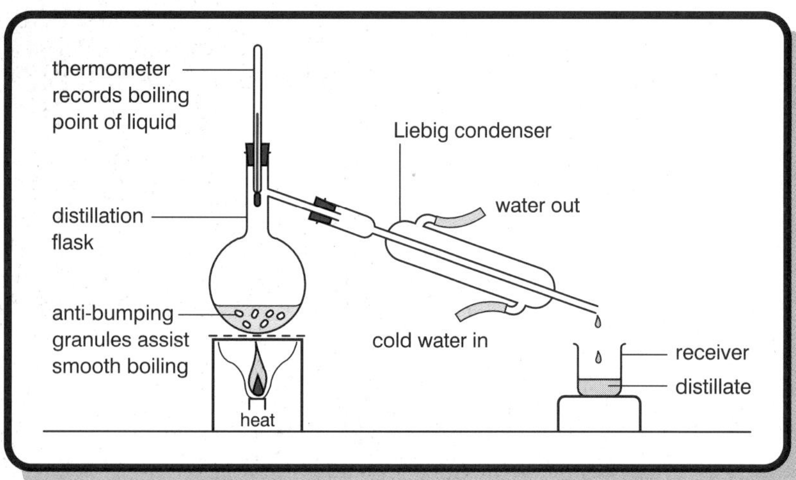

A laboratory distillation apparatus

3.6 Miscible liquids

Heat the mixture in the **fractional distillation** apparatus shown here. The lower boiling point liquid, e.g. ethanol, b.p. 78 °C, distils over first. Then the temperature rises as the liquid with the higher boiling point, e.g. water, b.p. 100 °C, distils over.

Fractional distillation can be run continuously (non-stop). Continuous fractional distillation is used to separate crude petroleum oil into a number of useful fuels (see pages 98–9).

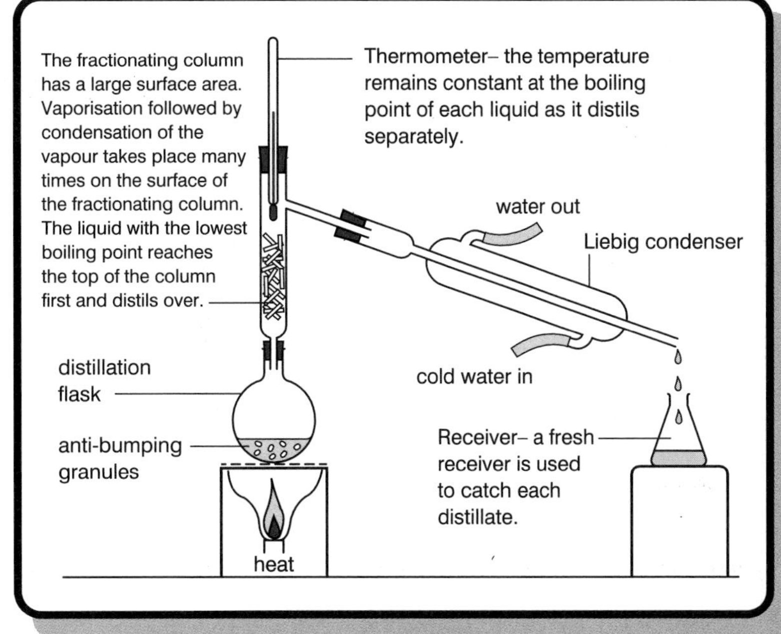

The fractionating column has a large surface area. Vaporisation followed by condensation of the vapour takes place many times on the surface of the fractionating column. The liquid with the lowest boiling point reaches the top of the column first and distils over.
Thermometer– the temperature remains constant at the boiling point of each liquid as it distils separately.
water out
Liebig condenser
cold water in
distillation flask
anti-bumping granules
heat
Receiver– a fresh receiver is used to catch each distillate.

Apparatus for fractional distillation

round-up

How much have you improved?
Work out your improvement index on page 128.

1 Suggest a method of separating steel drink cans from a collection of empty steel cans and aluminium cans. [2]

2 A mixture contains the salts C and D. Neither is soluble in water. C is soluble in ethanol. Suggest a method you could use to separate C and D. Mention any safety precautions. [5]

3 How are gasoline and diesel oil separated from crude oil? Explain why the method works. [3]

4 The manufacturer Colorit has a patent on three pigments A, B and C. The firm suspects that a rival firm which has brought out the pigments P1 and P2 is using Colorit's pigments. The works analytical chemist runs a chromatogram on all five pigments. The results of her analysis are shown in the diagram. What conclusions can you draw? [2]

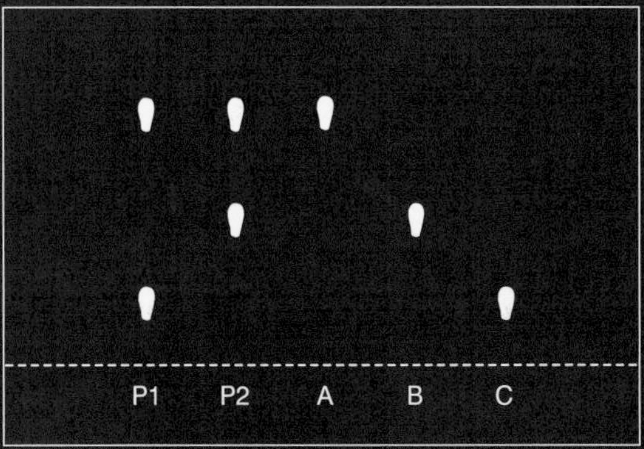

P1 P2 A B C

Chromatogram of A, B, C, P1 and P2

5 An oil tanker collides with a rocky promontory and thousands of litres of oil escape to form an oil slick. A salvage ship sucks up a mixture of oil and sea water from the surface. Suggest a method of separating the valuable oil from sea water. [3]

Well done if you've improved. Don't worry if you haven't. Take a break and try again.

The structure of the atom

preview

At the end of this topic you will:

- know the names of the particles of which atoms are composed
- know how particles are arranged in the atom
- understand the terms atomic number, mass number, relative atomic mass, relative molecular mass and isotope.

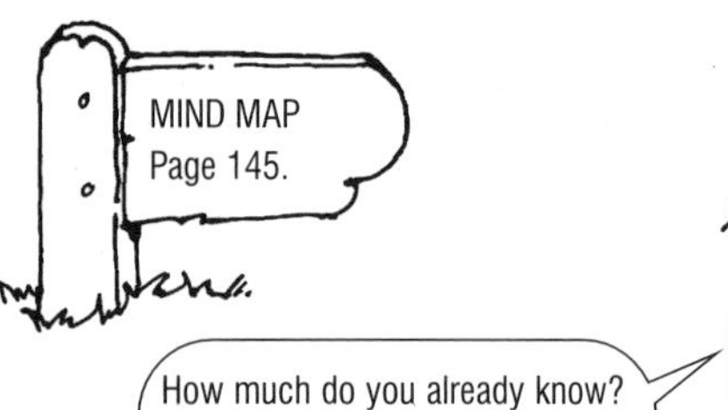

How much do you already know? Work out your score on page 128.

Test yourself

1 An atom is made of charged particles called protons and electrons. Why is an atom uncharged? [2]

2 An atom of potassium has mass number 39 and atomic number 19. What is **a)** the number of electrons and **b)** the number of neutrons? [2]

3 Why do the isotopes of an element have the same chemical reactions? [2]

4 What is meant by **a)** the atomic number and **b)** the mass number of an element? [3]

5 Write the symbol, with mass number and atomic number, for each of the following isotopes:
a) phosphorus with atomic number 15 and mass number 31 [2]
b) potassium with atomic number 19 and mass number 39. [2]

6 An atom of carbon has 6 electrons. Say how the electrons are divided between shells. [2]

4.1 Protons, neutrons and electrons

The concept map opposite gives a summary of the nature of the sub-atomic particles, their masses and charges and some ways of expressing the masses of atoms.

4.2 Focus on the atom

The diagram below shows how protons, neutrons and electrons are arranged in the atom.

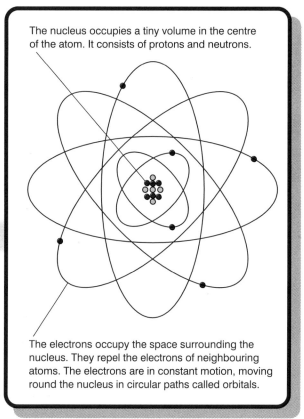

The nucleus occupies a tiny volume in the centre of the atom. It consists of protons and neutrons.

The electrons occupy the space surrounding the nucleus. They repel the electrons of neighbouring atoms. The electrons are in constant motion, moving round the nucleus in circular paths called orbitals.

The arrangement of particles in the atom

The electrons moving in orbitals further away from the nucleus have more energy than those close to the nucleus. A group of orbitals of similar energy is called a **shell** (see diagram on page 22). In the outermost shell of any atom, the maximum number of electrons is eight.

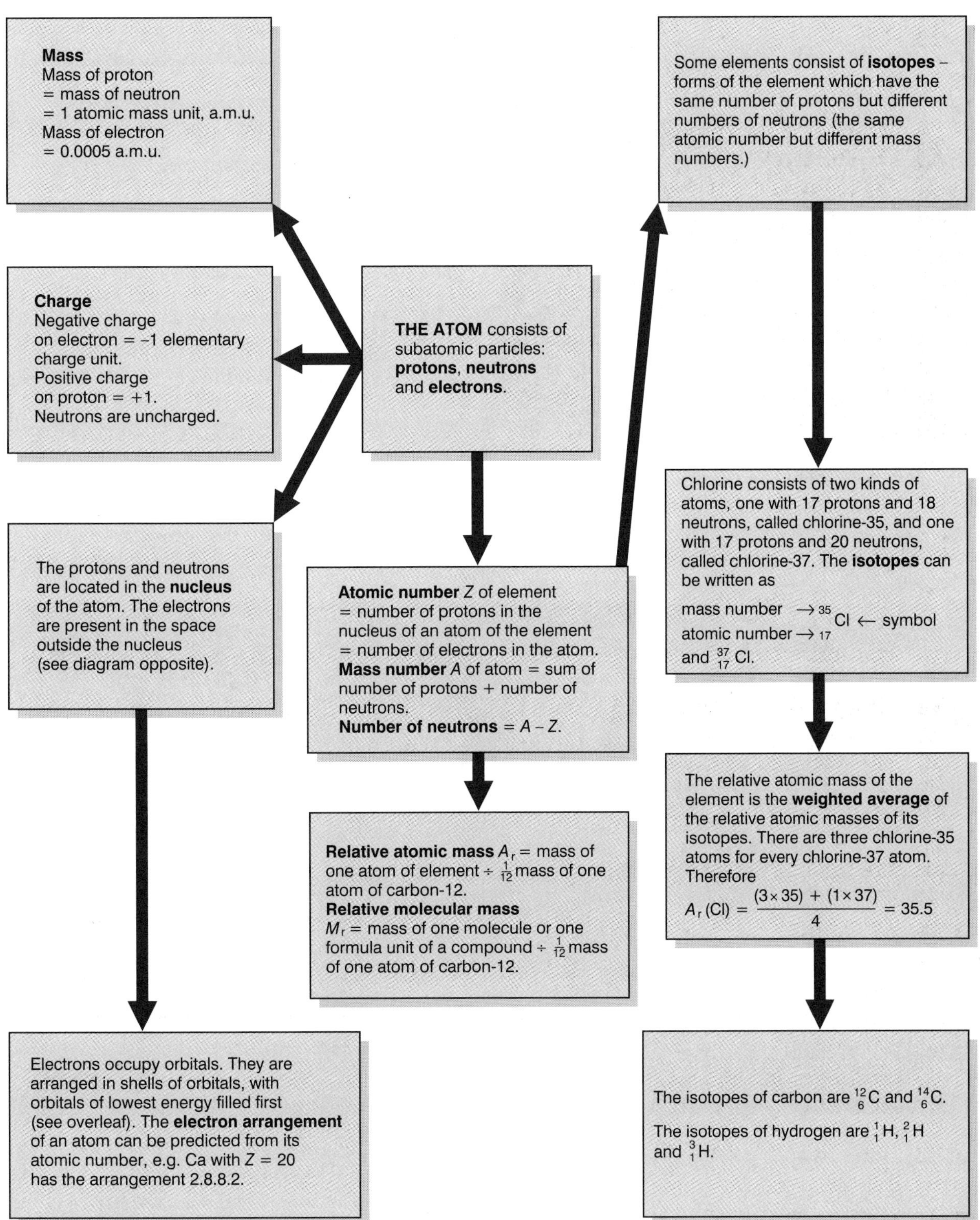

Mass
Mass of proton
= mass of neutron
= 1 atomic mass unit, a.m.u.
Mass of electron
= 0.0005 a.m.u.

Charge
Negative charge
on electron = –1 elementary
charge unit.
Positive charge
on proton = +1.
Neutrons are uncharged.

THE ATOM consists of
subatomic particles:
protons, **neutrons**
and **electrons**.

The protons and neutrons
are located in the **nucleus**
of the atom. The electrons
are present in the space
outside the nucleus
(see diagram opposite).

Atomic number Z of element
= number of protons in the
nucleus of an atom of the element
= number of electrons in the atom.
Mass number A of atom = sum of
number of protons + number of
neutrons.
Number of neutrons = $A - Z$.

Relative atomic mass A_r = mass of
one atom of element ÷ $\frac{1}{12}$ mass of one
atom of carbon-12.
Relative molecular mass
M_r = mass of one molecule or one
formula unit of a compound ÷ $\frac{1}{12}$ mass
of one atom of carbon-12.

Electrons occupy orbitals. They are
arranged in shells of orbitals, with
orbitals of lowest energy filled first
(see overleaf). The **electron arrangement**
of an atom can be predicted from its
atomic number, e.g. Ca with Z = 20
has the arrangement 2.8.8.2.

Some elements consist of **isotopes** –
forms of the element which have the
same number of protons but different
numbers of neutrons (the same
atomic number but different mass
numbers.)

Chlorine consists of two kinds of
atoms, one with 17 protons and 18
neutrons, called chlorine-35, and one
with 17 protons and 20 neutrons,
called chlorine-37. The **isotopes** can
be written as
mass number → $^{35}_{17}$Cl ← symbol
atomic number →
and $^{37}_{17}$Cl.

The relative atomic mass of the
element is the **weighted average** of
the relative atomic masses of its
isotopes. There are three chlorine-35
atoms for every chlorine-37 atom.
Therefore
$A_r(\text{Cl}) = \frac{(3 \times 35) + (1 \times 37)}{4} = 35.5$

The isotopes of carbon are $^{12}_{6}$C and $^{14}_{6}$C.
The isotopes of hydrogen are $^{1}_{1}$H, $^{2}_{1}$H
and $^{3}_{1}$H.

Concept map: the nature of the atom

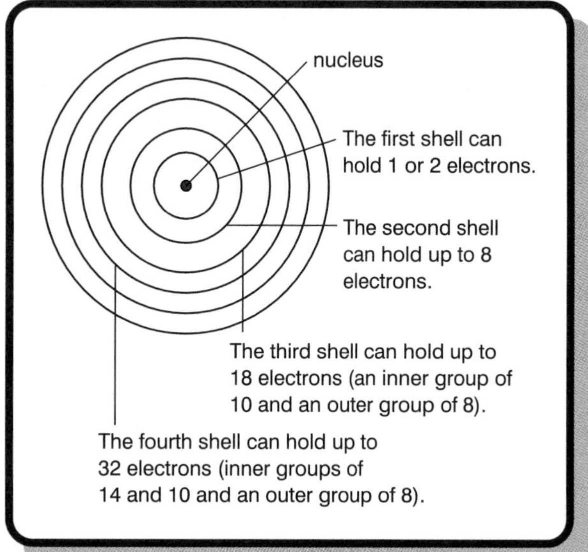

Shells of electrons

If you know the atomic number of an element, you can work out the arrangement of electrons. The lower energy levels are filled before the higher energy levels. The arrangements of electrons in an atom of carbon (atomic number 6) and an atom of magnesium (atomic number 12) are shown here.

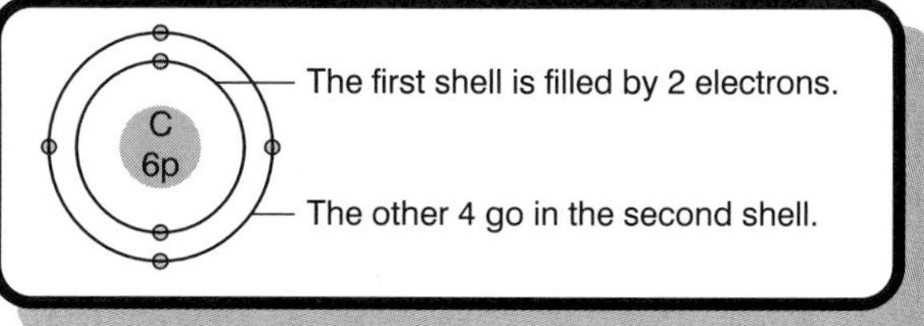

The arrangement of electrons in the carbon atom (2.4)

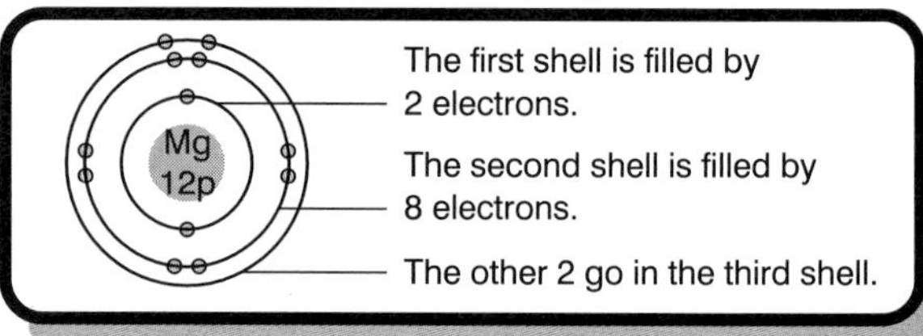

The arrangement of electrons in the magnesium atom (2.8.2)

The table opposite gives the electron arrangements of the first 20 elements.

round-up

RELATIVE ATOMIC MASSES Page 92.

How much have you improved? Work out your improvement index on pages 128–9.

1 a) How many times heavier is one atom of aluminium than one atom of hydrogen? [1]

b) How many times heavier is one atom of mercury than one atom of calcium? [1]

c) What is the ratio: $\frac{\text{mass of one Fe atom}}{\text{mass of one Br atom?}}$ [1]

d) How many atoms of nitrogen equal the mass of one atom of bromine? [1]

2 Write the symbol, with mass number and atomic number, for each of the following isotopes:

a) arsenic (atomic number 33 and mass number 75) [1]

b) uranium-235, uranium-238 and uranium-239 (atomic number 92). [3]

3 Calculate the relative atomic masses of the following elements:

a) copper, which consists of 69% of copper-63 and 31% of copper-65 [1]

b) gallium, which consists of 60% of gallium-69 and 40% of gallium-71. [1]

4 The electron arrangement of phosphorus is (2.8.5). Sketch the arrangement of electrons in the atom, as in the diagrams above. [1]

5 Sketch the arrangements of electrons in the atoms of
a) B (atomic number 5) **b)** N (atomic number 7)
c) F (atomic number 9) **d)** Al (atomic number 13). [4]

Well done if you've improved. Don't worry if you haven't. Take a break and try again.

Electron arrangements of the first 20 elements

element	symbol	atomic number	number of electrons in				electron arrangement
			1st level	2nd level	3rd level	4th level	
hydrogen	H	1	1				1
helium	He	2	2				2
lithium	Li	3	2	1			2.1
beryllium	Be	4	2	2			2.2
boron	B	5	2	3			2.3
carbon	C	6	2	4			2.4
nitrogen	N	7	2	5			2.5
oxygen	O	8	2	6			2.6
fluorine	F	9	2	7			2.7
neon	Ne	10	2	8			2.8
sodium	Na	11	2	8	1		2.8.1
magnesium	Mg	12	2	8	2		2.8.2
aluminium	Al	13	2	8	3		2.8.3
silicon	Si	14	2	8	4		2.8.4
phosphorus	P	15	2	8	5		2.8.5
sulphur	S	16	2	8	6		2.8.6
chlorine	Cl	17	2	8	7		2.8.7
argon	Ar	18	2	8	8		2.8.8
potassium	K	19	2	8	8	1	2.8.8.1
calcium	Ca	20	2	8	8	2	2.8.8.2

Electron arrangements of the first 20 elements

Electrolysis

5

preview

At the end of this topic you will be able to:

- **explain what happens when compounds are electrolysed**
- **predict which ions will be discharged in electrolysis**
- **give examples of the use of electrolysis in industry.**

MIND MAP
Page 146.
How much do you already know?
Work out your score on page 129.

Test yourself

1 Which of the following solids conduct electricity?
A zinc **B** sulphur **C** bronze
D crystalline copper(II) sulphate [2]

2 Which of the following liquids conduct electricity?
A a solution of dilute sulphuric acid
B a solution of sodium sulphate
C ethanol
D a solution of ethanoic acid [3]

3 What do the following terms mean?
a) an electrolyte **b)** an electrode [4, 1]

4 a) Explain the terms cation and anion, and give two examples of each. [6]
b) Explain why ions move towards electrodes. [2]
c) Explain why solid copper(II) chloride does not conduct electricity, but an aqueous solution of copper(II) chloride does. [2]

5 Sodium is obtained by the electrolysis of molten sodium chloride. Why is it important that the sodium chloride electrolysed to give sodium is anhydrous? [1]

6 Some parts of a car body are painted to protect against rusting, and others are chromium-plated. What advantage does chromium-plating have over painting? [1]

7 What is the advantage of gold-plated jewellery over
a) gold jewellery **b)** brass jewellery? [2]

8 Aluminium is obtained by the electrolysis of aluminium oxide.
a) Why is aluminium oxide dissolved in molten cryolite before electrolysis? [1]
b) Write the equations for the electrode processes. [5]
c) Suggest why this method of extracting aluminium is expensive. [1]

5.1 Conducting electricity

When substances conduct electricity changes happen at the electrodes. For example, a solution of copper chloride gives a deposit of copper at the negative electrode and a stream of chlorine at the positive electrode. The explanation is that copper chloride consists of positively charged particles of copper, called copper ions, and negatively charged particles of chlorine, called chloride ions. Experiments show that the copper ion carries two units of positive charge, Cu^{2+}, whereas the chloride ion carries one unit of negative charge, Cl^-. Copper chloride contains two chloride ions for every copper ion so that the charges balance, and the formula is $CuCl_2$.

In solid copper chloride, the ions are not free to move because they are held in a three-dimensional crystal structure, and the solid does not conduct electricity. When the salt is dissolved in water, the ions become free to move, the solution conducts electricity and electrolysis occurs.

There is another way of giving the ions freedom to move – to melt the solid. The electrolysis of molten sodium chloride is used for the extraction of sodium.

5.2 Ions

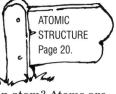

ATOMIC STRUCTURE
Page 20.

How is an ion formed from an atom? Atoms are uncharged. The number of protons in an atom is the same as the number of electrons. If an atom either gains or loses electrons, it will become electrically charged. Metal atoms and hydrogen atoms form positive ions (**cations**) by losing one or more electrons. Atoms of non-metallic elements form negative ions (**anions**) by gaining one or more electrons.

sodium atom Na → electron e^- +	sodium ion Na^+
(11 protons,	(11 protons,
11 electrons,	10 electrons,
charge = 0)	charge = +1)

chlorine atom Cl + electron e^- →	chloride ion Cl^-
(17 protons,	(17 protons,
17 electrons,	18 electrons,
charge = 0)	charge = –1)

The following table gives the symbols and formulas of some ions.

cations	anions
hydrogen ion H^+	bromide ion Br^-
sodium ion Na^+	chloride ion Cl^-
copper(II) ion Cu^{2+}	iodide ion I^-
lead(II) ion Pb^{2+}	hydroxide ion OH^-
aluminium ion Al^{3+}	nitrate ion NO_3^-
	sulphate ion SO_4^{2-}

5.3 At the electrodes

Copper(II) chloride solution

The diagram below shows what happens at the electrodes when copper(II) chloride is electrolysed.

Sodium chloride solution

The products of electrolysis are hydrogen and chlorine. Why is sodium not formed when sodium chloride solution is electrolysed? The water present in the solution is ionised to a very small extent:

water ⇌ hydrogen ions + hydroxide ions

$H_2O(l) \rightleftharpoons H^+(aq) + OH^-(aq)$

The hydrogen ions are attracted to the cathode (negative electrode). It is easier for the cathode to discharge a hydrogen ion than a sodium ion, and hydrogen is formed.

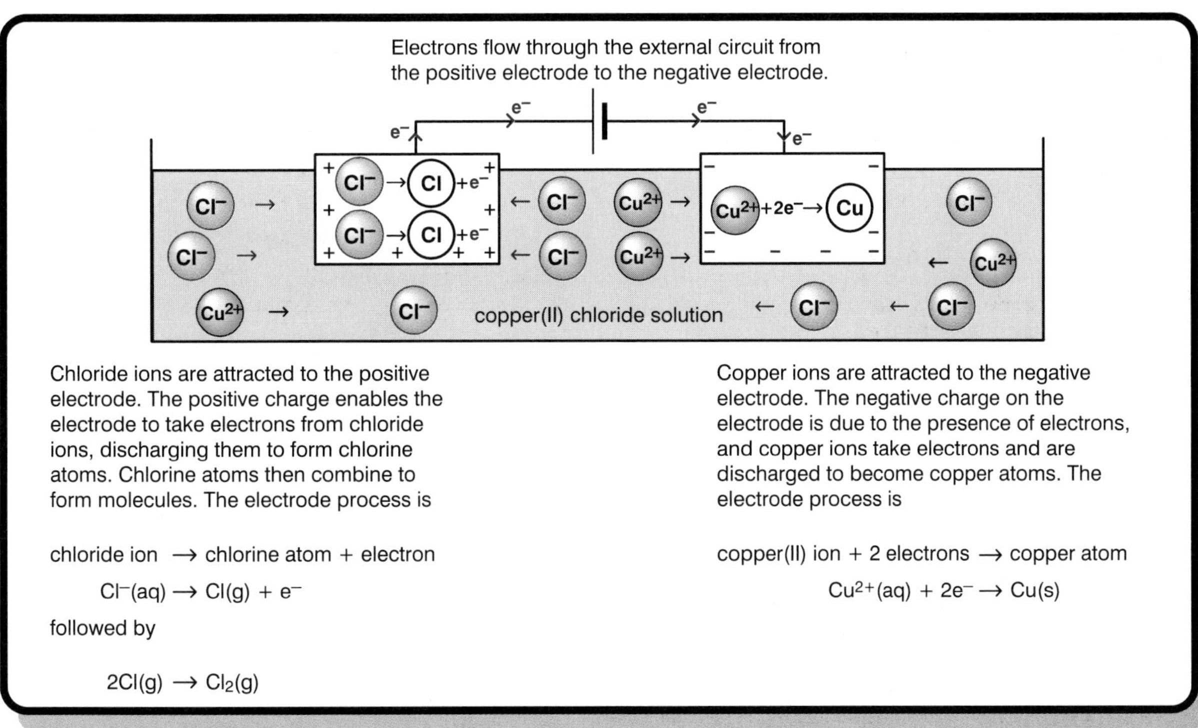

Electrons flow through the external circuit from the positive electrode to the negative electrode.
e^-
Cl^- → Cl + e^-
Cu^{2+} + $2e^-$ → Cu
copper(II) chloride solution
Chloride ions are attracted to the positive electrode. The positive charge enables the electrode to take electrons from chloride ions, discharging them to form chlorine atoms. Chlorine atoms then combine to form molecules. The electrode process is
chloride ion → chlorine atom + electron
$Cl^-(aq) \rightarrow Cl(g) + e^-$
followed by
$2Cl(g) \rightarrow Cl_2(g)$
Copper ions are attracted to the negative electrode. The negative charge on the electrode is due to the presence of electrons, and copper ions take electrons and are discharged to become copper atoms. The electrode process is
copper(II) ion + 2 electrons → copper atom
$Cu^{2+}(aq) + 2e^- \rightarrow Cu(s)$

The electrolysis of copper(II) chloride with carbon electrodes

electrode process $H^+(aq) + e^- \rightarrow H(g)$

followed by $2H(g) \rightarrow H_2(g)$

Although the concentration of hydrogen ions in water is small, when these hydrogen ions are discharged more water molecules ionise to replace them, and the discharge of hydrogen ions continues. As more water molecules ionise, the concentration of hydroxide ions increases and the solution of sodium chloride gradually turns into a solution of sodium hydroxide.

The electrolysis of sodium chloride solution is used commercially to obtain the important products sodium hydroxide, hydrogen and chlorine.

Copper(II) sulphate solution

The products of electrolysis are copper and oxygen. How is oxygen formed when an aqueous solution of copper(II) sulphate is electrolysed? Again, the dissociation of water molecules must be considered. Hydroxide ions formed by the ionisation of water molecules are present at the anode. It is easier for the anode to remove electrons from hydroxide ions than from sulphate ions. Consequently hydroxide ions are discharged, and the OH groups which are formed rearrange to give oxygen and water.

electrode process $OH^-(aq) \rightarrow OH(aq) + e^-$

followed by $4OH(aq) \rightarrow O_2(g) + 2H_2O(l)$

The hydroxide ions that are discharged are replaced by the ionisation of more water molecules. Hydrogen ions are also formed by the dissociation of water, and the solution gradually turns into a solution of sulphuric acid.

5.4 Which ions are discharged?

Anions

FACTS

★ Sulphate ions and nitrate ions are very difficult to discharge. In solutions of these ions, hydroxide ions are discharged to form oxygen.

Cations

★ The ions of very reactive metals, e.g. sodium and potassium, are difficult to discharge. In solutions of these ions, hydrogen ions are discharged instead.

★ The ions of less reactive metals, e.g. copper and lead, are easier to discharge. In a solution that contains a mixture of metal ions, the ions are discharged in order of the reactivity of the metals. Ions of the least reactive metals are discharged first. For example, in a solution containing Cu^{2+} ions and Zn^{2+} ions, Cu^{2+} ions are discharged while Zn^{2+} ions remain in solution.

5.5 Electrodes taking part

Sometimes electrodes are changed by the cell reaction. For example, when copper(II) sulphate is electrolysed with copper electrodes, the products differ from those just described. At the cathode, copper is deposited as before. The copper anode, the positive electrode, needs to gain electrons. Instead of gaining electrons by discharging SO_4^{2-} ions or OH^- ions, it gains electrons by ionising Cu atoms:

$$Cu(s) \rightarrow Cu^{2+}(aq) + 2e^-$$

The result of electrolysis is that copper is dissolved from the anode and an equal amount of copper is deposited on the cathode.

The table on the next page shows the products of electrolysis of some electrolytes.

5.6 Applications of electrolysis

Extraction of metals from their ores

★ **Sodium** is obtained from sodium chloride in the mineral rock salt. When molten anhydrous sodium chloride is electrolysed, the products are sodium and chlorine.

★ **Potassium**, **calcium** and **magnesium** are also obtained by electrolysis of molten anhydrous chlorides. The cost of electricity makes this method of extracting metals expensive.

★ **Aluminium** is mined as the ore bauxite, $Al_2O_3.2H_2O$. Purified anhydrous aluminium oxide is obtained from the ore. Before the oxide can be

electrolyte	products of electrolysis and electrode processes	
	cathode (negative electrode)	anode (positive electrode)
molten sodium chloride	sodium $Na^+(l) + e^- \rightarrow Na(l)$	chlorine $Cl^-(l) \rightarrow Cl(g) + e^-$ $2Cl(g) \rightarrow Cl_2(g)$
sodium chloride solution	hydrogen $H^+(aq) + e^- \rightarrow H(g)$ $2H(g) \rightarrow H_2(g)$	chlorine $Cl^-(aq) \rightarrow Cl(g) + e^-$ $2Cl(g) \rightarrow Cl_2(g)$
copper(II) sulphate solution	copper $Cu^{2+}(aq) + 2e^- \rightarrow Cu(s)$	oxygen $OH^-(aq) \rightarrow OH(aq) + e^-$ $4OH(aq) \rightarrow O_2(g) + 2H_2O(l)$
copper(II) sulphate solution, with copper electrodes	copper is discharged $Cu^{2+}(aq) + 2e^- \rightarrow Cu(s)$	copper dissolves $Cu(s) \rightarrow Cu^{2+}(aq) + 2e^-$
dilute sulphuric acid	hydrogen $H^+(aq) + e^- \rightarrow H(g)$ $2H(g) \rightarrow H_2(g)$	oxygen $OH^-(aq) \rightarrow OH(aq) + e^-$ $4OH(aq) \rightarrow O_2(g) + 2H_2O(l)$

electrolysed, it must be melted. The high melting point of aluminium oxide, 2050°C, makes this difficult so it is dissolved in molten cryolite, Na_3AlF_6, at 1000°C before electrolysis. See diagram below.

Purification of copper

The electrolysis of copper(II) sulphate with copper electrodes (see page 26) is used in the purification of copper. The diagram overleaf shows the setup.

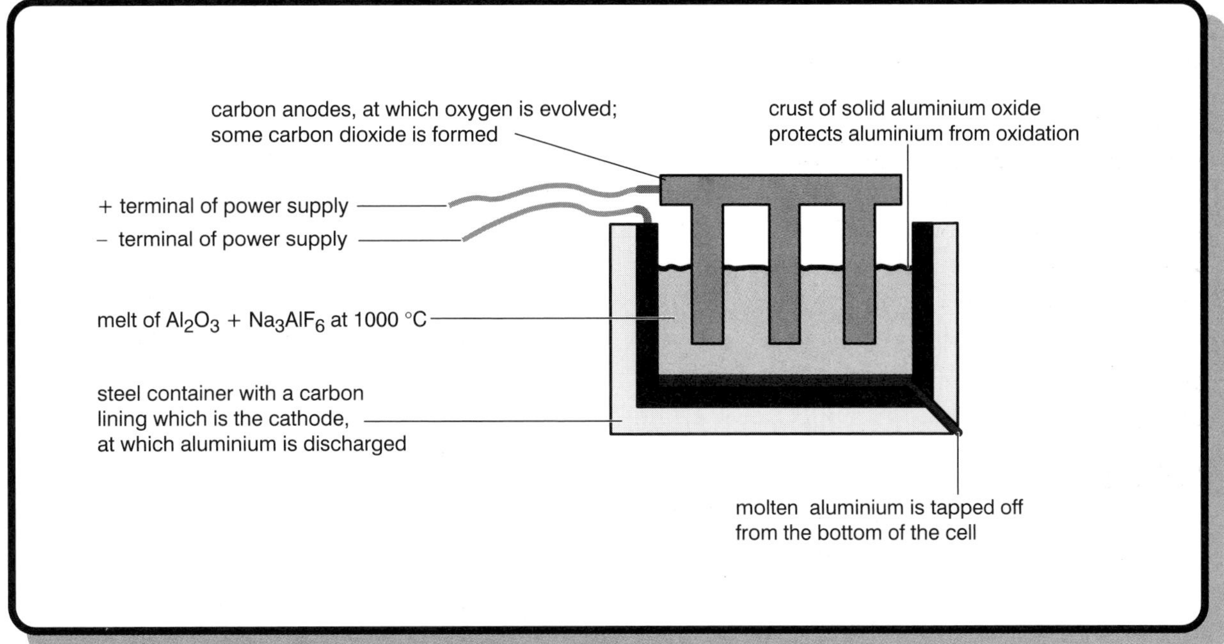

Electrolysis of molten aluminium oxide

Electroplating

Electrolysis is used to coat a metal with a thin even film of another metal, as shown in the diagram below.

1 A cheaper metal may be coated with a more beautiful and more expensive metal, e.g. silver or gold.

2 To prevent steel from rusting, it is electroplated with nickel and chromium which give the steel a bright surface that is not corroded in air.

3 Food cans are made of iron plated with a layer of tin. Tin is not corroded by food juices.

4 A layer of zinc is applied to iron in the manufacture of galvanised iron. Electroplating is one of the methods employed.

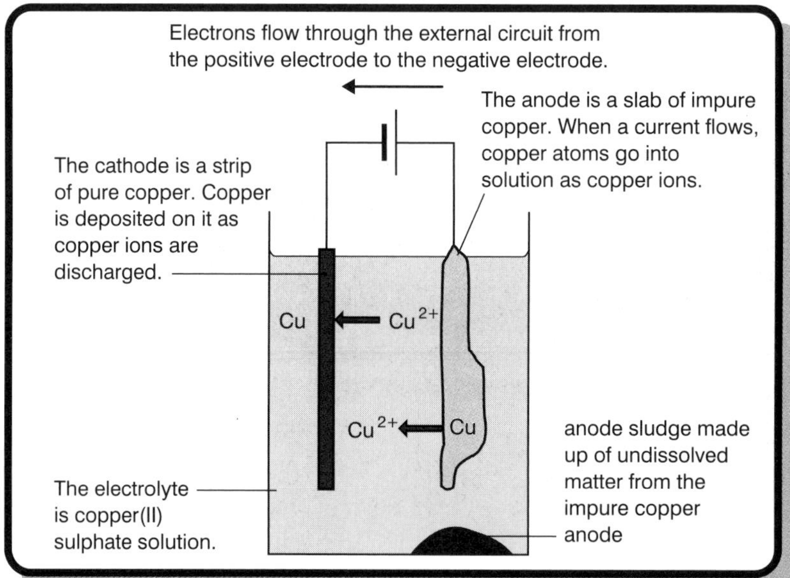
Electrons flow through the external circuit from the positive electrode to the negative electrode.
The anode is a slab of impure copper. When a current flows, copper atoms go into solution as copper ions.
The cathode is a strip of pure copper. Copper is deposited on it as copper ions are discharged.
Cu
Cu2+
Cu2+
Cu
The electrolyte is copper(II) sulphate solution.
anode sludge made up of undissolved matter from the impure copper anode

Electrolytic purification of copper ▲

Electroplating ▼

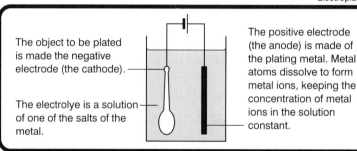

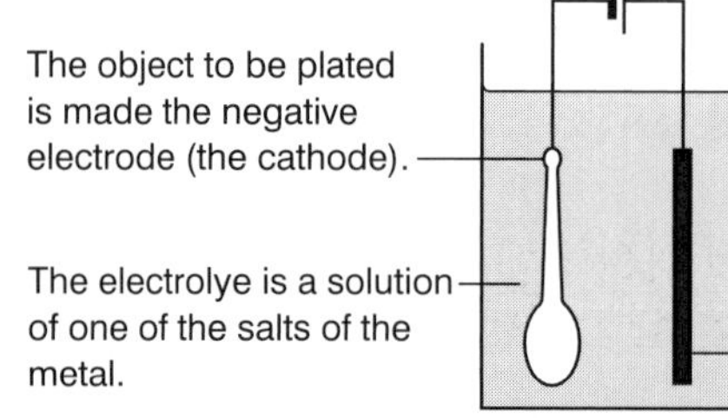
The object to be plated is made the negative electrode (the cathode).
The electrolye is a solution of one of the salts of the metal.
The positive electrode (the anode) is made of the plating metal. Metal atoms dissolve to form metal ions, keeping the concentration of metal ions in the solution constant.

round-up

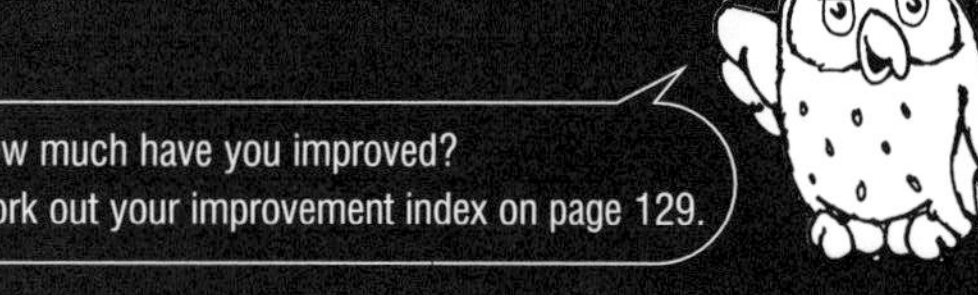
How much have you improved?
Work out your improvement index on page 129.

1 Copper is purified by an electrolytic method.
- **a)** Why do impurities in the copper such as zinc and iron not interfere? [1]
- **b)** What happens to impurities in the copper such as silver? [2]

2 Iron nails are electroplated with nickel to make them rust-resistant.
- **a)** Why is electroplating a good method of applying the nickel coating? [2]
- **b)** Sketch an apparatus which you could use to do this in the laboratory. [2]

3 When an aqueous solution of potassium bromide is electrolysed, a brown colour appears at one electrode.
- **a)** What is the brown substance? [1]
- **b)** At which electrode is it formed? [1]
- **c)** What is formed at the other electrode? [1]
- **d)** Name an ion which increases in concentration during the electrolysis. [1]
- **e)** Write equations for the electrode processes. [6]

4 Copper(II) sulphate solution can be electrolysed between platinum electrodes.
- **a)** State what products are formed at the electrodes. [2]
- **b)** Write equations for the electrode reactions. [7]
- **c)** What difference in the products of electrolysis is observed when copper electrodes are used? [2]
- **d)** Write the equations for the electrode reactions when copper electrodes are used. [4]

The chemical bond 6

preview

At the end of this topic you will:

- **understand how atoms combine by forming ionic bonds and covalent bonds**
- **understand how ionic compounds and covalent compounds differ in properties and structure.**

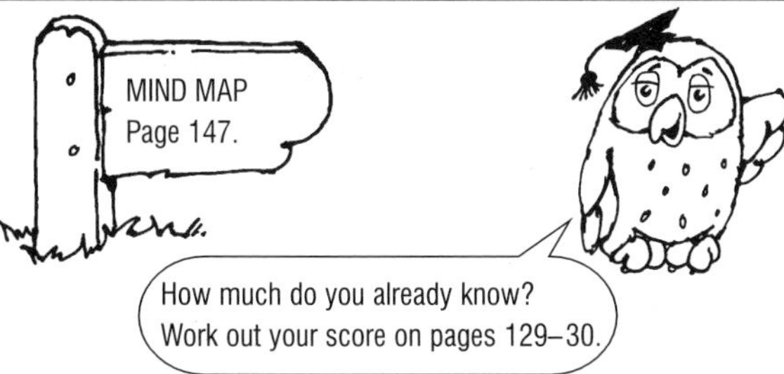

MIND MAP
Page 147.
How much do you already know?
Work out your score on pages 129–30.

Test yourself

1 Write words in the spaces to complete the sentences.

When an ionic compound is formed, some atoms lose electrons to become __________ ions while other atoms gain electrons to become __________ ions. Ions are held together by __________ attraction in a three-dimensional structure called a __________ . [4]

2 The element E has the electron arrangement E(2.8.2). The element Q has the electron arrangement Q(2.8.7). Explain what happens to atoms of E and Q when they combine to form an ionic compound, and give the formula of the compound. [3]

3 The element T has the electron arrangement T(2.7). Sketch the arrangement of electrons in an atom of T and in the molecule T_2. [2]

4 Name the following compounds:
a) $MgBr_2$ **b)** $FeCl_2$ **c)** $FeCl_3$ **d)** Na_2O **e)** $BaSO_4$. [5]

5 State the formulas of the following compounds:
a) potassium bromide **b)** calcium carbonate
c) lead(II) oxide **d)** lead(II) sulphate
e) silver chloride. [5]

6.1 Bond formation

When chemical reactions take place, it is the electrons in the outer shell that are involved in the formation of bonds. The resistance of the noble gases to chemical change is believed to be due to the stability of the full outer shell of eight electrons (two for helium). When atoms react, they gain, lose or share electrons to attain an outer shell of eight electrons. Metallic elements frequently combine with non-metallic elements to form compounds.

6.2 Ionic bonding

Example 1

Sodium burns in chlorine to form sodium chloride. This is what happens to the electrons:

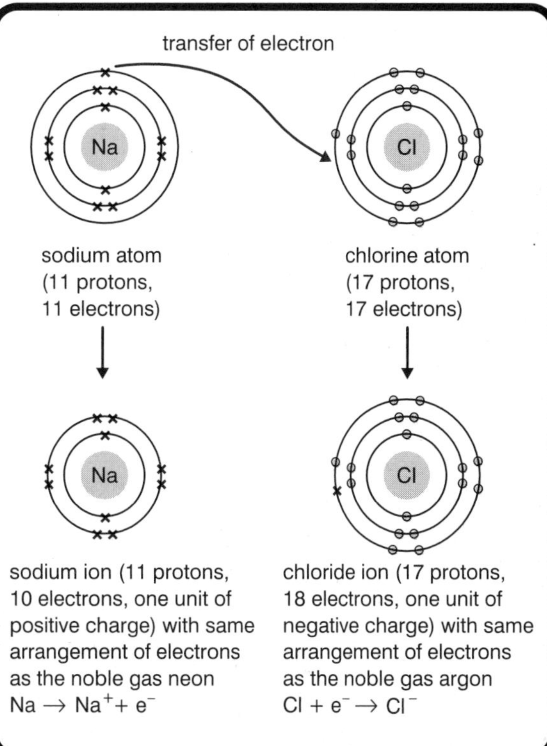

The formation of sodium chloride

There is an electrostatic force of attraction between oppositely charged ions. This force is called an **ionic bond** or **electrovalent bond**. The ions Na^+ and Cl^- are part of a **giant ionic structure** (a crystal). The ions cannot move out of their positions in the structure, and the crystal cannot conduct electricity. When the solid is melted or dissolved, the ions become free to move and conduct electricity (see page 24).

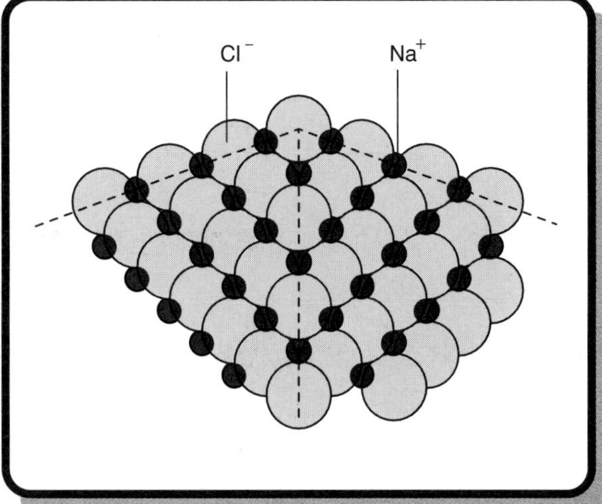

The structure of sodium chloride

Example 2

Magnesium + fluorine → magnesium fluoride

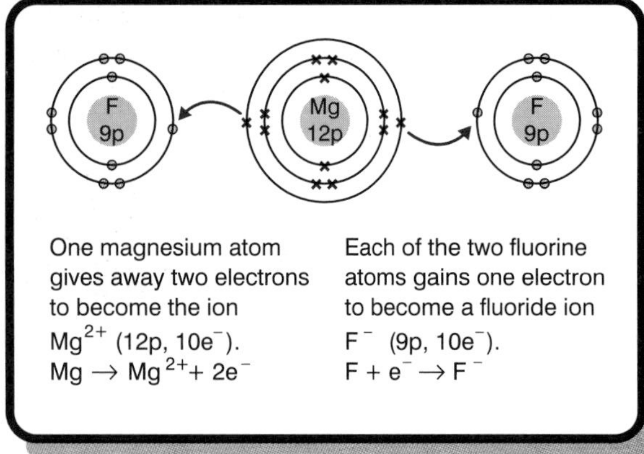

$Mg \rightarrow Mg^{2+} + 2e^-$
Each of the two fluorine atoms gains one electron to become a fluoride ion F^- (9p, 10e⁻).
$F + e^- \rightarrow F^-$

The formation of magnesium fluoride

The formula of magnesium fluoride is $Mg^{2+}2F^-$ or MgF_2.

Example 3

Magnesium + oxygen → magnesium oxide

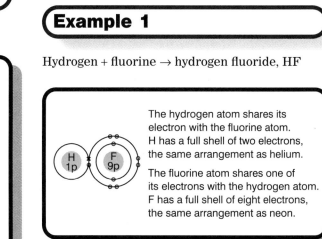

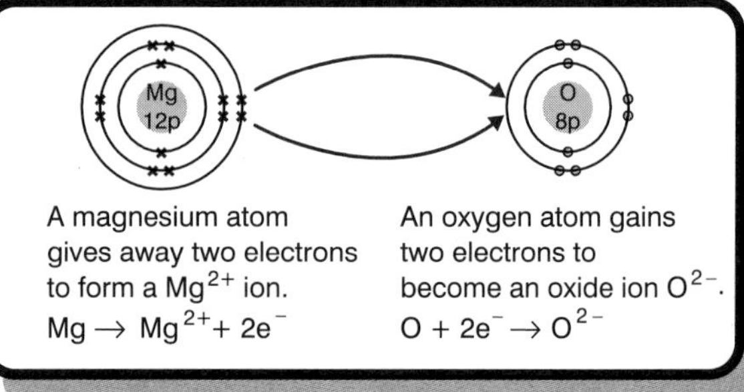

A magnesium atom gives away two electrons to form a Mg^{2+} ion.
$Mg \rightarrow Mg^{2+} + 2e^-$

$O + 2e^- \rightarrow O^{2-}$

The formation of magnesium oxide

The formula of magnesium oxide is $Mg^{2+}O^{2-}$ or MgO.

6.3 Covalent bonding

When two non-metallic elements combine, both want to gain electrons; neither wants to form positive ions. They combine by sharing electrons. A shared pair of electrons is a **covalent bond**. If two pairs of electrons are shared, the bond is a **double bond**.

Example 1

Hydrogen + fluorine → hydrogen fluoride, HF

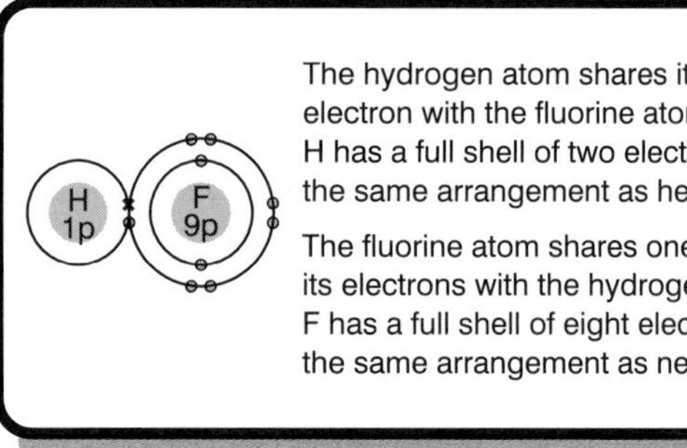

H 1p
F 9p
The hydrogen atom shares its electron with the fluorine atom.
H has a full shell of two electrons, the same arrangement as helium.
The fluorine atom shares one of its electrons with the hydrogen atom.
F has a full shell of eight electrons, the same arrangement as neon.

The formation of hydrogen fluoride

The shared pair of electrons is attracted to the hydrogen nucleus and to the fluorine nucleus, and bonds the two nuclei together.

Example 2

Hydrogen + oxygen → water, H_2O

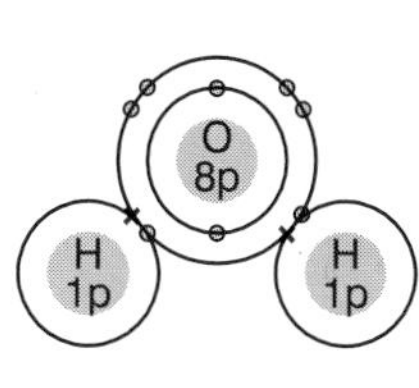

Two hydrogen atoms each share an electron with an oxygen atom. Each hydrogen atom has an outer shell of two electrons, and the oxygen atom has an outer shell of eight electrons.

The formation of water

Example 3

Nitrogen + hydrogen → ammonia, NH_3

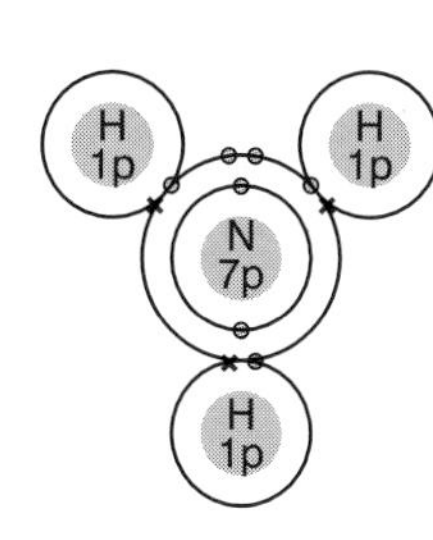

One nitrogen atom shares three electrons, one with each of three hydrogen atoms. The nitrogen atom has eight electrons in its outer shell (like neon), and each hydrogen has two electrons in its outer shell (like helium).

The formation of ammonia

Example 4

Carbon + hydrogen → methane, CH_4

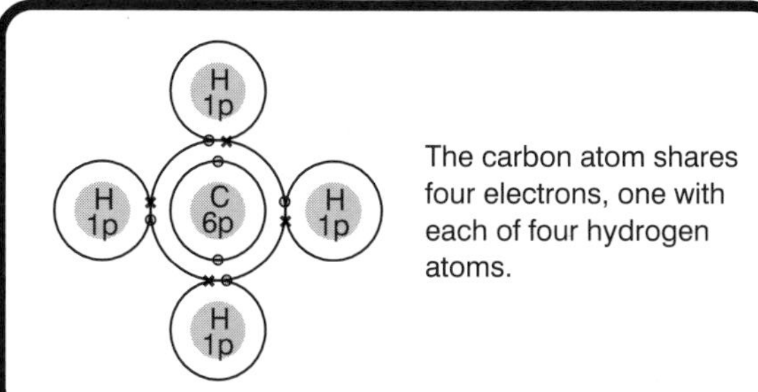

The carbon atom shares four electrons, one with each of four hydrogen atoms.

The formation of methane

Example 5

Carbon + oxygen → carbon dioxide, CO_2

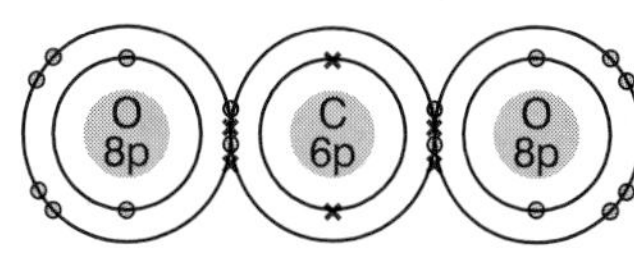

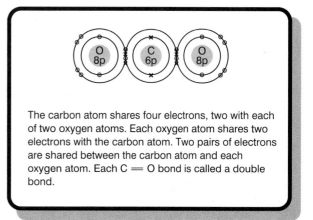

The carbon atom shares four electrons, two with each of two oxygen atoms. Each oxygen atom shares two electrons with the carbon atom. Two pairs of electrons are shared between the carbon atom and each oxygen atom. Each C ═ O bond is called a double bond.

The formation of carbon dioxide

6.4 Ionic and covalent substances

The concept map overleaf summarises the types of bonds formed by different substances.

6.5 The formula of an ionic compound

Ionic compounds consist of positive and negative ions. A sample of the compound is uncharged because the positive and negative charges balance exactly. In a sample of calcium chloride, $CaCl_2$, the number of chloride ions, Cl^-, is exactly twice the number of calcium ions, Ca^{2+}, so the formula is $Ca^{2+}2Cl^-$ or $CaCl_2$.

Worked example

Compound:	*sodium sulphate*
Ions present are:	Na^+ and SO_4^{2-}
To balance the charges:	two Na^+ are needed to balance one SO_4^{2-}
The ions needed are:	$2Na^+$ and SO_4^{2-}
The formula is:	Na_2SO_4

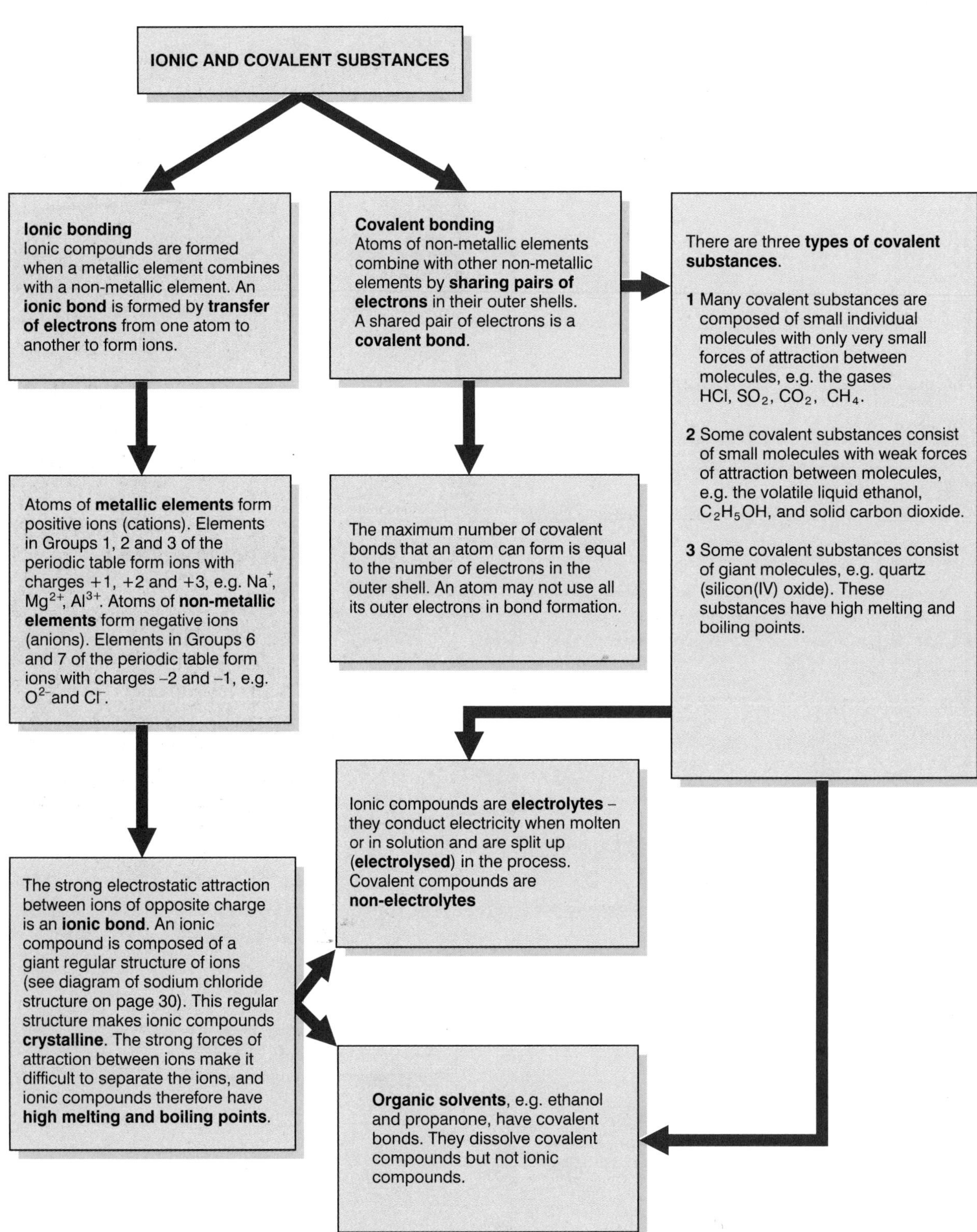

IONIC AND COVALENT SUBSTANCES
Ionic bonding
Ionic compounds are formed when a metallic element combines with a non-metallic element. An **ionic bond** is formed by **transfer of electrons** from one atom to another to form ions.
Covalent bonding
Atoms of non-metallic elements combine with other non-metallic elements by **sharing pairs of electrons** in their outer shells. A shared pair of electrons is a **covalent bond**.
There are three **types of covalent substances**.
1 Many covalent substances are composed of small individual molecules with only very small forces of attraction between molecules, e.g. the gases HCl, SO_2, CO_2, CH_4.
2 Some covalent substances consist of small molecules with weak forces of attraction between molecules, e.g. the volatile liquid ethanol, C_2H_5OH, and solid carbon dioxide.
3 Some covalent substances consist of giant molecules, e.g. quartz (silicon(IV) oxide). These substances have high melting and boiling points.
Atoms of **metallic elements** form positive ions (cations). Elements in Groups 1, 2 and 3 of the periodic table form ions with charges +1, +2 and +3, e.g. Na^+, Mg^{2+}, Al^{3+}. Atoms of **non-metallic elements** form negative ions (anions). Elements in Groups 6 and 7 of the periodic table form ions with charges −2 and −1, e.g. O^{2-} and Cl^-.
The maximum number of covalent bonds that an atom can form is equal to the number of electrons in the outer shell. An atom may not use all its outer electrons in bond formation.
Ionic compounds are **electrolytes** – they conduct electricity when molten or in solution and are split up (**electrolysed**) in the process. Covalent compounds are **non-electrolytes**
The strong electrostatic attraction between ions of opposite charge is an **ionic bond**. An ionic compound is composed of a giant regular structure of ions (see diagram of sodium chloride structure on page 30). This regular structure makes ionic compounds **crystalline**. The strong forces of attraction between ions make it difficult to separate the ions, and ionic compounds therefore have **high melting and boiling points**.
Organic solvents, e.g. ethanol and propanone, have covalent bonds. They dissolve covalent compounds but not ionic compounds.

Concept map: ionic and covalent substances

Compound:	*iron(II) sulphate*
Ions present are:	Fe^{2+} and SO_4^{2-}
To balance the charges:	one Fe^{2+} balances one SO_4^{2-}
The ions needed are:	Fe^{2+} and SO_4^{2-}
The formula is:	$FeSO_4$
Compound:	*iron(III) sulphate*
Ions present are:	Fe^{3+} and SO_4^{2-}
To balance the charges:	two Fe^{3+} balance three SO_4^{2-}
The ions needed are:	$2Fe^{3+}$ and $3SO_4^{2-}$
The formula is:	$Fe_2(SO_4)_3$

Note
The sulphates of iron are named iron(II) sulphate and iron(III) sulphate. The Roman numerals II and III show which type of ion, Fe^{2+} or Fe^{3+}, is present.

The symbols and charges of some ions

If you know the symbols and charges of these ions, you can work out the formulas of their compounds.

H^+ Na^+ K^+ Ag^+ NH_4^+	OH^- NO_3^- HCO_3^- Cl^- Br^- I^-
Ca^{2+} Cu^{2+} Zn^{2+} Pb^{2+} Mg^{2+} Fe^{2+} Ba^{2+}	SO_4^{2-} SO_3^{2-} CO_3^{2-} O^{2-} S^{2-}
Al^{3+} Fe^{3+}	

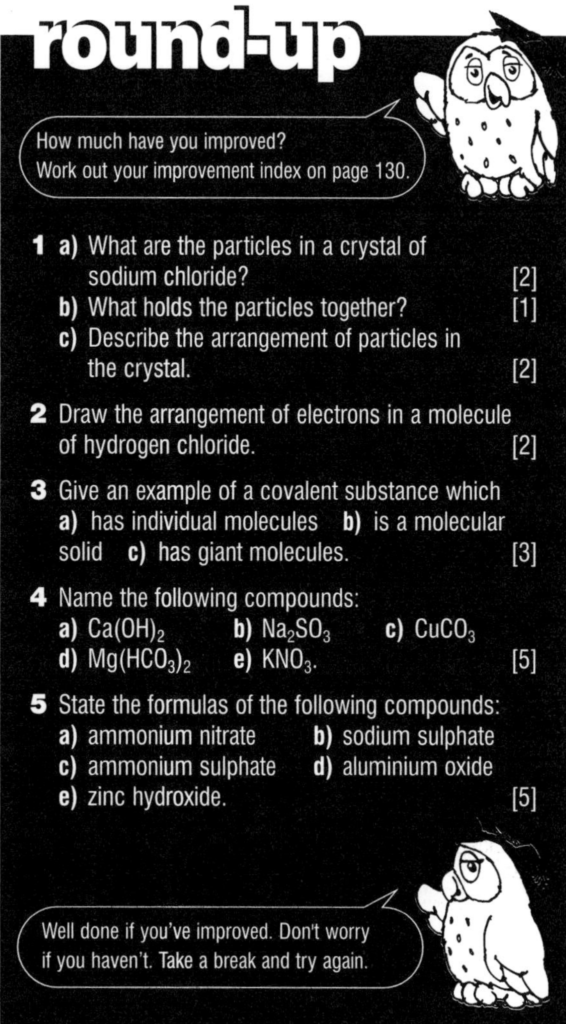

round-up
How much have you improved? Work out your improvement index on page 130.
Well done if you've improved. Don't worry if you haven't. Take a break and try again.

1 a) What are the particles in a crystal of sodium chloride? [2]
b) What holds the particles together? [1]
c) Describe the arrangement of particles in the crystal. [2]

2 Draw the arrangement of electrons in a molecule of hydrogen chloride. [2]

3 Give an example of a covalent substance which **a)** has individual molecules **b)** is a molecular solid **c)** has giant molecules. [3]

4 Name the following compounds:
a) $Ca(OH)_2$ **b)** Na_2SO_3 **c)** $CuCO_3$ **d)** $Mg(HCO_3)_2$ **e)** KNO_3. [5]

5 State the formulas of the following compounds:
a) ammonium nitrate **b)** sodium sulphate **c)** ammonium sulphate **d)** aluminium oxide **e)** zinc hydroxide. [5]

Can you summarise this topic in a Mind Map? Copy and complete:

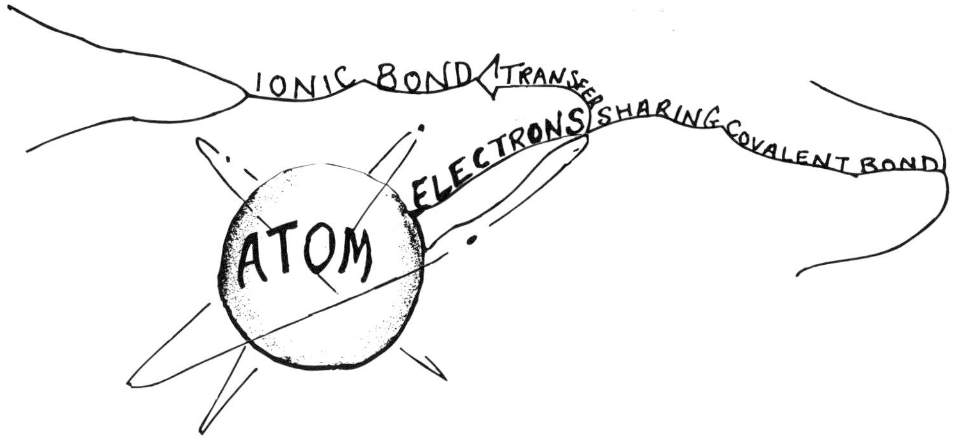

The periodic table

7

preview

At the end of this topic you will:

- **understand the structure of the periodic table**
- **know the nature of the elements in Groups 0, 1, 2, 7 and the transition elements**
- **understand oxidation–reduction reactions.**

How much do you already know? Work out your score on page 130.

Test yourself

1 **a)** What are the noble gases? [2]
b) In which group of the periodic table are they? [1]
c) What do the noble gases have in common regarding **(i)** their electron arrangements and **(ii)** their chemical reactions? [2]

2 X is a metallic element. It reacts slowly with water to give a strongly alkaline solution. In which group of the periodic table would you place X? [1]

3 Y is a non-metallic element. It reacts vigorously with sodium to give a salt of formula NaY. In which group of the periodic table would you place Y? [1]

4 Z is a metallic element which reacts rapidly with water to give a flammable gas and an alkaline solution. In which group of the periodic table would you place Z? [1]

5 **a)** Name the halogens. [4]
b) In which group of the periodic table are they? [1]
c) Does the chemical reactivity of the halogens increase or decrease with atomic number? [1]
d) Give the formulas of the products of the reactions of **(i)** sodium **(ii)** iron with each of the halogens. [8]

6 What is a transition metal? Name two transition metals. [2]

7 Complete the sentence.
Oxidation is the ____________ of oxygen or the ____________ of hydrogen or the ____________ of electrons. [3]

7.1 Classifying elements

Topic 2 dealt with the classification of elements as metallic and non-metallic elements. A major advance was made by John Newlands in 1866 and Dmitri Mendeleev in 1871 when they originated the periodic table. The modern periodic table arranges the elements in order of increasing atomic number. A vertical column of elements is a **group** and a horizontal row is a **period**.

The following patterns can be seen in the arrangement of the elements in the periodic table.

1 The reactive metals are at the left-hand side of the table, less reactive metallic elements in the middle block and non-metallic elements at the right-hand side.

2 The differences between the metals in Group 1, those in Group 2 and the transition metals are summarised in the table at the top of page 36.

3 Silicon and germanium are on the borderline between metals and non-metals. These elements are semiconductors, intermediate between metals, which are electrical conductors, and non-metals, which are non-conductors of electricity. Semiconductors are vital to the computer industry.

4 Group 7 is a set of very reactive non-metallic elements called the **halogens**. They react with metals to form salts; see the table on page 36.

5 When Mendeleev drew up his periodic table in 1871, only 55 elements were known. He left gaps in the table and predicted that new elements would be discovered which would fit the gaps. When the noble gases were discovered, one by one, their atomic numbers placed them in between Groups 1 and 7, and a new Group 0 had to be created for them.

metals **non-metals**

Group 1	2											3	4	5	6	7	0
			H														He
Li	Be											B	C	N	O	F	Ne
Na	Mg					transition metals						Al	Si	P	S	Cl	Ar
K	Ca	Sc	Ti	V	Cr	Mn	Fe	Co	Ni	Cu	Zn	Ga	Ge	As	Se	Br	Kr
Rb	Sr	Y	Zr	Nb	Mo	Tc	Ru	Rh	Pd	Ag	Cd	In	Sn	Sb	Te	I	Xe
Cs	Ba	La	Hf	Ta	W	Re	Os	Ir	Pt	Au	Hg	Tl	Pd	Bi	Po	At	Rn

The reactivity of metals increases **down** each group.

The reactivity of non-metals increases **up** each group.

reactive metals

less reactive metals

non-metals

Elements on or near this line are **metalloids**: they have some metallic characteristics and some non-metallic characteristics.

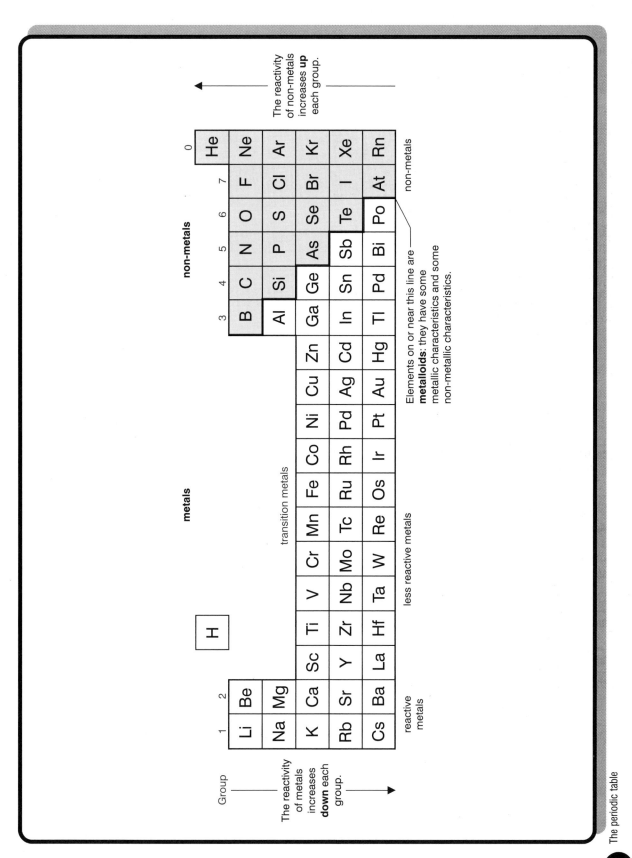

metal	reaction with air	reaction with water	reaction with dilute hydrochloric acid	trend
Group 1 the alkali metals				
lithium sodium potassium rubidium caesium	Burn vigorously to form the strongly basic oxide M_2O which dissolves in water to give the strong alkali MOH.	React vigorously to form hydrogen and a solution of the strong alkali MOH.	The reaction is dangerously violent.	The vigour of all these reactions increases down the group.
Group 2 the alkaline earths				
beryllium magnesium calcium strontium barium	Burn to form the strongly basic oxides MO, which are sparingly soluble or insoluble.	Reacts very slowly. Burns in steam. React readily to form hydrogen and the alkali $M(OH)_2$.	React readily to give hydrogen and a salt, e.g. MCl_2.	The vigour of all these reactions increases down the group. Group 2 elements are less reactive than Group 1.
Transition metals				
iron zinc copper	When heated, form oxides without burning. The oxides and hydroxides are weaker bases than those of Groups 1 and 2 and are insoluble.	Iron rusts slowly. Iron and zinc react with steam to form hydrogen and the oxide. Copper does not react.	Iron and zinc react to give hydrogen and a salt. Copper does not react.	Transition metals are less reactive than Groups 1 and 2. In general, their compounds are coloured; they are used as catalysts.

Some reactions of metals

Note
M stands for the symbol of a metallic element. Dilute sulphuric acid reacts with metals in the same way as dilute hydrochloric acid. Dilute nitric acid is an oxidising agent and attacks metals, e.g. copper, which are not sufficiently reactive to react with other dilute acids.

halogen	state at room temperature	reaction with sodium	reaction with iron	trend
fluorine	gas	explosive	explosive	The vigour of these reactions decreases down the group.
chlorine	gas	Heated sodium burns in chlorine to form sodium chloride.	Reacts vigorously with hot iron to form iron(III) chloride.	
bromine	liquid	Reacts less vigorously to form sodium bromide.	Reacts less vigorously to form iron(III) bromide.	
iodine	solid	Reacts less vigorously than bromine to form sodium iodide.	Reacts less vigorously than bromine to form iron(II) iodide.	

Some reactions of the halogens

7.2 A repeating pattern

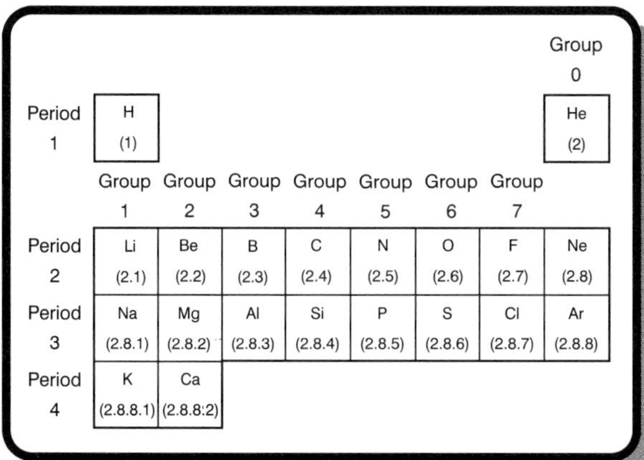

	Group 1	Group 2	Group 3	Group 4	Group 5	Group 6	Group 7	Group 0
Period 1	H (1)							He (2)
Period 2	Li (2.1)	Be (2.2)	B (2.3)	C (2.4)	N (2.5)	O (2.6)	F (2.7)	Ne (2.8)
Period 3	Na (2.8.1)	Mg (2.8.2)	Al (2.8.3)	Si (2.8.4)	P (2.8.5)	S (2.8.6)	Cl (2.8.7)	Ar (2.8.8)
Period 4	K (2.8.8.1)	Ca (2.8.8:2)						

A section of the periodic table

You can see that the arrangement above has the following features:

★ The elements are listed in order of increasing atomic number.

★ Elements which have the same number of electrons in the outermost shell fall into the same **group** (vertical column) of the periodic table.

★ The noble gases are in Group 0. For the rest of the elements, the group number is the number of electrons in the outermost shell.

★ The first **period** (horizontal row) contains only hydrogen and helium. The second period contains the elements lithium to neon. The third period contains the elements sodium to argon.

7.3 Oxidising and reducing agents

Oxidation–reduction reactions

Do you remember what is meant by an oxidising agent and a reducing agent?

★ An **oxidising agent** gives oxygen to a substance or takes hydrogen from a substance.

★ A **reducing agent** takes oxygen from a substance or gives hydrogen to a substance. For example, hydrogen reduces lead(II) oxide to lead.

this is reduction (lead(II) oxide → lead)

lead(II) oxide + hydrogen → lead + water

$$PbO(s) + H_2(g) \rightarrow Pb(s) + H_2O(l)$$

this is oxidation (hydrogen → water)

In this reaction, lead(II) oxide is reduced while hydrogen is oxidised. Lead(II) oxide is the oxidising agent, and hydrogen is the reducing agent. Oxidation and reduction always occur together, and these reactions are called **oxidation–reduction reactions** or **redox reactions**.

Metals as reducing agents

Metals are reducing agents; that is, they can accept oxygen from other substances, for example:

copper + oxygen → copper(II) oxide

$$2Cu(s) + O_2(g) \rightarrow 2CuO(s)$$

calcium + water → hydrogen + calcium hydroxide

$$Ca(s) + 2H_2O(l) \rightarrow H_2(g) + Ca(OH)_2(aq)$$

Some metals are more powerful reducing agents than others. The higher a metal is in the reactivity series, the more powerful a reducing agent it is. A metal high in the reactivity series can reduce the oxide of a metal lower in the reactivity series, for example:

aluminium + iron(III) oxide → aluminium oxide + iron

$$2Al(s) + Fe_2O_3(s) \rightarrow Al_2O_3(s) + 2Fe(s)$$

This is an oxidation–reduction reaction: while iron(III) oxide is reduced to iron, aluminium is oxidised to aluminium oxide.

The halogens as oxidising agents

The halogens are classified as oxidising agents, although they do not give oxygen to other substances. Their reactions are dominated by a readiness to gain electrons and form halide ions, for example:

chlorine molecules + electrons → chloride ions

$Cl_2(aq) + 2e^- \rightarrow 2Cl^-(aq)$

If halogens are oxidising agents, our definition of oxidation–reduction reactions must be extended to include this type of reaction.

An extended definition:

Oxidation is	**Reduction is**
• the gain of oxygen by a substance	• the loss of oxygen by a substance
• the loss of hydrogen by a substance	• the gain of hydrogen by a substance
• the loss of electrons by a substance.	• the gain of electrons by a substance.

An oxidising agent	**A reducing agent**
• gives oxygen to a substance	• takes oxygen from a substance
• takes hydrogen from a substance	• gives hydrogen to a substance
• takes electrons from a substance.	• gives electrons to a substance.

Handy hint

Loss or gain of electrons?

OIL RIG will help you to remember:

★ Oxidation Is Loss

★ Reduction Is Gain.

Reactions with metals: halogens react with metals to form salts, for example:

sodium + chlorine → sodium chloride

$2Na(s) + Cl_2(g) \rightarrow 2Na^+(s) + 2Cl^-(s)$

Halogen molecules are reduced (they gain electrons) to become halide ions, such as Cl^-.

Metal atoms are oxidised (they give electrons) to become metal ions, such as Na^+.

Reactions between halogens: in order of oxidising power, the halogens rank:

$F_2 > Cl_2 > Br_2 > I_2$

As a result of this difference in oxidising power,

1 Chlorine displaces bromine from bromides.

chlorine + bromide ion → chloride ion + bromine

$Cl_2(aq) + 2Br^-(aq) \rightarrow 2Cl^-(aq) + Br_2(aq)$

(reduction: $Cl_2 \rightarrow 2Cl^-$; oxidation: $2Br^- \rightarrow Br_2$)

Chlorine molecules are reduced to chloride ions, while bromide ions are oxidised to bromine molecules.

2 Chlorine displaces iodine from iodides.

3 Bromine displaces iodine from iodides.

Bromine from sea water

The oxidation of bromide ions by chlorine is used to extract bromine from sea water. The process is carried out in Anglesey, Wales and by the Dead Sea, Israel. This is the process:

1 Sea water is concentrated by evaporation.

2 Sodium chloride, potassium chloride and magnesium chloride crystallise out.

3 These salts are electrolysed to give chlorine.

4 Chlorine is passed through the concentrated sea water.

5 Liquid bromine is run off and distilled.

round-up

How much have you improved?
Work out your improvement index on pages 130–1.

1 Magnesium chloride, $MgCl_2$, is a solid of high melting point, and tetrachloromethane, CCl_4, is a volatile liquid. Explain how differences in chemical bonding account for these differences. [4]

2 Choose from the elements: Na, Mg, Al, Si, P, S, Cl, Ar.
a) List the elements that react readily with cold water to form alkaline solutions. [2]
b) List the elements that form sulphates. [3]
c) Name the elements which exist as molecules containing **(i)** one atom **(ii)** two atoms. [2]
d) Which element has both metallic and non-metallic properties? [1]

3 Write the symbol for the reducing agent in each of the following reactions.
a) $2Na(s) + 2H_2O(l) \rightarrow H_2(g) + 2NaOH(aq)$ [1]
b) $O_2(g) + S(s) \rightarrow SO_2(g)$ [1]
c) $2Al(s) + 3Cl_2(g) \rightarrow 2AlCl_3(s)$ [1]
d) $Cu(s) + S(s) \rightarrow CuS(s)$ [1]

4 Give the formulas of the oxides of sodium, magnesium, aluminium and silicon. [4]

5 What have the following compounds in common? the sulphate of chlorine, the carbonate of silicon and the hydride of argon [1]

6 The elements sodium and potassium have the electron arrangements Na(2.8.1) and K(2.8.8.1). How does this explain the similarity in their reactions? [2]

7 Radium, Ra, is a radioactive element of atomic number 88 which falls below barium in Group 2. What can you predict about
a) the nature of radium oxide [3]
b) the reaction of radium with water [3]
c) the reaction of radium with dilute hydrochloric acid? [4]
Give the physical state and type of bonding in any compounds you mention. Include the names and formulas of any compounds formed.

8 Astatine, At, is a radioactive element of atomic number 85 which follows fluorine in Group 7.
What can you predict about
a) the nature of its compound with hydrogen [3]
b) the reaction of astatine with sodium? [4]
Give the physical state and type of bonding in any compounds you mention. Include the names and formulas of any compounds formed.

9 Write a word equation and a balanced chemical equation
a) for the oxidation of sodium iodide by chlorine [4]
b) for the oxidation of potassium iodide by bromine. [4]

10 You are given three unmarked bottles containing crystalline white solids and three labels which read:

potassium chloride

potassium bromide

potassium iodide

You have to decide which label to stick on each bottle. You may use only a bottle of chlorine water and an organic solvent. What tests would you carry out? [10]

11 With which of the following pairs of reagents would a displacement reaction take place?
A aqueous bromine and aqueous potassium chloride
B aqueous bromine and aqueous sodium iodide
C aqueous chlorine and aqueous potassium iodide
D aqueous iodine and aqueous potassium bromide [2]

12 State which is **(i)** the oxidising agent and **(ii)** the reducing agent in each of these reactions:
a) aluminium + iron oxide → iron + aluminium oxide [2]
a)
b) tin sulphide + oxygen → tin oxide + sulphur dioxide [2]
c) tin oxide + carbon → tin + carbon monoxide [2]

Well done if you've improved. Don't worry if you haven't. Take a break and try again.

Acids, bases and salts

preview

At the end of this section you will:

- **be able to define the terms 'acid', 'base' and 'alkali'**
- **know the typical reactions of acids and bases**
- **know how to prepare salts and know the uses of some important salts.**

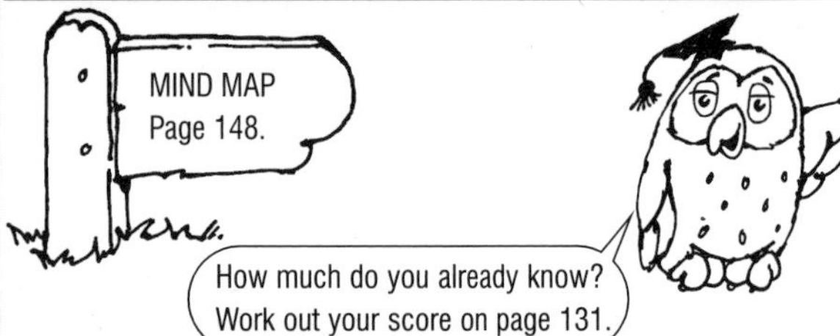

MIND MAP
Page 148.
How much do you already know?
Work out your score on page 131.

Test yourself

1 Say whether the substances listed are strongly acidic (SA), weakly acidic (WA), strongly basic (SB), weakly basic (WB) or neutral (N).

a) battery acid, pH 0 [1]
b) rainwater, pH 6.5 [1]
c) blood, pH 7.4 [1]
d) sea water, pH 8.5 [1]
e) cabbage juice, pH 5.0 [1]
f) saliva, pH 7.0 [1]
g) washing soda, pH 11.5 [1]

2 You are given two bottles labelled 'acid 1' and 'acid 2'. One is a weak acid and the other is a strong acid. Describe two tests you could do to find out which is which. [3]

3 Name

a) a strong acid present in your stomach [1]
b) a base present in indigestion tablets [1]
c) a weak acid present in fruits [1]
d) a weak base used as a domestic cleaning fluid. [1]

4 Kleenit is an oven spray for cleaning greasy ovens. It contains a concentrated solution of sodium hydroxide.

a) Why does sodium hydroxide remove grease? [1]
b) Why does sodium hydroxide work better than ammonia? [1]
c) What two safety precautions should you take when using Kleenit? [2]
d) Why does Moppit, a fluid used for cleaning floors, contain ammonia rather than sodium hydroxide? [1]
e) Why do soap manufacturers use sodium hydroxide, not ammonia? [1]

8.1 Acids

Where are acids found?

The following are strong acids:

- Hydrochloric acid occurs in the stomach, where it aids digestion.
- Nitric acid is used in the production of fertilisers and explosives.
- Sulphuric acid is used car batteries and in the production of fertilisers.

The following are weak acids:

- Carbonic acid is used in fizzy drinks.
- Citric acid occurs in lemons and other citrus fruits.
- Ethanoic acid occurs in vinegar.
- Lactic acid is present in sour milk.

What do acids do?

Acids are compounds that release hydrogen ions when dissolved in water. The hydrogen ions are responsible for the typical reactions of acids. Strong acids are completely ionised; for example, hydrochloric acid solution consists of the ions H^+ and Cl^- and water molecules. There are no molecules of HCl in the solution. Weak acids consist chiefly of molecules, but a small fraction of the molecules are ionised. Weak acids therefore have a low concentration of hydrogen ions in solution and react less readily than strong acids.

The concept map opposite gives a summary of the properties of acids.

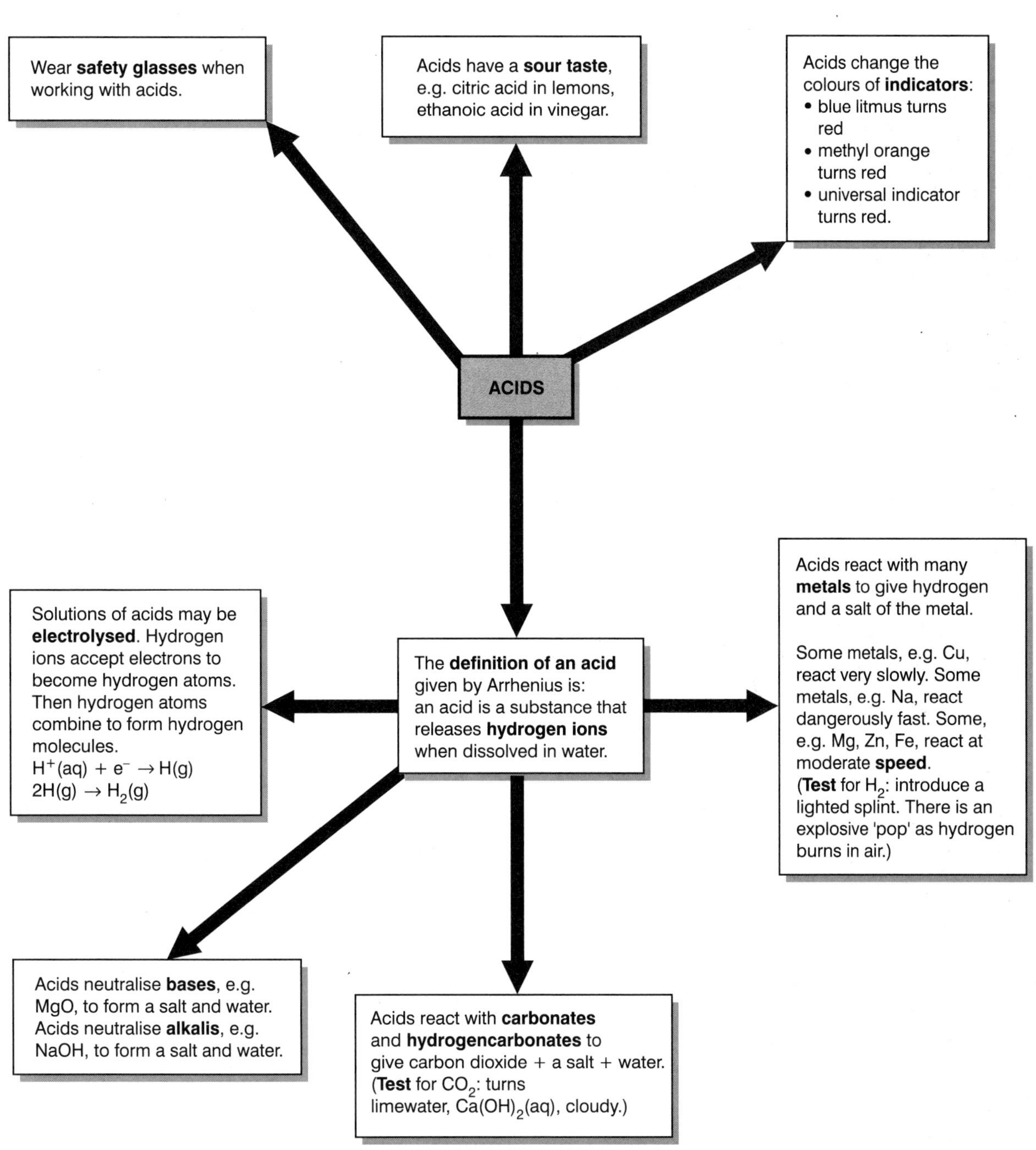

Wear **safety glasses** when working with acids.
Acids have a **sour taste**, e.g. citric acid in lemons, ethanoic acid in vinegar.
Acids change the colours of **indicators**:
• blue litmus turns red
• methyl orange turns red
• universal indicator turns red.
ACIDS
The **definition of an acid** given by Arrhenius is: an acid is a substance that releases **hydrogen ions** when dissolved in water.
Solutions of acids may be **electrolysed**. Hydrogen ions accept electrons to become hydrogen atoms. Then hydrogen atoms combine to form hydrogen molecules.
$H^+(aq) + e^- \rightarrow H(g)$
$2H(g) \rightarrow H_2(g)$
Acids react with many **metals** to give hydrogen and a salt of the metal.
Some metals, e.g. Cu, react very slowly. Some metals, e.g. Na, react dangerously fast. Some, e.g. Mg, Zn, Fe, react at moderate **speed**.
(**Test** for H_2: introduce a lighted splint. There is an explosive 'pop' as hydrogen burns in air.)
Acids neutralise **bases**, e.g. MgO, to form a salt and water. Acids neutralise **alkalis**, e.g. NaOH, to form a salt and water.
Acids react with **carbonates** and **hydrogencarbonates** to give carbon dioxide + a salt + water. (**Test** for CO_2: turns limewater, $Ca(OH)_2(aq)$, cloudy.)

Concept map: The properties of acids

Equations for some reactions in the concept map

With metals

zinc + sulphuric acid → hydrogen + zinc sulphate

$Zn(s) + H_2SO_4(aq) \rightarrow H_2(g) + ZnSO_4(aq)$

or the ionic equation:

$Zn(s) + 2H^+(aq) \rightarrow Zn^{2+}(aq) + H_2(g)$

With bases

magnesium oxide + sulphuric acid → magnesium sulphate + water

$MgO(s) + H_2SO_4(aq) \rightarrow MgSO_4(aq) + H_2O(l)$

or the ionic equation:

$O^{2-}(s) + 2H^+(aq) \rightarrow H_2O(l)$

calcium hydroxide + hydrochloric acid → calcium chloride + water

$Ca(OH)_2(s) + 2HCl(aq) \rightarrow CaCl_2(aq) + 2H_2O(l)$

or the ionic equation:

$OH^-(aq) + H^+(aq) \rightarrow H_2O(l)$

With carbonates

calcium carbonate + hydrochloric acid → carbon dioxide + calcium chloride + water

$CaCO_3(s) + 2HCl(aq) \rightarrow CO_2(g) + CaCl_2(aq) + H_2O(l)$

or the ionic equation:

$CO_3^{2-}(s) + 2H^+(aq) \rightarrow CO_2(g) + H_2O(l)$

With alkalis

ammonia + sulphuric acid → ammonium sulphate

$2NH_3(aq) + H_2SO_4(aq) \rightarrow (NH_4)_2SO_4(aq)$

8.2 Bases

Where do you find bases?

The following are strong bases:

- Calcium hydroxide is used to treat soil which is too acidic.
- Calcium oxide is used in the manufacture of cement and concrete.
- Magnesium hydroxide is used in anti-acid indigestion tablets.
- Sodium hydroxide is used in soap manufacture and as a degreasing agent.
- The weak base ammonia is used in cleaning fluids, as a degreasing agent and in the manufacture of fertilisers.

What do bases do?

A **base** is a substance that reacts with an acid to form a salt and water as the only products.
A soluble base is called an **alkali**. Sodium hydroxide, NaOH, is a strong base and a strong alkali. It is completely ionised in solution as Na^+ and OH^- ions. Ammonia is only slightly ionised and the concentration of hydroxide ions in the solution is small. Ammonia is therefore a weak base.

The concept map opposite gives a summary of the properties of bases.

Equations for some reactions in the concept map

With acids

magnesium oxide + hydrochloric acid → magnesium chloride + water

$MgO(s) + 2HCl(aq) \rightarrow MgCl_2(aq) + H_2O(l)$

or the ionic equation:

$O^{2-}(s) + 2H^+(aq) \rightarrow H_2O(l)$

sodium hydroxide + hydrochloric acid → sodium chloride + water

$NaOH(aq) + HCl(aq) \rightarrow NaCl(aq) + H_2O(l)$

sodium hydroxide + sulphuric acid → sodium sulphate + water

$2NaOH(aq) + H_2SO_4(aq) \rightarrow Na_2SO_4(aq) + 2H_2O(l)$

or the ionic equation:

$OH^-(aq) + H^+(aq) \rightarrow H_2O(l)$

With metal salts

sodium hydroxide + iron(II) sulphate → iron(II) hydroxide + sodium sulphate

$2NaOH(aq) + FeSO_4(aq) \rightarrow Fe(OH)_2(s) + Na_2SO_4(aq)$

or the ionic equation:

$Fe^{2+}(aq) + 2OH^-(aq) \rightarrow Fe(OH)_2(s)$

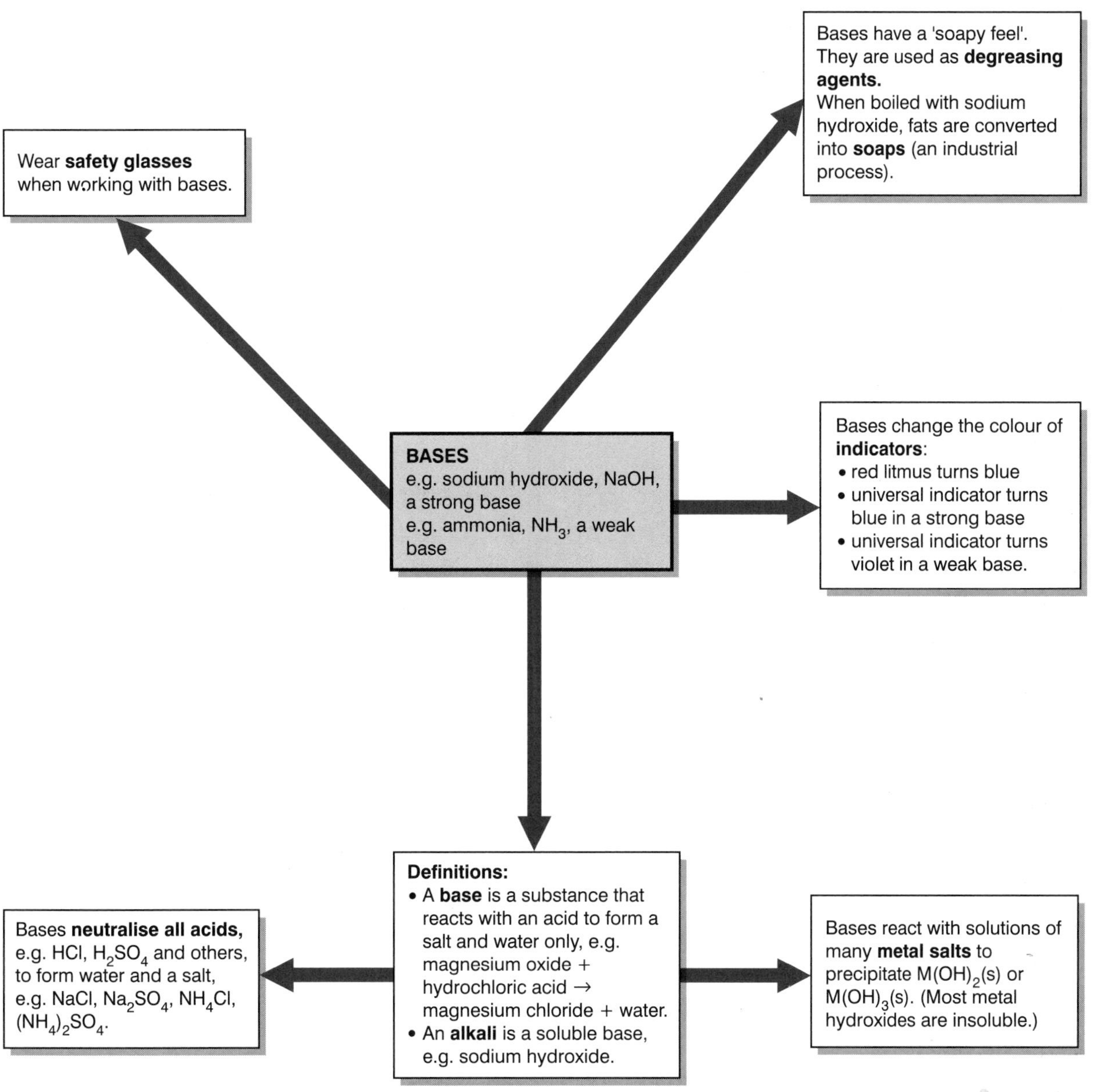

Wear **safety glasses** when working with bases.

Bases have a 'soapy feel'. They are used as **degreasing agents.** When boiled with sodium hydroxide, fats are converted into **soaps** (an industrial process).

BASES
e.g. sodium hydroxide, NaOH, a strong base
e.g. ammonia, NH_3, a weak base

Bases change the colour of **indicators**:
• red litmus turns blue
• universal indicator turns blue in a strong base
• universal indicator turns violet in a weak base.

Definitions:
• A **base** is a substance that reacts with an acid to form a salt and water only, e.g. magnesium oxide + hydrochloric acid → magnesium chloride + water.
• An **alkali** is a soluble base, e.g. sodium hydroxide.

Bases **neutralise all acids,** e.g. HCl, H_2SO_4 and others, to form water and a salt, e.g. NaCl, Na_2SO_4, NH_4Cl, $(NH_4)_2SO_4$.

Bases react with solutions of many **metal salts** to precipitate $M(OH)_2(s)$ or $M(OH)_3(s)$. (Most metal hydroxides are insoluble.)

Concept map: The properties of bases

sodium hydroxide + iron(III) sulphate → iron(III) hydroxide + sodium sulphate

$6NaOH(aq) + Fe_2(SO_4)_3(aq) \rightarrow 2Fe(OH)_3(s) + 3Na_2SO_4(aq)$

or the ionic equation:

$Fe^{3+}(aq) + 3OH^-(aq) \rightarrow Fe(OH)_3(s)$

8.3 Neutralisation

Neutralisation is the combination of hydrogen ions (from an acid) and hydroxide ions (from an alkali) or oxide ions (from an insoluble base) to form water. In the process a salt is formed. For example, with an alkali:

hydrochloric acid + sodium hydroxide → sodium chloride + water

$HCl(aq) + NaOH(aq) \rightarrow NaCl(aq) + H_2O(l)$

acid + **alkali** → **salt** + **water**

The hydrogen ions and hydroxide ions combine to form water molecules.

$$H^+(aq) + OH^-(aq) \rightarrow H_2O(l)$$

Sodium ions and chloride ions remain in the solution, which becomes a solution of sodium chloride.

With a base:

sulphuric acid + copper(II) oxide → copper(II) sulphate + water

$H_2SO_4(aq) + CuO(s) \rightarrow CuSO_4(aq) + H_2O(l)$

acid + **base** → **salt** + **water**

Hydrogen ions and oxide ions combine to form water:

$$2H^+(aq) + O^{2-}(s) \rightarrow H_2O(l)$$

Copper(II) ions and sulphate ions remain in the solution, which becomes a solution of copper(II) sulphate.

8.4 Indicators

indicator	acidic colour	neutral colour	alkaline colour
litmus	red	purple	blue
phenolphthalein	colourless	colourless	red
methyl orange	red	orange	yellow

Universal indicator can distinguish between strong and weak bases, as shown in the diagram below.

8.5 Salts

Common salt

The importance of common salt, sodium chloride, NaCl, is outlined in the concept map opposite.

Some useful salts

★ **Sodium carbonate-10-water**, $Na_2CO_3.10H_2O$, 'washing soda', is used as a water softener, an ingredient of washing powders and bath salts.

★ **Sodium hydrogencarbonate**, $NaHCO_3$, 'baking soda', is added to self-raising flour. It decomposes at oven temperature to give carbon dioxide and steam, which make bread and cakes rise.

★ **Calcium sulphate-$\frac{1}{2}$-water**, $CaSO_4.\frac{1}{2}H_2O$, is plaster of Paris. When mixed with water it combines and sets to form a strong 'plaster cast'. It is also used for plastering walls.

★ **Silver bromide**, AgBr, is used in black-and-white photographic film.

★ **Iron(II) sulphate-7-water**, $FeSO_4.7H_2O$, is used in some kinds of 'iron tablets' which people take for anaemia.

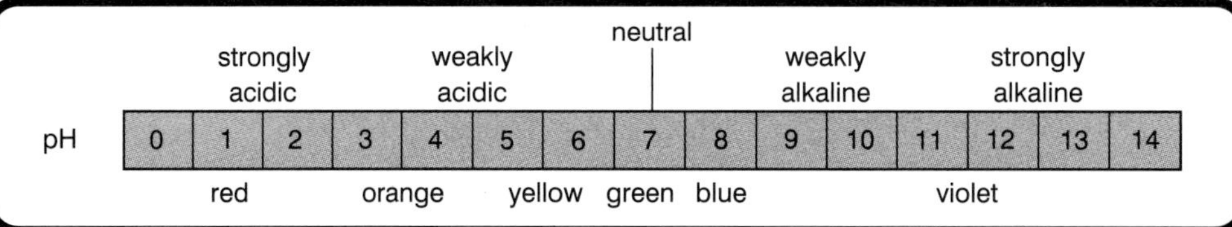

The colour of universal indicator in solutions of different pH

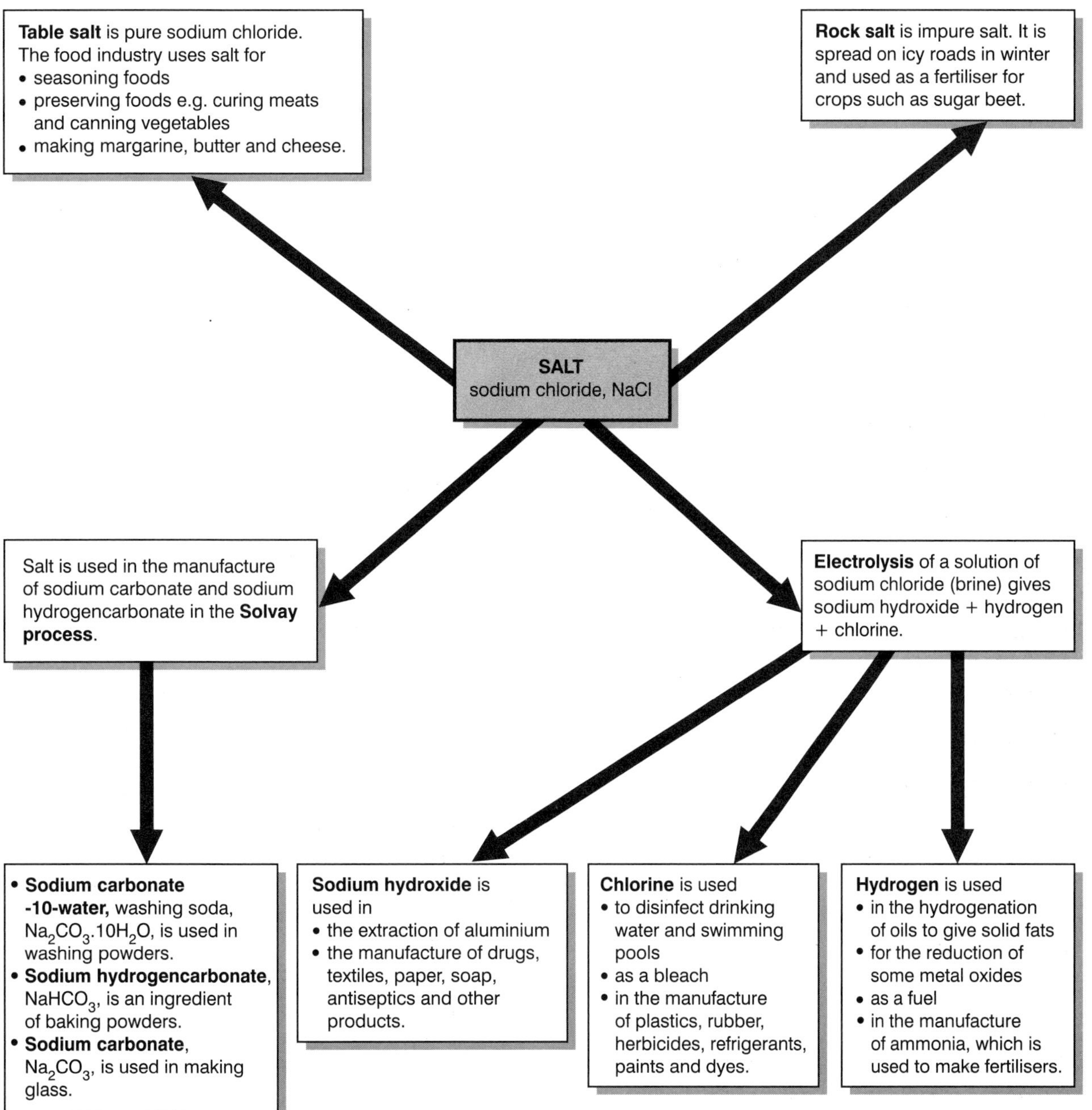

Table salt is pure sodium chloride. The food industry uses salt for
• seasoning foods
• preserving foods e.g. curing meats and canning vegetables
• making margarine, butter and cheese.
Rock salt is impure salt. It is spread on icy roads in winter and used as a fertiliser for crops such as sugar beet.
SALT
sodium chloride, NaCl
Salt is used in the manufacture of sodium carbonate and sodium hydrogencarbonate in the **Solvay process**.
Electrolysis of a solution of sodium chloride (brine) gives sodium hydroxide + hydrogen + chlorine.
• **Sodium carbonate -10-water,** washing soda, $Na_2CO_3.10H_2O$, is used in washing powders.
• **Sodium hydrogencarbonate**, $NaHCO_3$, is an ingredient of baking powders.
• **Sodium carbonate**, Na_2CO_3, is used in making glass.
Sodium hydroxide is used in
• the extraction of aluminium
• the manufacture of drugs, textiles, paper, soap, antiseptics and other products.
Chlorine is used
• to disinfect drinking water and swimming pools
• as a bleach
• in the manufacture of plastics, rubber, herbicides, refrigerants, paints and dyes.
Hydrogen is used
• in the hydrogenation of oils to give solid fats
• for the reduction of some metal oxides
• as a fuel
• in the manufacture of ammonia, which is used to make fertilisers.

Concept map: common salt

★ **Barium sulphate**, $BaSO_4$, is used in 'barium meals' because barium ions show up well on X-rays and reveal the position of a stomach ulcer.

★ **Copper(II) sulphate**, $CuSO_4$, is used as a fungicide for spraying grapes, potatoes and other crops.

★ **Calcium fluoride**, CaF_2, is added to toothpastes. Tooth enamel reacts with fluorides to form a harder enamel which is better at resisting attack by mouth acids. Many water companies add a small amount of calcium fluoride to drinking water.

★ **NPK fertilisers** contain ammonium nitrate, NH_4NO_3, and ammonium sulphate, $(NH_4)_2SO_4$, as sources of nitrogen; calcium phosphate, $Ca_3(PO_4)_2$, as a source of phosphorus; and potassium chloride, KCl, as a source of potassium.

Making soluble salts

To make a soluble salt, an acid is neutralised by adding a metal, a solid base, a solid metal carbonate or a solution of an alkali.

★ **Method 1:** acid + metal → salt + hydrogen

★ **Method 2:** acid + metal oxide → salt + water

★ **Method 3:**

acid + metal carbonate → salt + water + carbon dioxide

★ **Method 4:** acid + alkali → salt + water

Here are the practical details for methods **1**, **2** and **3**.

a) Carry out the neutralisation as shown in the table and diagram below.

b) Filter to remove the excess of solid, using a filter funnel and filter paper.

c) Evaporate the filtrate, preferably on a water bath.

d) As the solution cools, crystals of the salt form. Separate the crystals by filtration. Using a little distilled water, wash the crystals in the filter funnel. Leave the crystals to dry.

method 1 (acid + metal)	**method 2** (acid + metal oxide)	**method 3** (acid + metal carbonate)
Warm the acid, then switch off the Bunsen burner.	Warm the acid.	
Add an excess of the metal to the acid. When no more hydrogen is evolved, the reaction is complete.	Add an excess of the metal oxide to the acid. When the solution no longer turns blue litmus paper red, the reaction is complete.	Add an excess of the metal carbonate to the acid. When no more carbon dioxide is evolved, the reaction is complete.

Neutralisation details for methods **1** to **3**

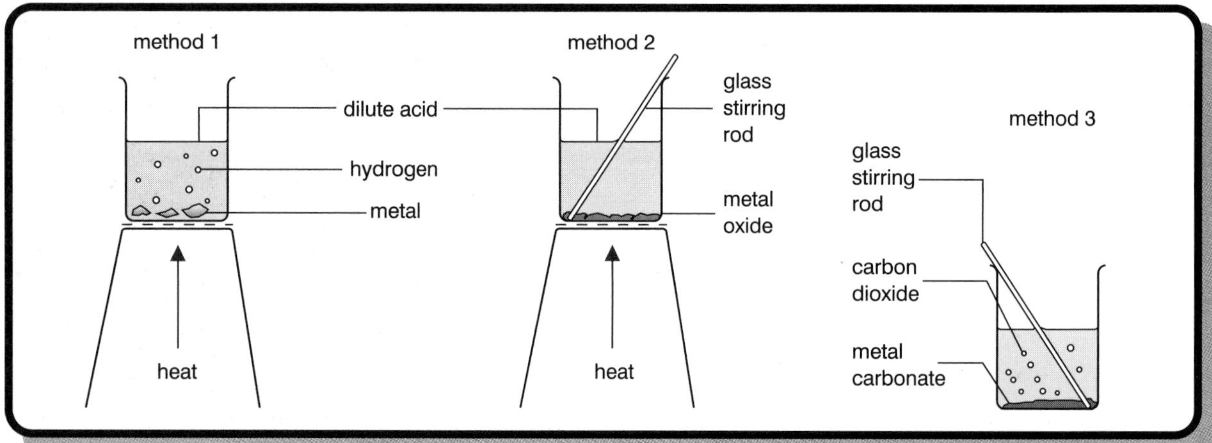

Adding an excess of a solid reactant to an acid

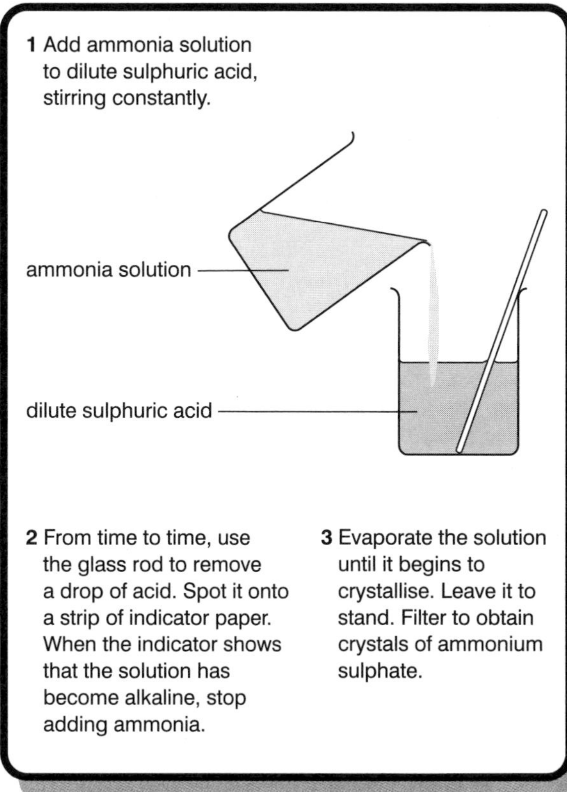

1 Add ammonia solution to dilute sulphuric acid, stirring constantly.
ammonia solution
dilute sulphuric acid
2 From time to time, use the glass rod to remove a drop of acid. Spot it onto a strip of indicator paper. When the indicator shows that the solution has become alkaline, stop adding ammonia.
3 Evaporate the solution until it begins to crystallise. Leave it to stand. Filter to obtain crystals of ammonium sulphate.

Laboratory preparation of ammonium sulphate

Here are the practical details for method **4** (acid + alkali). For example, the neutralisation of an acid by ammonia solution can be used to make ammonium salts. The diagram above shows the steps in the preparation of ammonium sulphate.

Making insoluble salts: precipitation

Insoluble salts are made by mixing two solutions. For example, barium sulphate is insoluble. A soluble barium salt and a soluble sulphate must be chosen to make barium sulphate. The precipitate is separated by filtering or centrifuging.

The equation for the reaction is:

barium chloride + sodium sulphate → barium sulphate + sodium chloride

$$BaCl_2(aq) + Na_2SO_4(aq) \rightarrow BaSO_4(s) + 2NaCl(aq)$$

or the ionic equation:

$$Ba^{2+}(aq) + SO_4^{2-}(aq) \rightarrow BaSO_4(s)$$

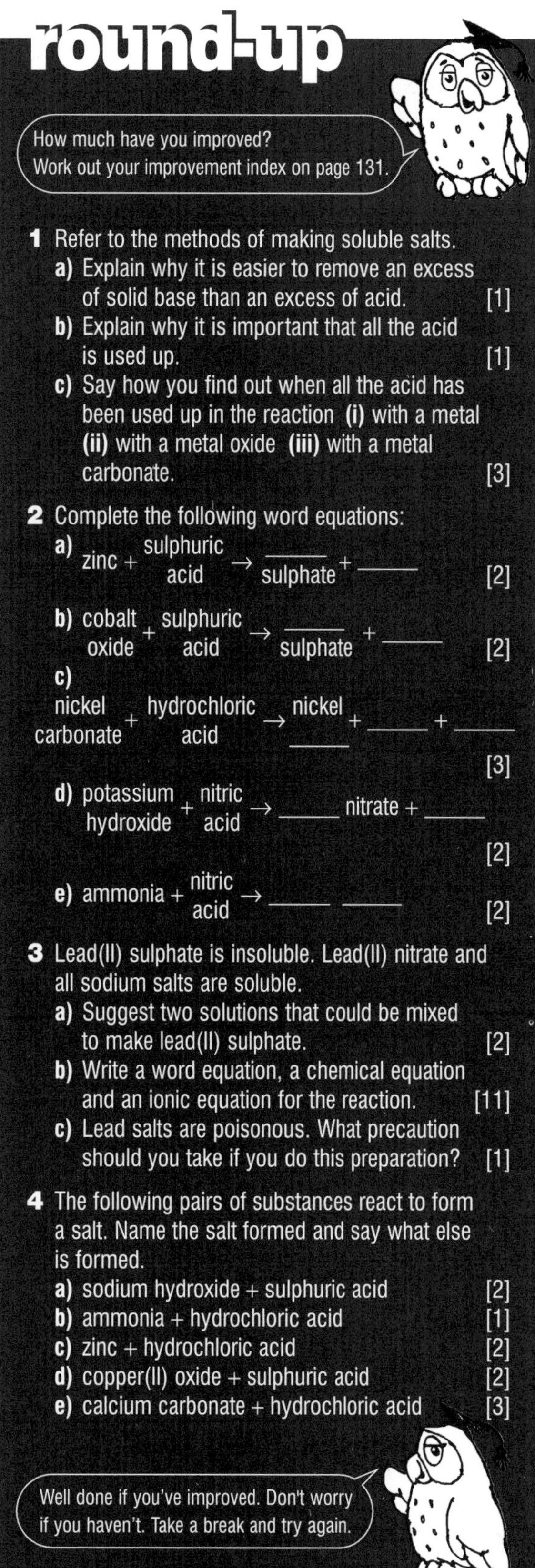

round-up

How much have you improved? Work out your improvement index on page 131.

1 Refer to the methods of making soluble salts.

a) Explain why it is easier to remove an excess of solid base than an excess of acid. [1]

b) Explain why it is important that all the acid is used up. [1]

c) Say how you find out when all the acid has been used up in the reaction **(i)** with a metal **(ii)** with a metal oxide **(iii)** with a metal carbonate. [3]

2 Complete the following word equations:

a) zinc + sulphuric acid → _____ sulphate + _____ [2]

b) cobalt oxide + sulphuric acid → _____ sulphate + _____ [2]

c) nickel carbonate + hydrochloric acid → nickel _____ + _____ + _____ [3]

d) potassium hydroxide + nitric acid → _____ nitrate + _____ [2]

e) ammonia + nitric acid → _____ _____ [2]

3 Lead(II) sulphate is insoluble. Lead(II) nitrate and all sodium salts are soluble.

a) Suggest two solutions that could be mixed to make lead(II) sulphate. [2]

b) Write a word equation, a chemical equation and an ionic equation for the reaction. [11]

c) Lead salts are poisonous. What precaution should you take if you do this preparation? [1]

4 The following pairs of substances react to form a salt. Name the salt formed and say what else is formed.

a) sodium hydroxide + sulphuric acid [2]

b) ammonia + hydrochloric acid [1]

c) zinc + hydrochloric acid [2]

d) copper(II) oxide + sulphuric acid [2]

e) calcium carbonate + hydrochloric acid [3]

Well done if you've improved. Don't worry if you haven't. Take a break and try again.

Air

9

preview

At the end of this topic you will:

- know how Earth's atmosphere originated
- know the reactions and importance of oxygen
- know the importance of the nitrogen cycle and the carbon cycle
- appreciate the effects of pollutants in the atmosphere.

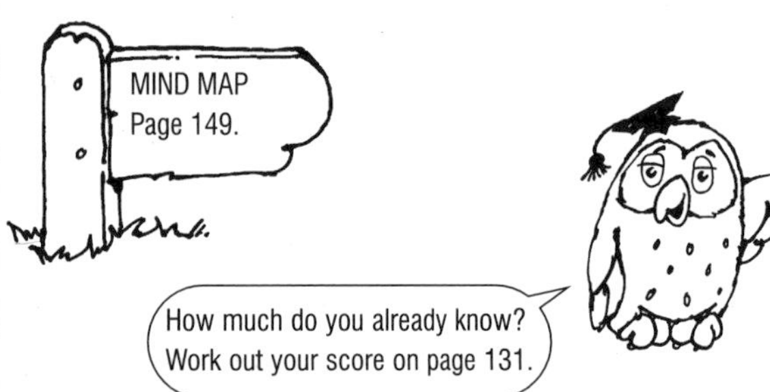

MIND MAP
Page 149.
How much do you already know?
Work out your score on page 131.

Test yourself

1 How did Earth's original atmosphere, formed billions of years ago, differ from today's atmosphere in its content of water vapour, carbon dioxide, oxygen and nitrogen? [4]

2 Give the percentage by volume in pure dry air of oxygen and nitrogen. [2]

3 Give two industrial uses for oxygen. [2]

4 What is the name for an oxidation reaction in which energy is released? [1]

5 Describe a test for oxygen. [1]

6 Suggest identities for the following elements. [4]
A burns with a blue flame to give an acidic gas.
B burns with a yellow flame to give a basic solid.
C burns with a bright white flame to give a basic solid.
D burns with a red glow to give an invisible gas.

7 Name two processes which turn atmospheric nitrogen into compounds. [2]

8 Name two processes which take carbon dioxide out of the atmosphere. [2]

9 How would you test an invisible gas to find out if it is carbon dioxide? [2]

10 Name four atmospheric pollutants and state one source of each. [8]

9.1 How the atmosphere evolved

A mixture of gases was released from the interior of Earth about 4.6 billion years ago. The mixture was probably similar to the gases released from volcanoes today: water vapour 64% by mass, carbon dioxide 24%, sulphur dioxide 10%, nitrogen 1.5%. Water vapour condensed to make oceans. Carbon dioxide dissolved in the oceans, where it was used by the first living things in a process which developed into photosynthesis:

$$\text{carbon dioxide} + \text{water} + \text{sunlight} \rightarrow \text{organic matter} + \text{oxygen}$$

$$CO_2 + H_2O \rightarrow (CH_2O) + O_2$$

The oxygen formed in photosynthesis would have poisoned primitive plants. It was not released into the air, but was converted into iron oxides.

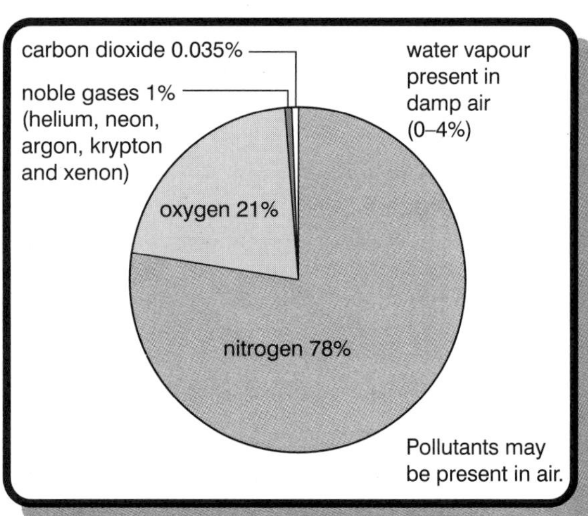

The composition of pure, dry air in percentage by volume

Eventually bacteria living in the ocean developed the ability to use oxygen in respiration. Oxygen began to accumulate in the atmosphere, and the ozone layer formed. This shields Earth from receiving too much radiation from the Sun, and makes Earth an environment in which things can live. About 450 million years ago land plants emerged, followed by land animals 400 million years ago. The composition of the atmosphere has remained the same for about 300 million years.

Separating gases from air

Oxygen, nitrogen and argon are obtained by fractional distillation of liquid air. Liquid air at –190°C is fed into an insulated fractionation column. Nitrogen (boiling point –196°C) vaporises at the top of the column, argon (boiling point –186°C) vaporises from the middle of the column, and oxygen (boiling point –183°C) is left at the bottom of the column.

9.2 Oxygen

Plants and animals need oxygen for respiration. Aquatic plants and animals depend on the oxygen dissolved in water. Pollutants such as excess decaying organic matter use up dissolved oxygen and put aquatic animals and plants at risk.

Uses of pure oxygen

★ Aeroplanes which fly at high altitude, and all space flights, carry oxygen.

★ Deep-sea divers carry cylinders which contain a mixture of oxygen and helium.

★ An oxyacetylene torch (which burns ethyne, C_2H_2, in oxygen) has a very hot flame, about 4000°C, and is used for welding and cutting metals.

★ Cast iron contains carbon, which is burnt off in a stream of oxygen to make steel.

★ Oxygen is pumped into polluted rivers and lakes.

9.3 Reactions of oxygen

Oxygen is colourless, odourless and slightly soluble in water. Many elements react with oxygen to form oxides as shown in the table below.

★ Combination with oxygen is called **oxidation**.

★ Oxidation in which energy is given out is called **combustion**.

★ Combustion accompanied by a flame is **burning**.

★ Substances which undergo combustion to give out a lot of energy are called **fuels**.

★ Many substances burn in oxygen, and all substances burn more rapidly in oxygen than in air.

★ **Test for oxygen:** a glowing wooden splint lowered into oxygen starts to burn brightly.

The concept map overleaf shows the properties of oxides.

FACTS

element	observation	product	action of product on water
calcium (metal)	burns with a red flame	calcium oxide (white solid)	dissolves to give a strongly alkaline solution
copper (metal)	turns black without burning	copper(II) oxide (black solid)	insoluble
iron (metal)	burns with yellow sparks	iron oxide, Fe_3O_4	insoluble
magnesium (metal)	burns with a white flame	magnesium oxide (white solid)	dissolves slightly to give an alkaline solution
sodium (metal)	burns with a yellow flame	sodium oxide	dissolves readily to give a strongly alkaline solution
carbon (non-metal)	glows red	carbon dioxide (invisible gas)	dissolves slightly to give a weakly acidic solution
sulphur (non-metal)	burns with a blue flame	sulphur dioxide (fuming gas)	dissolves readily to give a strongly acidic solution

Reactions of oxygen with some elements

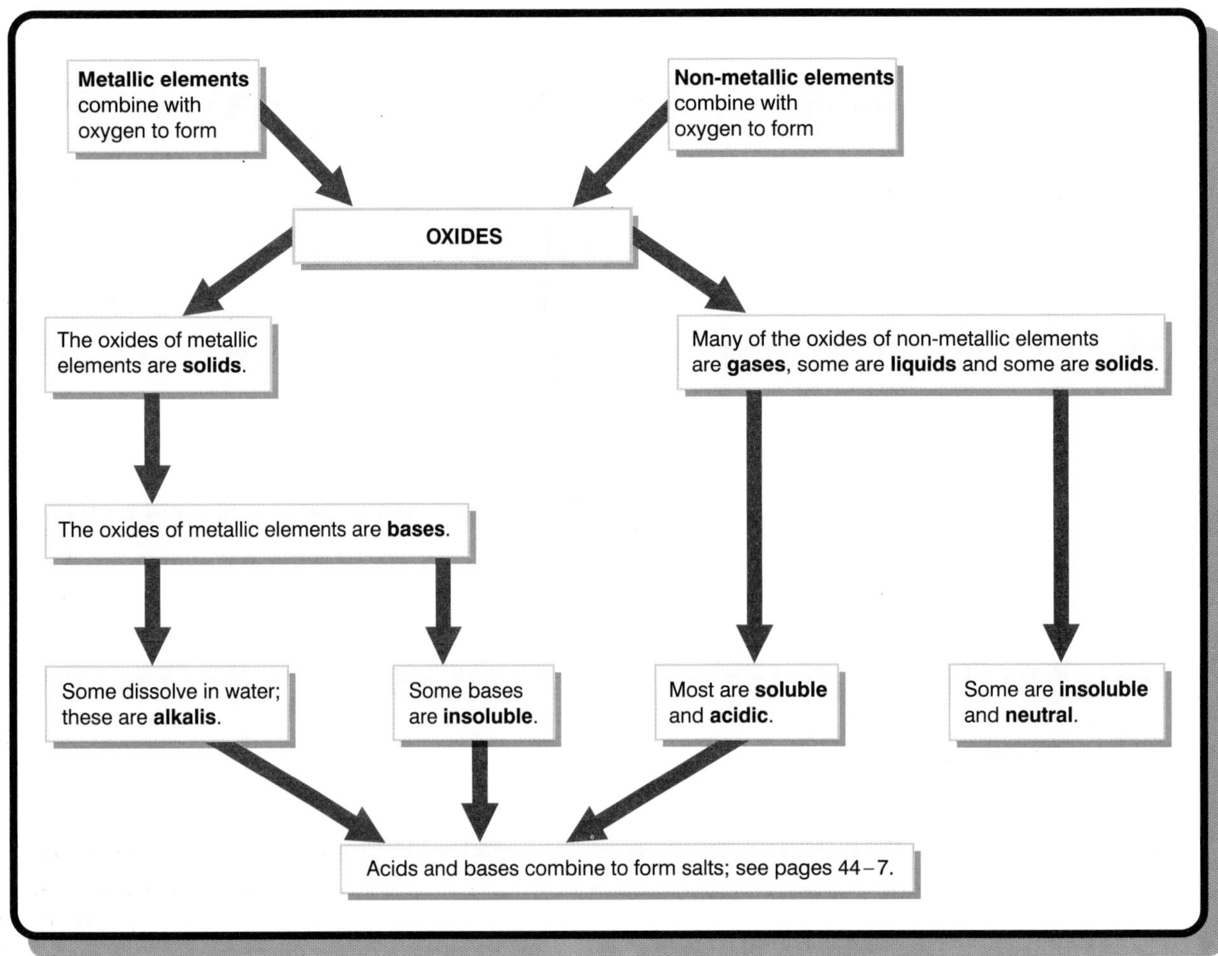

Concept map: properties of oxides

9.4 Nitrogen

Nitrogen is a gas which does not take part in many chemical reactions. It combines with hydrogen to form ammonia. This reaction is the basis of the fertiliser industry; see opposite. Many uses of nitrogen arise from its lack of reactivity.

★ Liquid nitrogen is used in the fast-freezing of foods.

★ Many foods are packed in an atmosphere of nitrogen to prevent oils and fats in the foods from being oxidised to rancid products.

★ Oil tankers, road tankers and grain silos are flushed out with nitrogen as a precaution against fire.

9.5 The nitrogen cycle

Nitrogen circulates from air to soil to living things and back again in a process called the **nitrogen cycle**, shown on the opposite page.

9.6 Ammonia and fertilisers

Ammonia

The nitrogen in the air is used to make nitrogenous fertilisers. Under the conditions of the **Haber process** (named after the chemist Fritz Haber) nitrogen will combine with hydrogen.

$$\text{nitrogen} + \text{hydrogen} \rightleftharpoons \text{ammonia}$$

$$N_2(g) + 3H_2(g) \rightleftharpoons 2NH_3(g)$$

The reaction is reversible: some of the ammonia formed dissociates into nitrogen and hydrogen.

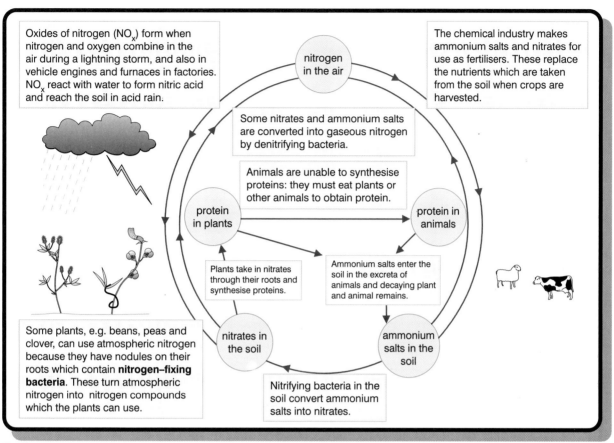

The nitrogen cycle

The product is a mixture of nitrogen, hydrogen and ammonia. Two factors increase the percentage of ammonia in the mixture: a **high pressure** and a **low temperature**. However, the reaction is very slow to reach equilibrium at a low temperature, and industrial plants use a compromise temperature and a catalyst to speed up the reaction, as shown in the flow diagram. The ammonia made by the Haber process can be oxidised to nitric acid.

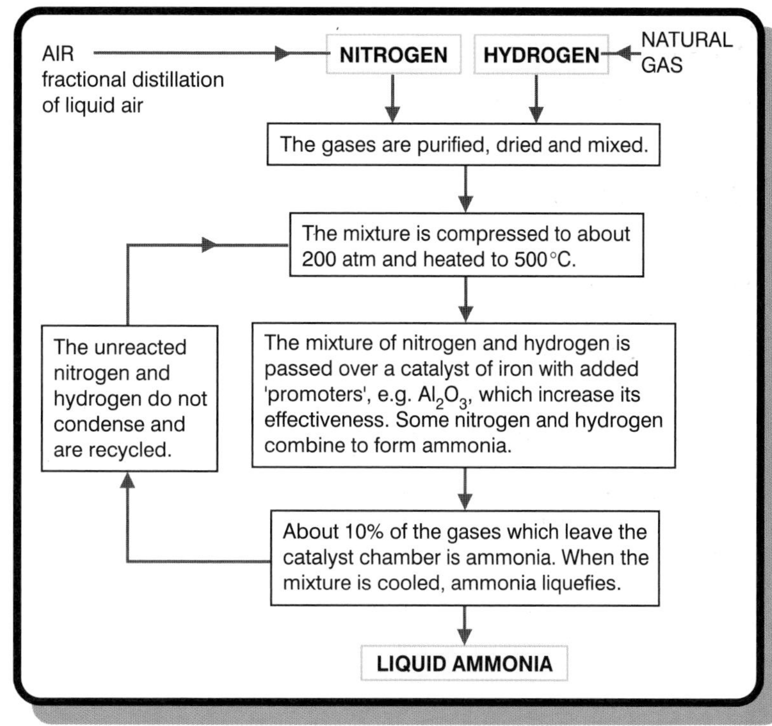

Flow diagram of the Haber process

NPK fertilisers

Ammonia solution can be used as a fertiliser. However, it is more common to use the solid fertilisers ammonium nitrate, ammonium sulphate and ammonium phosphate.

Mixtures of ammonium nitrate, ammonium phosphate and potassium chloride contain the elements nitrogen, phosphorus and potassium, which are essential for plant growth and are sold as **NPK fertilisers**.

9.7 Carbon dioxide

The carbon cycle

Plants are able to make sugars by the process of **photosynthesis:**

carbon dioxide + water + sunlight $\xrightarrow{\text{catalysed by chlorophyll}}$ glucose + oxygen

The energy of sunlight is converted into the energy of the chemical bonds in the sugar glucose.

Animals obtain energy by **cellular respiration:**

glucose + oxygen → carbon dioxide + water + energy

The balance between the processes which take carbon dioxide from the air and those which put carbon dioxide into the air is called the **carbon cycle**. The cycle is shown below.

Uses of carbon dioxide

- ★ Soft drinks are made by dissolving carbon dioxide in water under pressure and adding sugar and flavourings.
- ★ Solid carbon dioxide sublimes (turns into a vapour on warming). It is used as the refrigerant 'dry ice'.
- ★ Carbon dioxide is used in fire extinguishers because it does not support combustion and is denser than air.

Test for carbon dioxide

Carbon dioxide reacts with a solution of calcium hydroxide (limewater) to form a white precipitate of calcium carbonate.

carbon dioxide + calcium hydroxide → calcium carbonate + water

$$CO_2(g) + Ca(OH)_2(aq) \rightarrow CaCO_3(s) + H_2O(l)$$

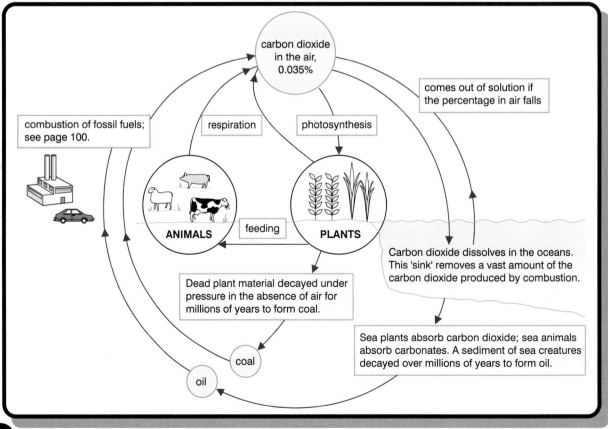

carbon dioxide in the air, 0.035%

combustion of fossil fuels; see page 100.

respiration

photosynthesis

comes out of solution if the percentage in air falls

ANIMALS

feeding

PLANTS

Carbon dioxide dissolves in the oceans. This 'sink' removes a vast amount of the carbon dioxide produced by combustion.

Dead plant material decayed under pressure in the absence of air for millions of years to form coal.

Sea plants absorb carbon dioxide; sea animals absorb carbonates. A sediment of sea creatures decayed over millions of years to form oil.

coal

oil

The greenhouse effect

The Earth receives radiation from the Sun, and also radiates heat into space. Carbon dioxide and water vapour reduce the escape of heat energy from the Earth by means of the **greenhouse effect** (see diagram below). Without these 'blankets' of water vapour and carbon dioxide, the temperature of the Earth's surface would be at −40°C, and life on Earth would be impossible.

The combustion of fossil fuels is causing an increase in the level of carbon dioxide at a rate which could raise the average temperature of the Earth. One result would be that the massive icecaps of the Arctic and Antarctic regions would slowly begin to melt. The levels of oceans would rise, and coastal areas would be flooded. A rise in temperature could decrease food production over vast areas, e.g. the mid-west USA and Russia.

Secondary effects would make matters worse. The increase in temperature would make more water vaporise from the oceans and drive out some of the carbon dioxide dissolved in the oceans to add to a still thicker greenhouse blanket. Other 'greenhouse gases' are methane, chlorofluorocarbons (CFCs), nitrogen oxides and ozone.

9.8 The noble gases

Helium, neon, argon, krypton and xenon are the noble gases.

★ Helium is used in airships because of its low density.

★ Neon and other noble gases are used in illuminated signs.

★ Argon is used to fill light bulbs.

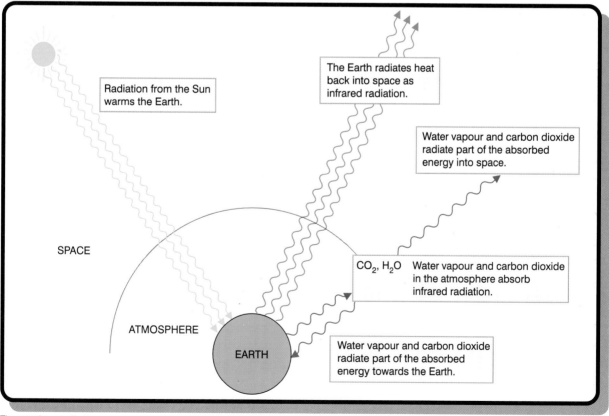

Radiation from the Sun warms the Earth.

The Earth radiates heat back into space as infrared radiation.

Water vapour and carbon dioxide radiate part of the absorbed energy into space.

SPACE

CO_2, H_2O Water vapour and carbon dioxide in the atmosphere absorb infrared radiation.

ATMOSPHERE

EARTH

Water vapour and carbon dioxide radiate part of the absorbed energy towards the Earth.

The greenhouse effect

9.9 The problem of pollution

Carbon monoxide

Source: most of the carbon monoxide in the air comes from vehicle engines, where it is formed by the incomplete combustion of petrol. Soil organisms remove carbon monoxide from the air. However, in cities, where the concentration of carbon monoxide is high, there is little soil to remove it.

Effects: carbon monoxide combines with haemoglobin, the red pigment in the blood, and prevents haemoglobin from combining with oxygen. At a level of 1%, carbon monoxide will kill quickly; at lower levels, it causes headaches and dizziness and affects reaction times. Being colourless and odourless, carbon monoxide gives no warning of its presence.

Solutions to the problem may come from

- tuning vehicle engines to use more air and produce only carbon dioxide and water. However, this increases the emission of oxides of nitrogen.
- fitting vehicles with catalytic converters
- using fuels which burn more cleanly than hydrocarbons, e.g. ethanol.

Sulphur dioxide

Sources: major sources of the sulphur dioxide in the air are

- the extraction of metals from sulphide ores
- the burning of coal, which contains 0.5–5% sulphur, mostly in electricity power stations
- oil-burning power stations, because fuel oil contains sulphur compounds.

Effects: sulphur dioxide is a colourless gas with a very penetrating and irritating smell. Atmospheric sulphur dioxide is thought to contribute to bronchitis and lung diseases. It is a cause of acid rain.

Solutions to the problem: see below.

Acid rain

Rain is naturally weakly acidic because it dissolves carbon dioxide from the air. The pH of natural rainwater is 5.2. Rain with a pH below this is described as **acid rain**.

There are many effects of acid rain:

- damage to lakes and the fish and plants in them; see diagram on opposite page
- washing of nutrients out of topsoil, resulting in poor crops and damage to trees
- costly damage to building materials, e.g. limestone, concrete, cement and metal.

What can be done?

Sweden has tackled the problem by spraying tonnes of calcium hydroxide into acid lakes.

Members of the European Community (EC) have agreed to make a 60% to 70% cut in their emissions of sulphur dioxide by 2003. Power stations must make a big contribution to solving the problem. Some lines of attack are:

1. Coal can be crushed and washed with a solvent to remove much of the sulphur content.
2. Fuel oil can be purified at the refinery – at a cost.
3. Sulphur dioxide can be removed from the exhaust gases of power stations. In **flue gas desulphurisation (FGD)**, jets of wet powdered limestone neutralise acidic gases as they pass up the chimney of the power station.
4. In a **pulverised fluidised bed combustion (PFBC)** furnace, the coal is pulverised (broken into small pieces) and burnt on a bed of powdered limestone, which is 'fluidised' (kept in motion by an upward flow of air). As the coal burns, sulphur dioxide reacts with the limestone.
5. Nuclear power stations do not send pollutants into the air. However, they create the problem of storing radioactive waste.

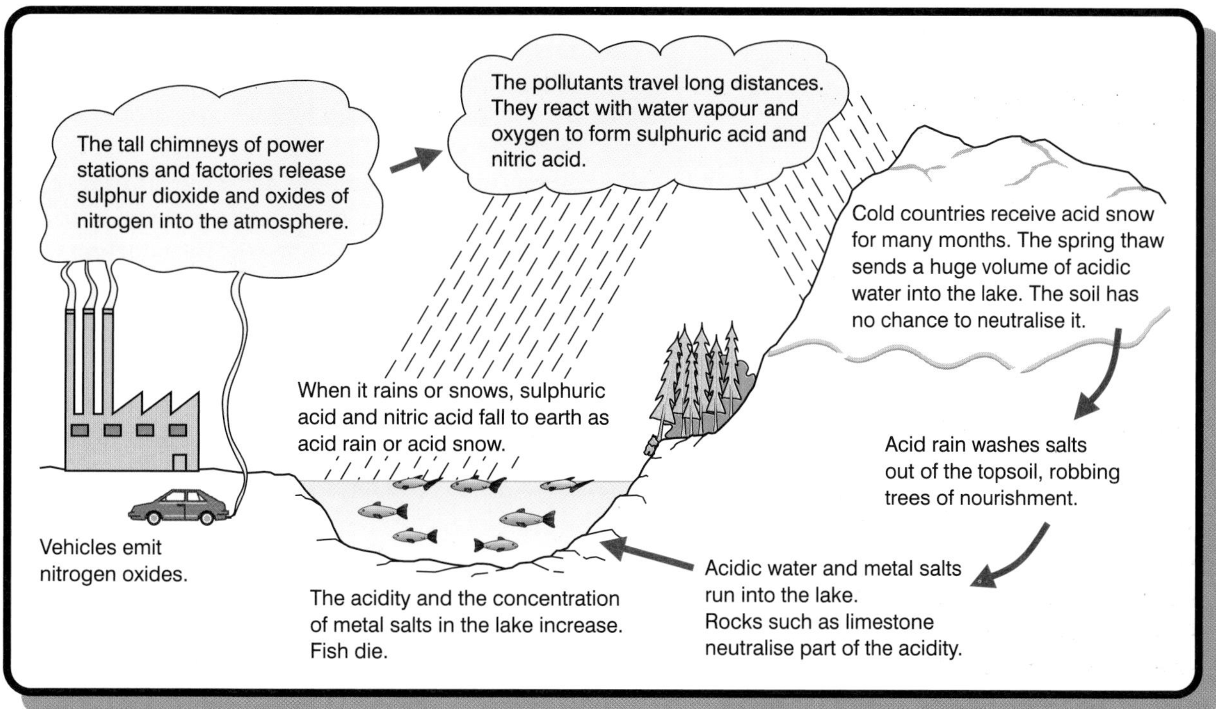

Acid rain; its source and its effect on lake water

Smoke, dust and grit

Particles enter the air from natural sources such as dust storms, forest fires and volcanic eruptions. Coal-burning power stations, incinerators, industries and vehicles add to the pollution. When smoke particles mix with fog, **smog** is formed. Smog contains sulphuric acid, which has been formed from sulphur dioxide in the smoke. Breathing smog makes the lungs produce mucus, making it more difficult to breathe.

Methods of removing particles include:

- using sprays of water to wash out particles from waste gases
- passing exhaust gases through filters
- using electrostatic precipitators which attract particles to charged plates.

The exhaust gases of vehicles are not treated by any of these methods.

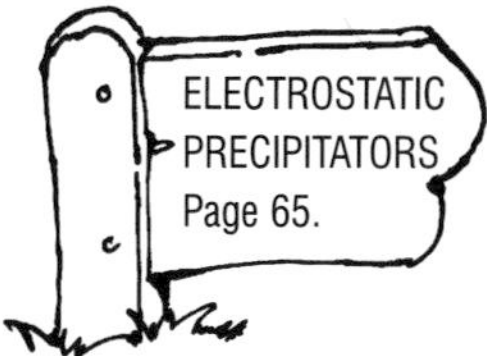

Oxides of nitrogen

Source: when fuels are burned in air, the temperature rises. Some of the nitrogen and oxygen in the air combine to form nitrogen monoxide, NO, and nitrogen dioxide, NO_2. This mixture (shown as NO_x) is emitted by power stations, factories and vehicles.

Effects: nitrogen monoxide is soon converted into nitrogen dioxide which is highly toxic, and which contributes to the formation of acid rain.

Solution to the problem: the presence of a catalyst (platinum) brings about the reaction:

$$\text{nitrogen monoxide} + \text{carbon monoxide} \rightarrow \text{nitrogen} + \text{carbon dioxide}$$

$$2NO(g) + 2CO(g) \rightarrow N_2(g) + 2CO_2(g)$$

The **catalytic converters** which are now fitted in the exhausts of cars reduce the emission of oxides of nitrogen in this way. Unleaded petrol must be used because lead compounds in the exhaust gases would stop the catalyst working.

Hydrocarbons

Sources: the hydrocarbons in the air come from natural sources, such as the decay of plant material (85%), and from vehicles (15%).

Effects: in sunlight, hydrocarbons react with oxygen and oxides of nitrogen to form **photochemical smog**. This contains irritating and toxic compounds.

Solutions to the problem: if the air supply in a vehicle engine is increased, the petrol burns completely. However, at the same time, the formation of NO_X increases. A solution may be found by running the engine at a lower temperature and employing a catalyst to promote combustion.

Lead

Sources: lead compounds enter the air from the combustion of coal, the roasting of metal ores and from vehicle engines. Since the introduction of unleaded petrol, the level of lead in the atmosphere has fallen.

Effects: lead causes depression, tiredness, irritability and headaches. Higher levels of lead cause damage to the brain, liver and kidneys.

round-up

How much have you improved?
Work out your improvement index on page 132.

1 zinc oxide + carbon → zinc + carbon monoxide

$$ZnO(s) + C(s) \rightarrow Zn(s) + CO(g)$$

a) In this reaction, name
(i) the oxidising agent
(ii) the reducing agent. [2]
b) Say which substance is
(i) oxidised
(ii) reduced. [2]

2 a) Why is air not used for 'airships'? [1]
b) Helium has a density twice that of hydrogen. Why is helium used in preference to hydrogen for filling airships? [2]

3 Explain the danger to health from the presence in the air of **a)** carbon monoxide **b)** sulphur dioxide and **c)** particles of smoke and dust.
Say how nature removes each of these pollutants from the air. [6]

4 a) How do oxides of nitrogen get into the air?
b) What damage do they cause?
c) What is the solution to this problem? [3]

5 a) Explain how the 'greenhouse effect' makes life on Earth possible. [2]
b) Explain why people are worried about an 'enhanced greenhouse effect'. [2]
c) If Earth warms up, what do people predict will happen
(i) at the North Pole **(ii)** in Thailand
(iii) in the mid-west of the USA? [3]

6 Explain why power stations have tall chimneys. Would the problem of pollution from power stations be solved by still taller chimneys? [2]

7 a) Why do cold countries, e.g. Sweden, suffer badly from acid rain? [1]
b) In Sweden, the base calcium hydroxide is added to acid lakes. Write a word equation and a chemical equation for the reaction between calcium hydroxide and sulphuric acid in the lake water. [4]
c) What name is given to this type of reaction? [1]

8 What chemical reactions take place between acid rain and **a)** iron railings **b)** marble statues **c)** fresh mortar? [2, 3, 2]

9 a) In petrol engines and diesel engines, hydrocarbons burn to form a number of products. What are these products? [4]
b) What other substances are present in vehicle exhaust gases? [3]

Water

10

preview

At the end of this topic you will:

- appreciate the importance of the water cycle
- know how to purify water and how to test for water
- appreciate the dangers of water pollution
- know how tap water is treated and how sewage is treated
- understand the action of soaps and soapless detergents
- know how hard water is softened.

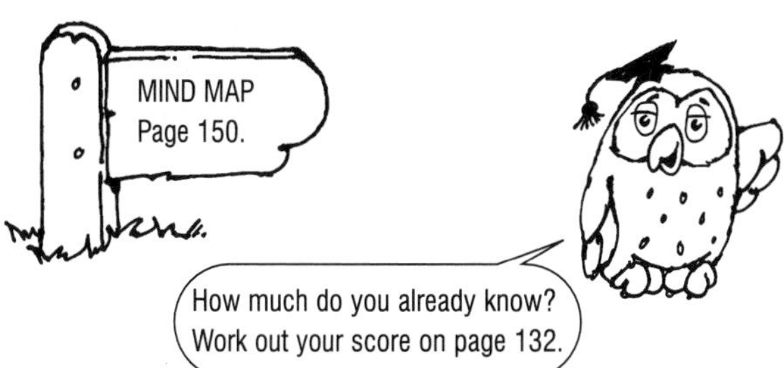

MIND MAP
Page 150.
How much do you already know?
Work out your score on page 132.

Test yourself

1 Name three processes which send water vapour into the atmosphere. [3]

2 Explain why rainwater is weakly acidic. [1]

3 Explain how weakly acidic rainwater leads to the formation of underground caves in limestone regions. Write a word equation and a chemical equation for the process. [5]

4 State **a)** a test to find out whether a liquid contains water **b)** a test to show whether a liquid is pure water. [3]

5 Name three types of living things for which dissolved oxygen is important. [3]

6 Name three steps in water treatment. [3]

7 Explain how a soap works to remove oil and grease from a fabric. [8]

8 Explain the difference between hard and soft water with respect to **a)** the action of soap and **b)** chemical composition. [4]

9 State two methods of softening 'permanently hard water'. [2]

10.1 The water cycle

The water cycle is shown in the diagram overleaf.

10.2 Water underground

Rainwater dissolves carbon dioxide as it falls through the air, and natural rainwater is therefore weakly acidic. In limestone regions, rain trickles over rocks containing calcium carbonate and magnesium carbonate. The acidic rainwater reacts with the rocks:

calcium carbonate + water + carbon dioxide → calcium hydrogencarbonate

$$CaCO_3(s) + H_2O(l) + CO_2(aq) \rightarrow Ca(HCO_3)_2(aq)$$

Over a period of thousands of years, calcium carbonate and magnesium carbonate have been dissolved out of the rocks to form the underground caves and potholes that occur in limestone regions.

The reverse reaction can take place. In an underground cavern, dissolved calcium hydrogencarbonate can turn into a grain of solid calcium carbonate. Over thousands of years, tiny grains of calcium carbonate can build up into **stalactites** and **stalagmites**.

10.3 Dissolved oxygen

The solubility of oxygen in water is 10 p.p.m. (parts per million), only about 10 g oxygen per tonne of water. Fish and other water-living animals and plants depend on this dissolved oxygen. **Aerobic** bacteria which feed on plant and animal debris in the water also depend on the dissolved oxygen. If the oxygen is used up, for example to oxidise untreated sewage, the aerobic bacteria die and **anaerobic** bacteria take over. They digest biomass to produce unpleasant-smelling decay products.

5 Clouds are blown by the wind. As they rise over higher ground, larger drops of water form.

4 Water vapour cools and condenses to form clouds of tiny droplets.

3 Transpiration in plants produces water vapour.

6 Water returns to land and sea as rain and snow.

7 Rain collects in streams.

2 Respiration in plants and animals produces water vapour.

1 Warmed by the sun, water evaporates from oceans, rivers and lakes.

8 Streams flow into rivers. Rivers flow into the sea, completing the cycle.

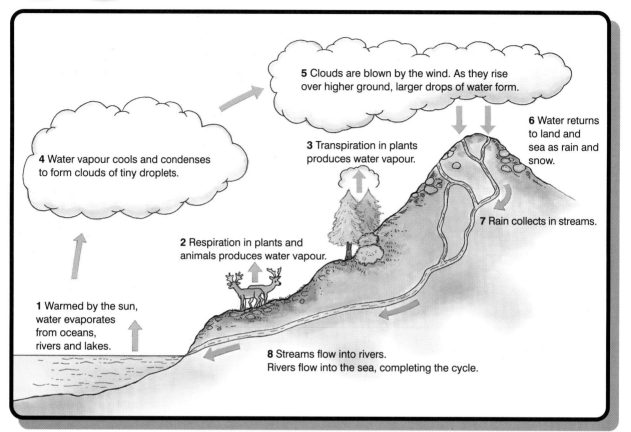

The water cycle

10.4 Pure water

Tests for water

or for any liquid that contains water:

1 Water turns white anhydrous copper(II) sulphate blue:

$$\text{copper(II) sulphate} + \text{water} \rightarrow \text{copper(II) sulphate-5-water}$$

$$CuSO_4(s) + 5H_2O(l) \rightarrow CuSO_4.5H_2O$$

2 Water turns blue anhydrous cobalt(II) chloride pink:

$$\text{cobalt(II) chloride} + \text{water} \rightarrow \text{cobalt(II) chloride-6-water}$$

$$CoCl_2(s) + 6H_2O(l) \rightarrow CoCl_2.6H_2O$$

The water in copper(II) sulphate-5-water and cobalt(II) chloride-6-water is combined as **water of crystallisation**. It gives these hydrates their crystalline form and their colour.

Tests for pure water

1 The boiling point is 100°C at 1 atm.
2 The freezing point is 0°C at 1 atm.

Methods of obtaining pure water

1 **Distillation** (see page 18).

2 **Deionisation**: water can be passed through an **ion-exchange column**, which contains a resin. An exchange takes place between cations (M^+) and anions (A^-) in the water and H^+ and OH^- ions bonded to the resin.

$$M^+(aq) + H^+(resin) \rightarrow M^+(resin) + H^+(aq)$$

$$A^-(aq) + OH^-(resin) \rightarrow A^-(resin) + OH^-(aq)$$

Then hydrogen ions and hydroxide ions combine to form water:

$$H^+(aq) + OH^-(aq) \rightarrow H_2O(l)$$

10.5 Pollution of water

Pollution by industry

Many industrial firms have their factories on the banks of rivers and estuaries and discharge waste into the water. The National Rivers Authority was set up in 1989 to watch over the quality of rivers and prosecute polluters. It does not watch over tidal waters, and much sewage and industrial waste is poured into coastal waters and estuaries.

Pollution by sewage

Much sewage is discharged into rivers and estuaries without being treated. This gives swimmers at some of Britain's bathing beaches some nasty surprises. Dozens of British beaches fail to meet European Community standards because they have too high a level of coliform bacteria and faecal bacteria in the water.

Pollution by agriculture

Fertilisers: when an excess of fertiliser is used, some of it is not absorbed by the crop. Rain washes it out of the soil, and it accumulates in groundwater. The water industry uses groundwater as a source of drinking water. There is concern that nitrates in drinking water can lead to the formation of nitrosoamines, compounds which cause cancer.

Fertiliser which plants fail to absorb may be carried into the water of a lake, where it nourishes the growth of algae and water plants. This accidental enrichment of the water causes algae to form a thick mat of **algal bloom**, and weeds flourish. When algae die and decay, they use up dissolved oxygen. The fish in the lake are deprived of oxygen and die. The lake becomes a 'dead lake'. This process is called **eutrophication**.

Pesticides: these may enter lakes and become part of a food chain.

Thermal pollution

Industries take water from rivers to use as a coolant and return it at a higher temperature. At the higher temperature, the solubility of oxygen in the water is decreased. At the same time, fish and aerobic bacteria become more active and need more oxygen. The **biochemical oxygen demand** has increased.

Pollution by oil

Modern oil tankers are huge, each carrying up to 500 000 tonnes of crude oil.

If a tanker has an accident at sea, oil is spilt, and a huge oil slick floats on the surface of the ocean. It is very slowly oxidised by air and decomposed by bacteria. While the oil slick remains, it poisons fish and glues the feathers of sea birds together so that they cannot fly. When the oil slick washes ashore, it fouls beaches. The following methods can be used to deal with oil slicks:

1. **dispersants** – powerful detergents
2. **sinking** the oil by spreading it with e.g. powdered chalk
3. **absorption** in e.g. straw and polystyrene
4. **booms** placed in the water to prevent oil from spreading
5. **natural processes** if the oil spill occurs far out to sea.

10.6 Water treatment

A **water treatment** plant is illustrated overleaf.

10.7 Sewage works

Sewers carry used water to the **sewage works,** where it is purified sufficiently to allow it to be discharged into a river or the sea. A diagram of a sewage works is shown overleaf.

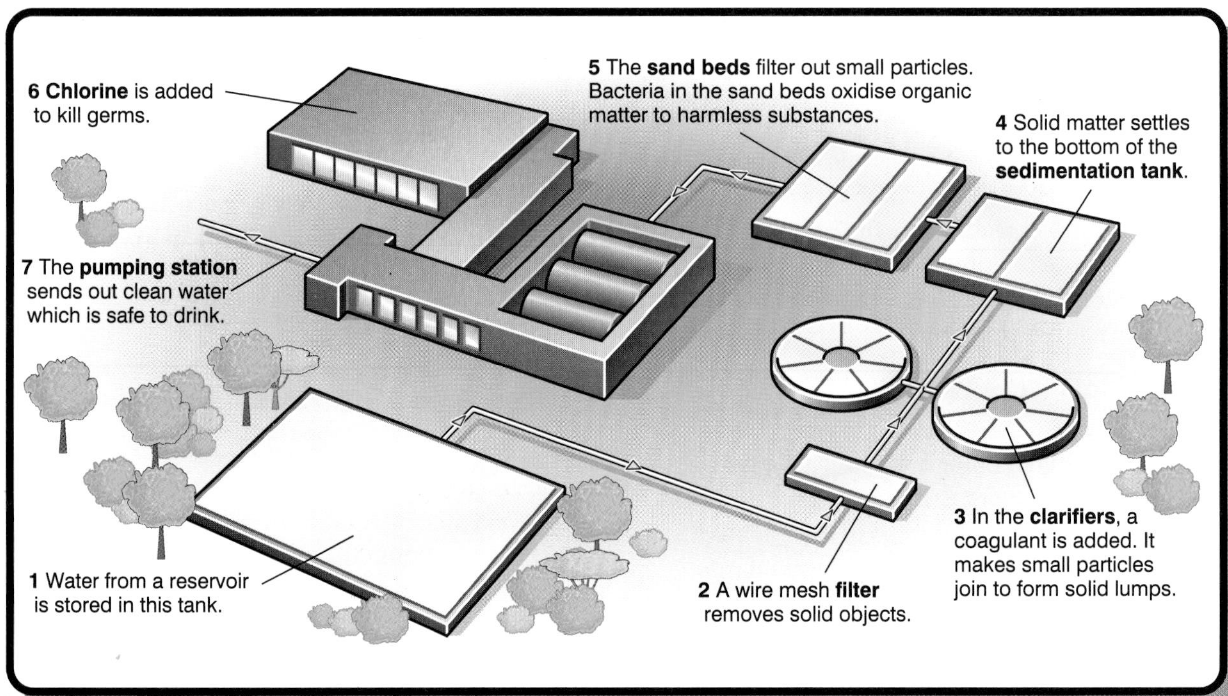

6 **Chlorine** is added to kill germs.
5 The **sand beds** filter out small particles. Bacteria in the sand beds oxidise organic matter to harmless substances.
4 Solid matter settles to the bottom of the **sedimentation tank**.
7 The **pumping station** sends out clean water which is safe to drink.
3 In the **clarifiers**, a coagulant is added. It makes small particles join to form solid lumps.
1 Water from a reservoir is stored in this tank.
2 A wire mesh **filter** removes solid objects.

A water treatment plant

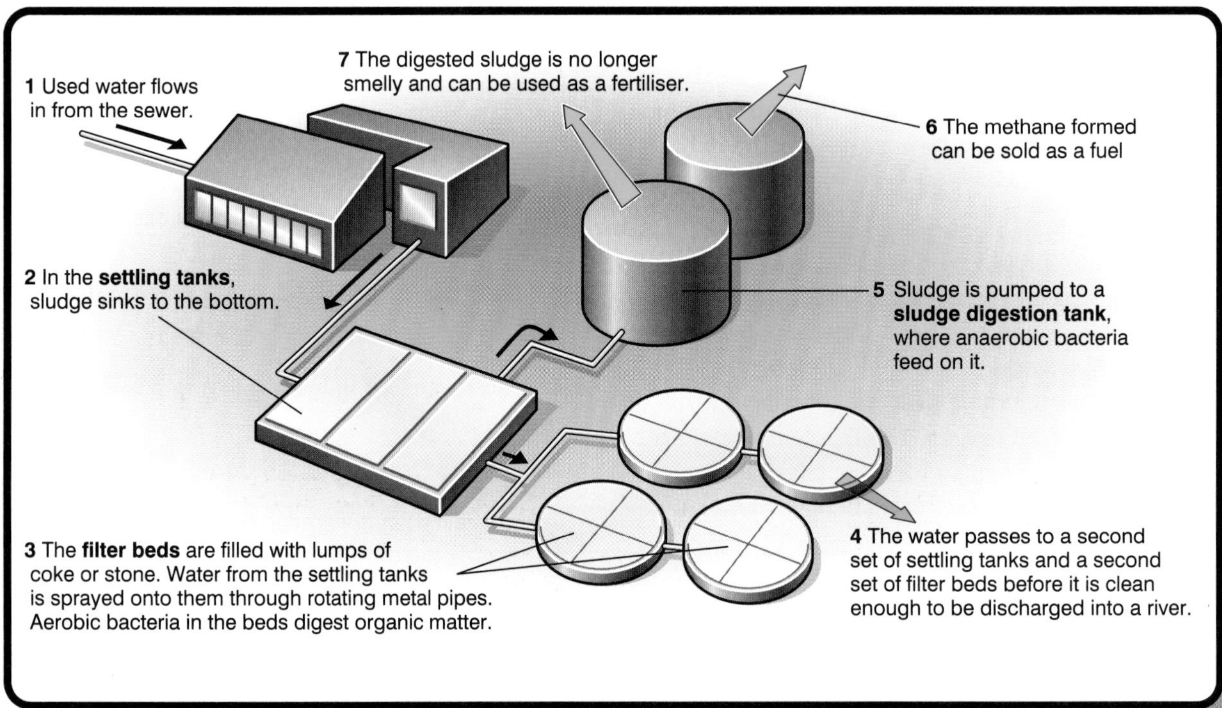

1 Used water flows in from the sewer.
7 The digested sludge is no longer smelly and can be used as a fertiliser.
6 The methane formed can be sold as a fuel
2 In the **settling tanks**, sludge sinks to the bottom.
5 Sludge is pumped to a **sludge digestion tank**, where anaerobic bacteria feed on it.
3 The **filter beds** are filled with lumps of coke or stone. Water from the settling tanks is sprayed onto them through rotating metal pipes. Aerobic bacteria in the beds digest organic matter.
4 The water passes to a second set of settling tanks and a second set of filter beds before it is clean enough to be discharged into a river.

A sewage works

10.8 Soaps and detergents

Water is a very good solvent and therefore a good cleaning agent. Oil and grease, however, do not dissolve in water. To wash oil and grease off your hands or clothes, you need a **detergent** or cleaning agent. Detergents are **wetting agents** (which help water to spread over skin and fabrics) and **emulsifying agents** (which can emulsify oil and water; that is, make them mix).

There are two kinds of detergents: **soaps**, which are made from animal fats, and **soapless detergents**, which are made from petroleum oil. Both soaps and soapless detergents are sodium or potassium salts of organic acids. Their ions contain a group of atoms which will dissolve in water and a group of atoms which will dissolve in oil and grease.

Soaps

The structure of a soap ion is shown in the diagram opposite.

The diagram below shows how a soap works.

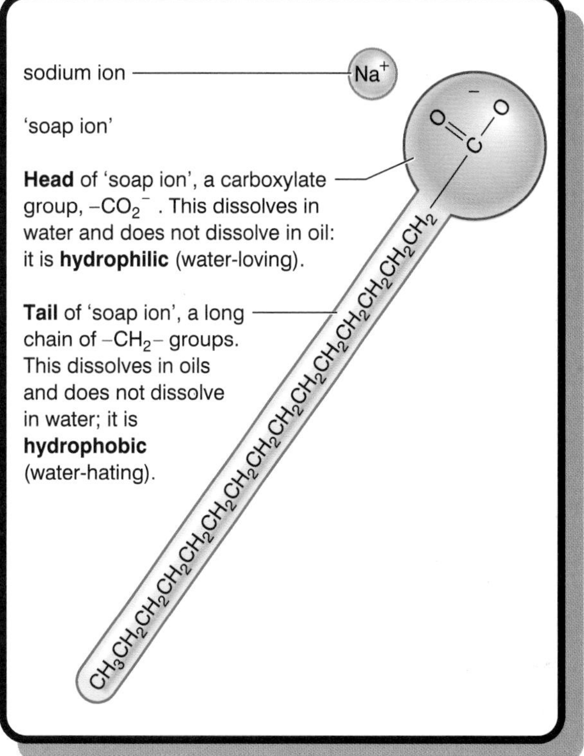

sodium ion
Na^+
'soap ion'
Head of 'soap ion', a carboxylate group, $-CO_2^-$. This dissolves in water and does not dissolve in oil: it is **hydrophilic** (water-loving).
Tail of 'soap ion', a long chain of $-CH_2-$ groups. This dissolves in oils and does not dissolve in water; it is **hydrophobic** (water-hating).
$CH_3CH_2CH_2CH_2CH_2CH_2CH_2CH_2CH_2CH_2CH_2CH_2CH_2CH_2CH_2$

The formula unit of the soap sodium hexadecanoate

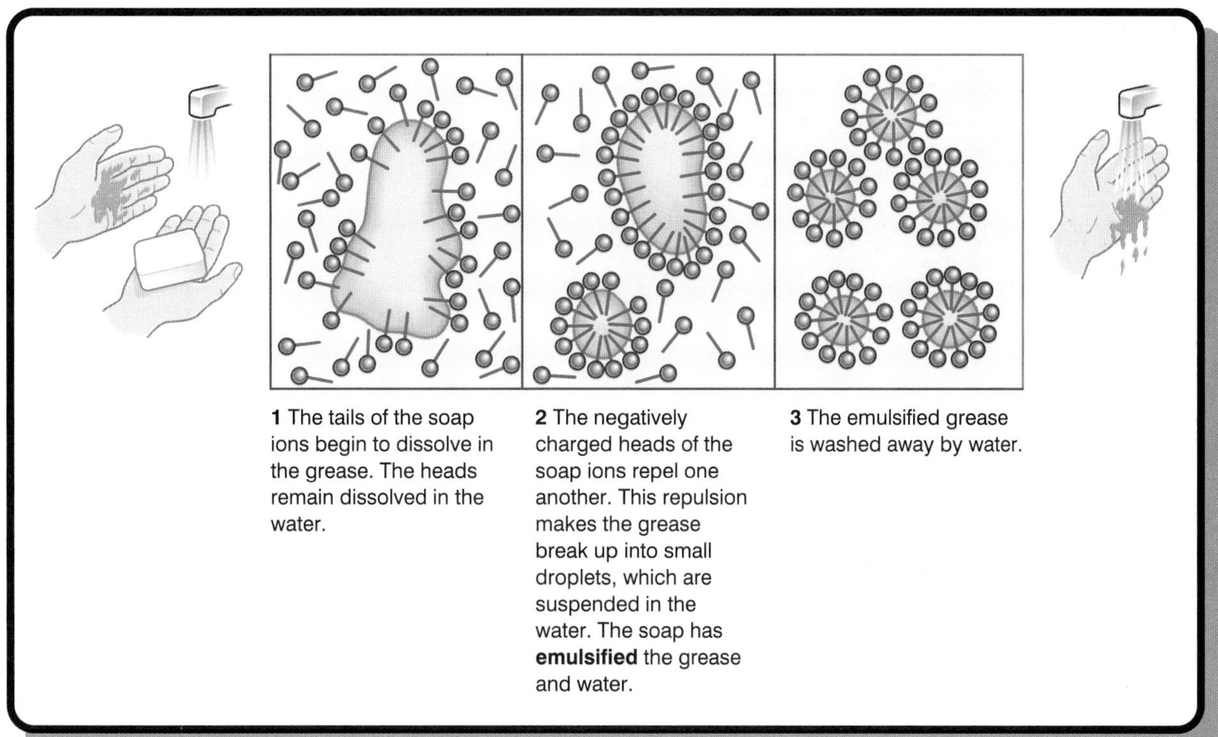

1 The tails of the soap ions begin to dissolve in the grease. The heads remain dissolved in the water.
2 The negatively charged heads of the soap ions repel one another. This repulsion makes the grease break up into small droplets, which are suspended in the water. The soap has **emulsified** the grease and water.
3 The emulsified grease is washed away by water.

The washing action of soap

The manufacture of soap – saponification

Fats consist of glycerol combined with a fatty acid, such as stearic acid. In soap-making, these two parts are split up by sodium hydroxide to give glycerol and the sodium salt of the acid, sodium stearate in this example. The fat is first boiled with concentrated alkali, cooled and then the soap is salted out.

FATS
Page 122.

fat + sodium hydroxide → glycerol + sodium stearate

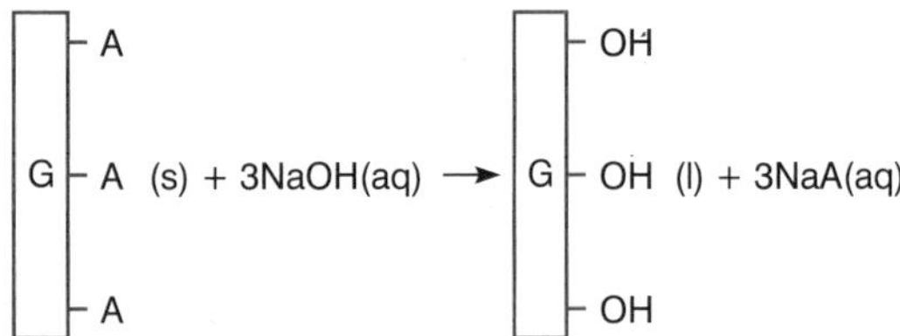

Soapless detergents

1 **Formula:** soapless detergents are sodium salts of sulphonic acids and sodium salts of organic sulphates.

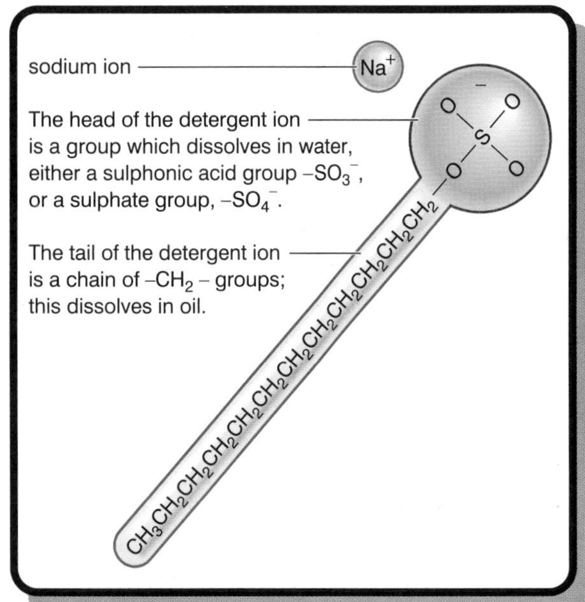

The formula unit of a soapless detergent

2 **Manufacture:** these detergents are made by the action of concentrated sulphuric acid on hydrocarbons. In a washing powder, bleach, brighteners, foam stabilisers and in some cases enzymes are added to the detergent. The enzymes speed up the breakdown of proteins, so digesting food stains.

3 **Caution:** it is not advisable to have your hands in detergents for long periods. By emulsifying oil in the skin, detergents make the skin dry and cracked.

Comparing soaps and detergents

1 **Resources:** soaps are made from animal fats and vegetable oils. Detergents are made from petroleum oil.

2 **Environmental effects:** natural products (including soaps) are biodegradable. The first detergents were not biodegradable, but formed a blanket of detergent foam in rivers which damaged plants and fish. Chemists solved the problem by making biodegradable detergents. The phosphates which are added to detergents cause eutrophication of rivers and lakes.

EUTROPHICATION
Page 59.

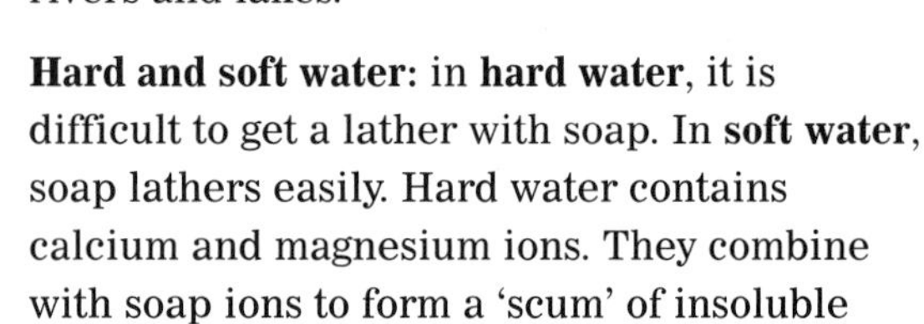

3 **Hard and soft water:** in **hard water**, it is difficult to get a lather with soap. In **soft water**, soap lathers easily. Hard water contains calcium and magnesium ions. They combine with soap ions to form a 'scum' of insoluble calcium and magnesium salts:

soap ions + calcium ions → scum

$2\ soap^-(aq) + Ca^{2+}(aq) \rightarrow Ca(soap)_2(s)$

If enough soap is added, all the calcium and magnesium ions are precipitated. After that, the soap is able to work, but a lot of soap has been wasted.

Soapless detergents work as well in hard water as they do in soft water because their calcium and magnesium salts are soluble.

10.9 Softening hard water

For some purposes, hard water is better than soft water.

★ The calcium in hard water is an aid to building strong bones and teeth.
★ Calcium has a protective effect against heart disease.
★ Hard water is better for beer-making.

There are two types of hardness:

- **temporary hardness**, removed by boiling
- **permanent hardness**, which cannot be removed by boiling.

Methods of softening water

1 **Boiling** removes temporary hardness, which is caused by calcium hydrogencarbonate and magnesium hydrogencarbonate.

$$Ca(HCO_3)_2(aq) \rightarrow CaCO_3(s) + CO_2(g) + H_2O(l)$$

2 Both temporary and permanent hardness are softened by adding **washing soda,** sodium carbonate-10-water, $Na_2CO_3.10H_2O$. Calcium ions and magnesium ions are precipitated as insoluble carbonates.

$$\text{calcium ions} + \text{carbonate ions} \rightarrow \text{calcium carbonate}$$

$$Ca^{2+}(aq) + CO_3^{2-}(aq) \rightarrow CaCO_3(s)$$

3 **Exchange resins,** such as permutits, take calcium and magnesium ions out of water and replace them with sodium ions.

$$\text{calcium ions} + \text{sodium permutit} \rightarrow \text{sodium ions} + \text{calcium permutit}$$

The water supply is run through a cylinder containing permutit, and the water that comes out of the taps is soft.

10.10 Alkaline cleaners and bleaches

Many powerful cleaning substances are alkalis. They react with oil and grease to form an emulsion of glycerol and soap, which can be washed away. Oven cleaners contain sodium hydroxide, washing powders contain sodium carbonate, and ammonia solution is used as a domestic cleaner.

Household bleaches contain sodium chlorate(I), NaClO, and calcium chlorate(I), $Ca(ClO)_2$. They are powerful oxidising agents which kill germs and oxidise dirt.

Remember

★ Do not use an acidic cleaner together with a bleach, because they react to form chlorine, which is poisonous.

★ Do not use ammonia together with a bleach, because they react to form poisonous chloroamines.

10.11 Colloids

What are colloids?

Solutions are homogeneous mixtures – they are the same all the way through. The particles of the solute are of atomic or molecular size (about one nanometre long; 1 nm = 10^{-9}m).

Suspensions are heterogeneous mixtures – they are not the same all the way through. They contain relatively large particles (over 1000 nm long) of insoluble solid or liquid suspended in another liquid. In time, the particles settle out. For example, in blood the red and white blood cells are in suspension in the plasma.

Suspensions of solid particles in a liquid can be separated by filtration and by centrifugation.

Colloids are heterogeneous mixtures, in which the suspended particles are smaller than in suspensions. Colloids are also called **colloidal dispersions** and **colloidal suspensions**. They consist of particles of one phase (solid, liquid or gas) suspended or dispersed (spread) through the second phase (solid, liquid or gas). The particles are the **disperse phase**, and the second phase is the **dispersion phase** or **dispersion medium**. The particles are between 1 nm and 1000 nm long, larger than the molecules and ions that form solutions but smaller than the particles in suspensions. The particles cannot be separated by filtration through filter paper. The table overleaf shows some types of colloids.

Some types of colloids

disperse phase	dispersion medium	type of colloid	examples
liquid	gas	aerosol	fog, mist from aerosol spray can, clouds
solid	gas	aerosol	smoke, dust-laden air
gas	liquid	foam	soap suds, whipped cream
liquid	liquid	emulsion	oil in water, milk, mayonnaise, protoplasm
solid	liquid	sol	clay, starch in water, protein in water, gelatine in water
gas	solid	solid foam	lava, pumice, styrofoam, marshmallows
liquid	solid	solid emulsion	pearl, jellies, butter, cheese
solid	solid	solid sol	some gems, some alloys

Emulsifiers

The oil and water in an emulsion such as mayonnaise tend to separate. An **emulsifier** is added to keep the components together. An emulsifier ion has two parts, as shown in the diagram below. When the emulsifier is added to a mixture of oil and water, the emulsifier ions align themselves with their polar heads dissolved in water and their hydrocarbon tails dissolved in the oil. The polar heads on the surface of each droplet repel one another, so the drops do not collect together.

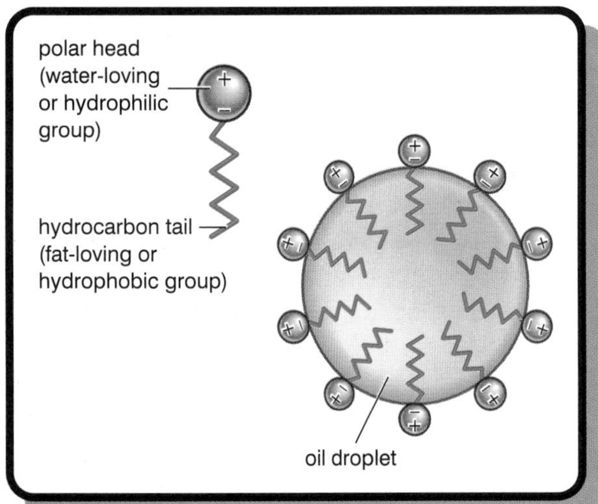

An emulsifier ion   A drop of oil surrounded by emulsifier

Optical properties of colloids

The particles of a colloid are large enough to scatter light, as shown below. This effect is named the **Tyndall effect** after its discoverer.

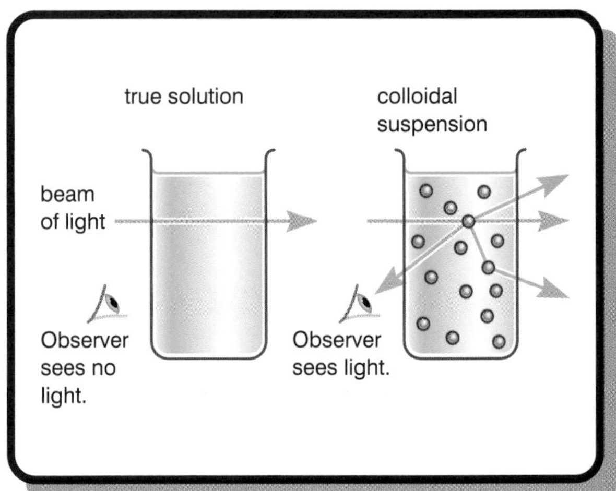

The scattering of light by a colloid

Coagulating colloids

The reason why colloidal particles do not precipitate is that they are charged. Repulsion between the charged particles keeps them apart and in suspension. In order to precipitate a colloid, the charge on the particles must be neutralised. This can be done by adding ions of opposite charge.

1 When water is purified for drinking, it may be treated with aluminium sulphate. Aluminium ions, Al^{3+}, are small in size and highly charged. They neutralise the negative charges on colloidal particles such as clay, which are then able to clump together and settle out of solution.

2 Blood contains colloidal proteins, which are negatively charged. Small cuts can be treated with styptic pencils, which contain Al^{3+} or Fe^{3+} ions. They cancel the charges on the colloidal particles and help the blood to clot.

3 Gases can be freed of colloidal particles by electrostatic precipitation, as shown below.

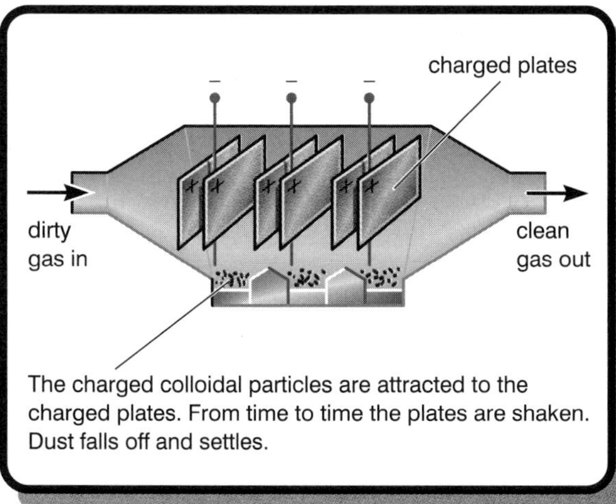
charged plates
dirty gas in
clean gas out
The charged colloidal particles are attracted to the charged plates. From time to time the plates are shaken. Dust falls off and settles.

Electrostatic precipitation

Electrophoresis

Colloidal particles migrate in an electric field, as ions do. Depending on their charge, the particles are attracted to one electrode and repelled by the other. This movement under the influence of an electric field is called **electrophoresis**. Electrophoresis can be used to separate different colloids, according to the nature of the charges and the different rates at which the particles migrate. An example is the separation of blood proteins by electrophoresis.

Dialysis

Dialysing membranes allow ions and small molecules to pass through them, but not large molecules or colloidal particles. The movement of ions and small molecules through dialysing membranes is called **dialysis**. Most animal membranes are dialysing membranes. Dialysis can be used to separate colloids from solutions that contain both colloidal particles and small molecules or ions in solution, as shown in the diagram below.

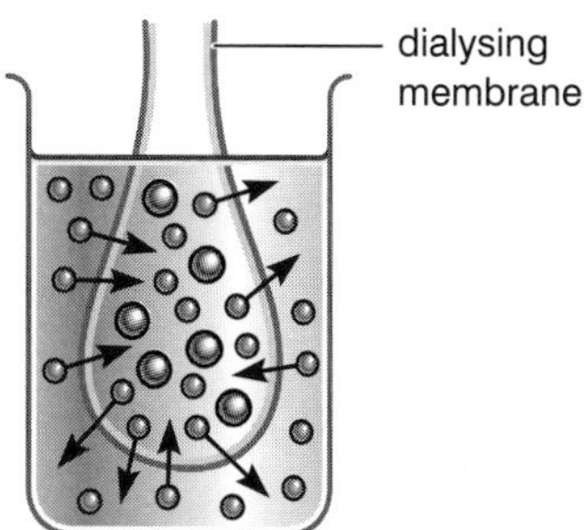
dialysing membrane

Small molecules and ions pass through the membrane, while colloidal particles cannot. The concentrations of small particles inside and outside the bag reach equilibrium.

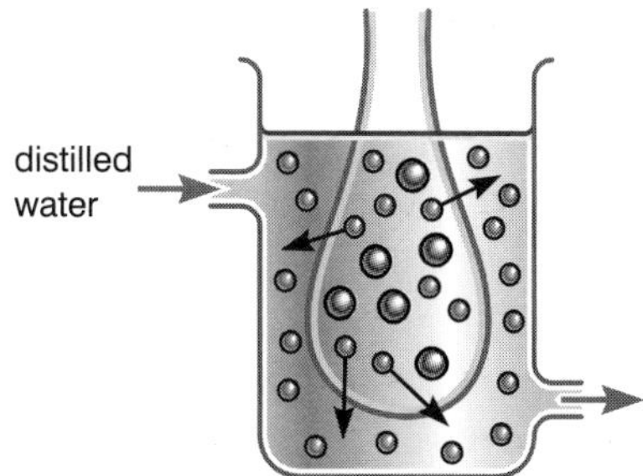
distilled water

With distilled water flowing slowly through the system, equilibrium cannot be established. Small particles pass out of the bag until only colloidal particles remain.

● = colloidal particle   ● = small molecule or ion

Dialysis

If someone's kidneys do not work properly, waste substances build up in the blood. A dialysis machine called an **artificial kidney** can be used to clean the blood. Blood from one of the patient's arteries runs through a coil of dialysis tubing immersed in a solution of salts and glucose, called the dialysis fluid. Small molecules of waste substances pass out of the blood into the dialysis fluid. Blood cells and large molecules such as protein molecules are retained in the blood. After dialysis, the purified blood is returned to the patient's body through a vein.

round-up

How much have you improved?
Work out your improvement index on pages 132–3.

1 a) What is a food chain? [2]
b) Explain how the existence of a food chain can lead to poisoning even when the concentration of a pollutant in a body of water is low. [3]

2 What are the effects of thermal pollution? [4]

3 When they change the oil in their car engine, some people pour the waste oil down the drain. Why is this wrong? [2]

4 Why has the incidence of pollution by oil increased? [2]

5 Accidental oil spills from tankers cause oil slicks at sea. List four methods of treating oil slicks. [4]

6 a) Why do some lakes develop an algal bloom? [1]
b) Why is algal bloom less common in rivers? [1]
c) What harm does algal bloom do to a lake that is used as **(i)** a reservoir **(ii)** a boating lake **(iii)** a fishing lake? [3]

7 The concentration of nitrates in drinking water is rising. Explain **a)** why this is happening and **b)** why some people are worried about the increase. [3]

8 a) What makes water hard? [2]
b) Describe one method of softening hard water. Explain how it works. [2]
c) Compare the action of soaps and detergents in hard water. [2]

9 A greasy oven is wiped with a pad of oven cleaner, which contains sodium hydroxide, and left for a few minutes. Then the grease can be washed off with water.
a) Explain how sodium hydroxide makes the grease easier to remove. [2]
b) Explain why you should wear rubber gloves when using this kind of oven cleaner. [1]
c) What effect does it have on the cleaning if you warm the oven first? [1]
d) Why is it better to use distilled water, rather than tap water, in a steam iron? [1]

10 a) Which would you recommend for washing hair in hard water, a mild soapless detergent or a soap? Explain your choice. [2]
b) What is there in hard water that makes it better for health than soft water? [2]
c) Explain why emulsified oil droplets do not stick together but spread out through the water. [3]
d) Why is it necessary to rinse clothes after washing them? [2]

11 a) Explain the difference between a soap and a soapless detergent. [2]
b) Compare soaps and detergents with respect to use of the Earth's resources. [4]

12 Name three steps in the treatment of drinking water. [3]

13 How can you tell the difference between
a) a solution and a suspension
b) a suspension and a colloid
c) a solution and a colloid? [3]

14 How can solid colloidal particles be made to separate **a)** from a sol **b)** from an aerosol? [2]

15 An emulsifier ion consists of two parts. Say how the two parts differ in structure, and explain how this enables an emulsifier to keep oil in colloidal suspension in water. [3]

16 a) What is a dialysing membrane? [2]
b) Briefly explain how dialysis can help a person whose kidneys do not function properly. [2]

Well done if you've improved. Don't worry if you haven't. Take a break and try again.

11

Planet Earth

preview

At the end of this topic you will:

- **know how Earth and its atmosphere evolved**
- **understand the theory of plate tectonics**
- **know about the different types of rock**
- **know how useful materials are obtained from rocks.**

MIND MAP
Page 151.
How much do you already know?
Work out your score on page 133.

Test yourself

1 The age of Earth is estimated to be
A 46 000 years **B** 1000 million years
C 460 000 years **D** 4 600 000 000 years. [1]

2 The average density of the whole Earth is
A 1.0 g/cm³ **B** 3.0 g/cm³
C 5.5 g/cm³ **D** 12.0 g/cm³. [1]

3 The diameter of the Earth is
A 127 000 km **B** 12 700 km
C 1270 km **D** 127 km. [1]

4 The Moho lies between
A the inner and outer core
B the crust and the mantle
C the oceanic and continental crust
D the outer core and the mantle. [1]

5 Name the following parts of the Earth:
a) the solid zone made of nickel and iron [1]
b) a zone which lies beneath ocean floors [1]
c) a zone which forms continents [1]
d) the zone of gases [1]
e) the zone where Earth's magnetism arises [1]
f) the outermost solid zone. [1]

6 Name
a) the type of rock which is formed when lava solidifies
b) the type of rock which is formed by compressing deposits of solid particles
c) the type of rock formed by the action of heat and pressure on types **a** and **b**. [3]

7 Of which type of rock was the original crust of Earth made? [1]

8 The original atmosphere of Earth contained about 25% carbon dioxide by volume. Why is the percentage of carbon dioxide in today's atmosphere so much lower? [2]

9 Name three weathering agents which act on rocks and shape the landscape. [3]

10 What theory says that Earth's crust is made up of separate pieces? [1]

11 State three uses for limestone. [3]

12 Name two materials that can be made from silica (sand). [2]

11.1 Structure of the Earth

The planet called Earth was formed as a molten mass of material cooled over a period of millions of years (see diagram overleaf).

As Earth cooled, water vapour condensed and rivers, lakes and oceans formed on its surface.

Earth's crust is of two kinds: **continental crust** and **oceanic crust**.

continental crust	oceanic crust
forms continents and their shelves	beneath deep sea floors
50–70 km thick	6 km thick on average
density 2.7 g/cm³	density 3.0 g/cm³
aged up to 3700 million years	aged up to 210 million years
has the same composition as granite	has the same composition as basalt

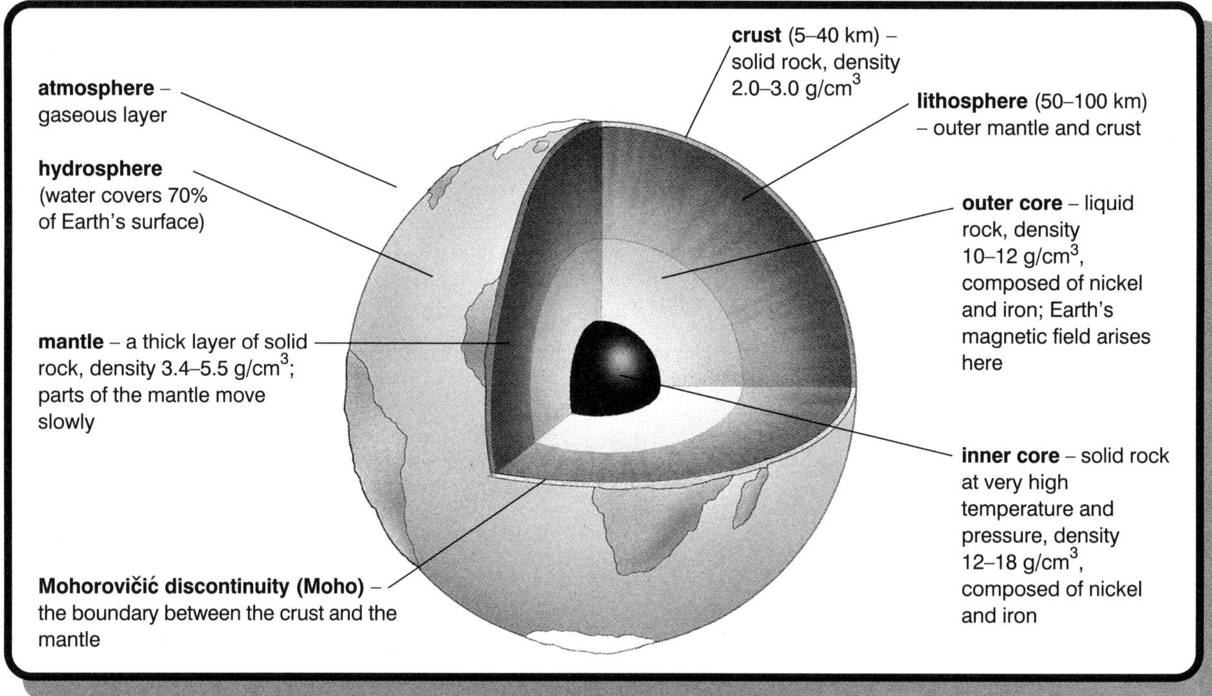

crust (5–40 km) – solid rock, density 2.0–3.0 g/cm³
atmosphere – gaseous layer
lithosphere (50–100 km) – outer mantle and crust
hydrosphere (water covers 70% of Earth's surface)
outer core – liquid rock, density 10–12 g/cm³, composed of nickel and iron; Earth's magnetic field arises here
mantle – a thick layer of solid rock, density 3.4–5.5 g/cm³; parts of the mantle move slowly
inner core – solid rock at very high temperature and pressure, density 12–18 g/cm³, composed of nickel and iron
Mohorovičić discontinuity (Moho) – the boundary between the crust and the mantle

The layered structure of the Earth

11.2 Plate tectonics

Earthquakes and volcanoes occur in belts of activity, which run

- along chains of high mountains, e.g. the Alps and the Andes. Deep **oceanic trenches** in the sea floor run alongside mountain ranges near the edges of continents.
- along chains of high mountains beneath the sea called **oceanic ridges**
- through chains of volcanic islands, e.g. the Philippines. Oceanic trenches run close to these belts.

Why do earthquakes and volcanoes occur in some parts of Earth's crust and not others? The theory of **plate tectonics** holds that the lithosphere (crust + outer mantle) is made up of a number of separate **plates** (see diagram on opposite page). Movements in the mantle make the plates move very slowly, at a rate of about 5 cm a year. As a result, plates may push against each other, creating stress. As the stress builds up, the plates may bend more and more until suddenly and violently they spring back into shape. Then the shock is felt as an earthquake. The energy required for the movements of the mantle comes from the decay of radioactive elements in the lithosphere.

Plate boundaries

FACTS

There are three types of boundaries between plates.

★ **Destructive boundaries** occur where plates are in collision. The edge of the oceanic plate slides beneath the less dense continental plate. As the oceanic plate moves downwards it melts and becomes part of the mantle. The process is called **subduction**. It causes oceans to shrink in size.

★ **Constructive boundaries** occur where lava erupts from volcanoes along the oceanic ridges and cools to form new oceanic crust. The new crust adds to the plates on each side and pushes them apart, increasing the width of the ocean floor. The process is called **sea-floor spreading**.

★ **Conservative boundaries** occur where two plates slide past one another, e.g. the San Andreas fault in California. No lithosphere is added or lost.

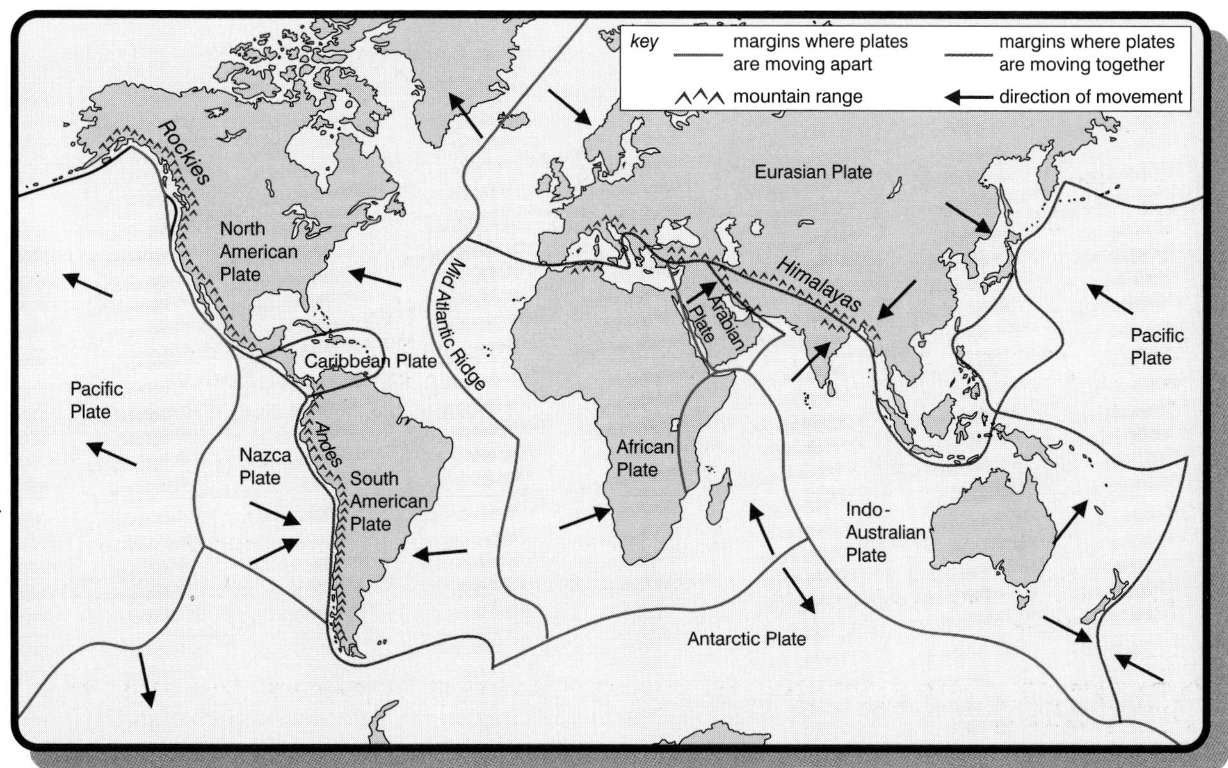

The plates that make up Earth's crust

The movement of plates

Material is subducted from plates at oceanic trenches and added at oceanic ridges. As a result, there is a movement of plates which has been described as a **conveyor belt** (see diagram below). As plates ride on the mobile mantle, the continents on them move. This has been happening for thousands of millions of years. Although continents move only a few centimetres a year, they have already travelled thousands of kilometres. About 300 million years ago, northern Europe was near the equator, and tropical forests grew there. These later decayed to form coal deposits.

Evidence for the theory of plate tectonics

There is a similarity between the east coastline of South America and the west coastline of Africa. This led scientists to suggest the theory of

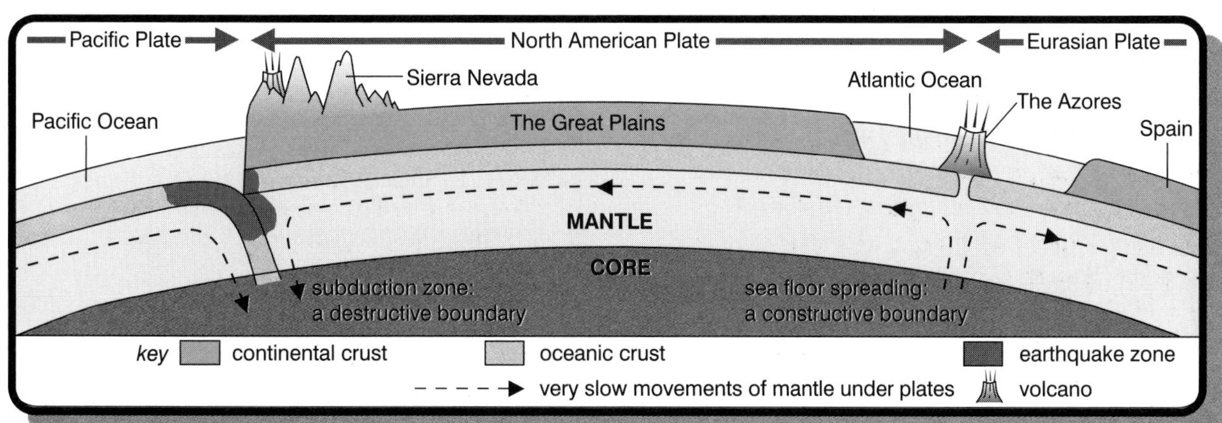

Movement of plates on the 'conveyor belt'

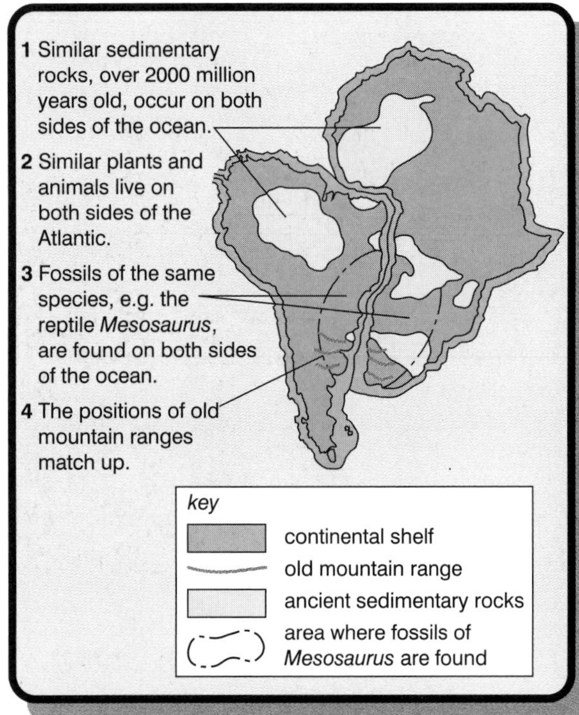

1 Similar sedimentary rocks, over 2000 million years old, occur on both sides of the ocean.
2 Similar plants and animals live on both sides of the Atlantic.
3 Fossils of the same species, e.g. the reptile *Mesosaurus*, are found on both sides of the ocean.
4 The positions of old mountain ranges match up.
key
continental shelf
old mountain range
ancient sedimentary rocks
area where fossils of *Mesosaurus* are found

South America and Africa – were they joined?

continental drift. There is evidence that geological ages ago the two continents were joined together, and later split up and slowly drifted apart.

According to the theory of continental drift, there was one original land mass, Pangaea, which split 180 million years ago into two parts. The two land masses, Laurasia and Gondwanaland, drifted apart. Oceans widened between them. Over millions of years the original land masses split up and drifted apart to form the five continents that we have today. What was the source of the energy needed to drive the continents apart? An enormous quantity of heat is produced by radioactive decay inside the Earth. Some of the heat drives convection currents in the magma. These currents power the continental drift.

11.3 Types of rock

Igneous rocks

Molten rock beneath Earth's crust is called **magma**. Magma tends to rise, and, when cracks appear in the Earth's crust, magma is forced out from the mantle as lava. It erupts on to the surface of the Earth as a volcano. When volcanic lava cools, it crystallises to form **extrusive igneous rocks**. The faster the rate of cooling, the smaller the crystals that are formed. When magma crystallises below Earth's surface, **intrusive igneous rocks** are formed. Igneous rocks include

- basalt, an extrusive igneous rock formed by free-flowing mobile lava
- granite, an intrusive igneous rock
- pumice, formed from a foam of lava and volcanic gases.

Sedimentary rocks

The rocks on Earth's surface are worn down by weathering and by erosion. The fragments that are worn away are carried by winds, ice and rivers and eventually deposited as a **sediment**. A bed of sediment may form on a sea shore, on an ocean floor or in a desert. As more material is deposited on top, the pressure makes the sediment **lithify** – form a sedimentary rock. Sedimentary rocks may contain fossils – imprints of dead plants or animals which were included in the rocks as they formed. Fossils are used to date rocks. If a rock contains the marks of creatures known to have been alive 250 million years ago, the rock must be 250 million years old. Sedimentary rocks include

- limestone, formed from the shells of dead animals
- coal, formed from the remains of dead plants
- sandstone, compacted grains of sand.

Metamorphic rocks

Metamorphic rocks are formed from igneous and sedimentary rocks at high temperature or high pressure. Included among metamorphic rocks are

- marble, formed from limestone at high temperature
- slate, formed from clay, mud and shale at high pressure.

Earth's crust is composed of 8% sedimentary rocks, 65% igneous rocks and 27% metamorphic rocks.

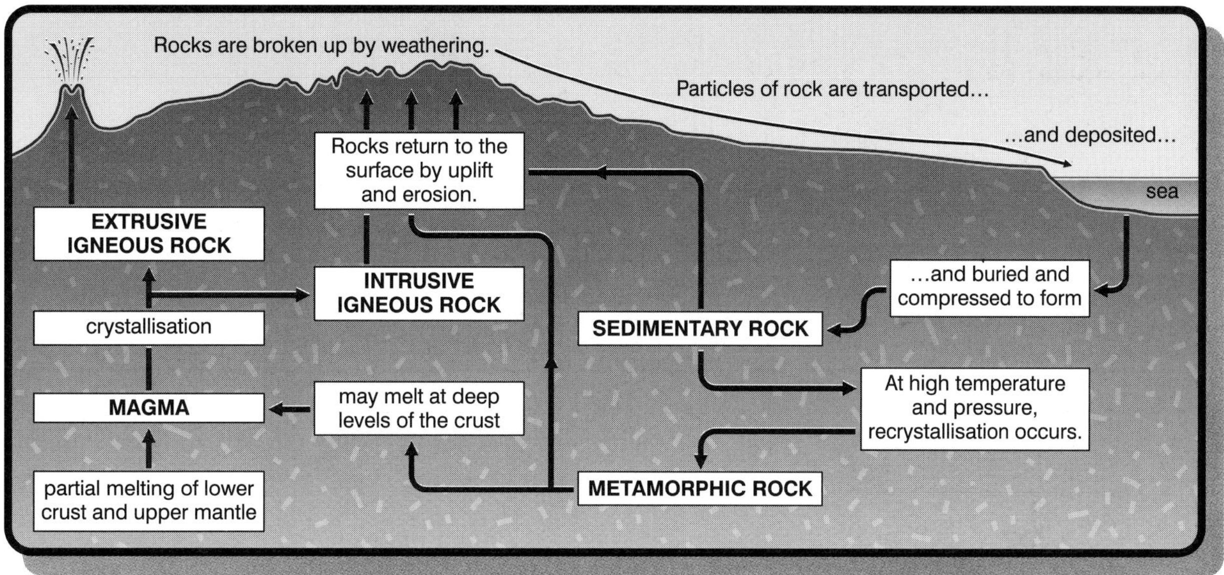

The rock cycle

The rock cycle

The interconversion between igneous rocks, sedimentary rocks and metamorphic rocks is called the **rock cycle** (see diagram above).

11.4 The landscape

Rocks are constantly being slowly broken down into smaller particles by **physical forces**, such as the wind, and **chemical reactions** which attack rocks. These processes are called **weathering**. When rocks are broken down and the particles are carried away by an agent such as water or wind, the process is called **erosion**. Weathering and erosion shape the landscape. The following agents shape the landscape:

- rainwater enters cracks in a rock, freezes, expands and opens the cracks wider
- rivers and streams carry material in solution and in suspension
- erosion happens when minerals dissolve slightly in water
- chemical reactions occur, e.g. between acidic water and limestone rocks
- glaciers move slowly over a landscape, wearing down rocks
- wind has a landscaping effect which is strongest in desert areas.

11.5 Materials from rocks

Many useful materials are obtained from rocks. Metals are extracted from compounds which occur in rocks; see page 77. Limestone and silica are important rocks.

Limestone

The concept map overleaf shows the uses of limestone.

A lime kiln

The reaction that takes place in a lime kiln is

calcium carbonate (limestone) → calcium oxide (quicklime) + carbon dioxide

$$CaCO_3(s) \rightarrow CaO(s) + CO_2(g)$$

This reaction is **reversible**; it can take place in the reverse direction as well as in the forward direction:

calcium oxide (a base) + carbon dioxide (an acid) → calcium carbonate (a salt)

In the lime kiln, a draught of air blowing through the kiln carries away carbon dioxide so that it cannot recombine with calcium oxide.

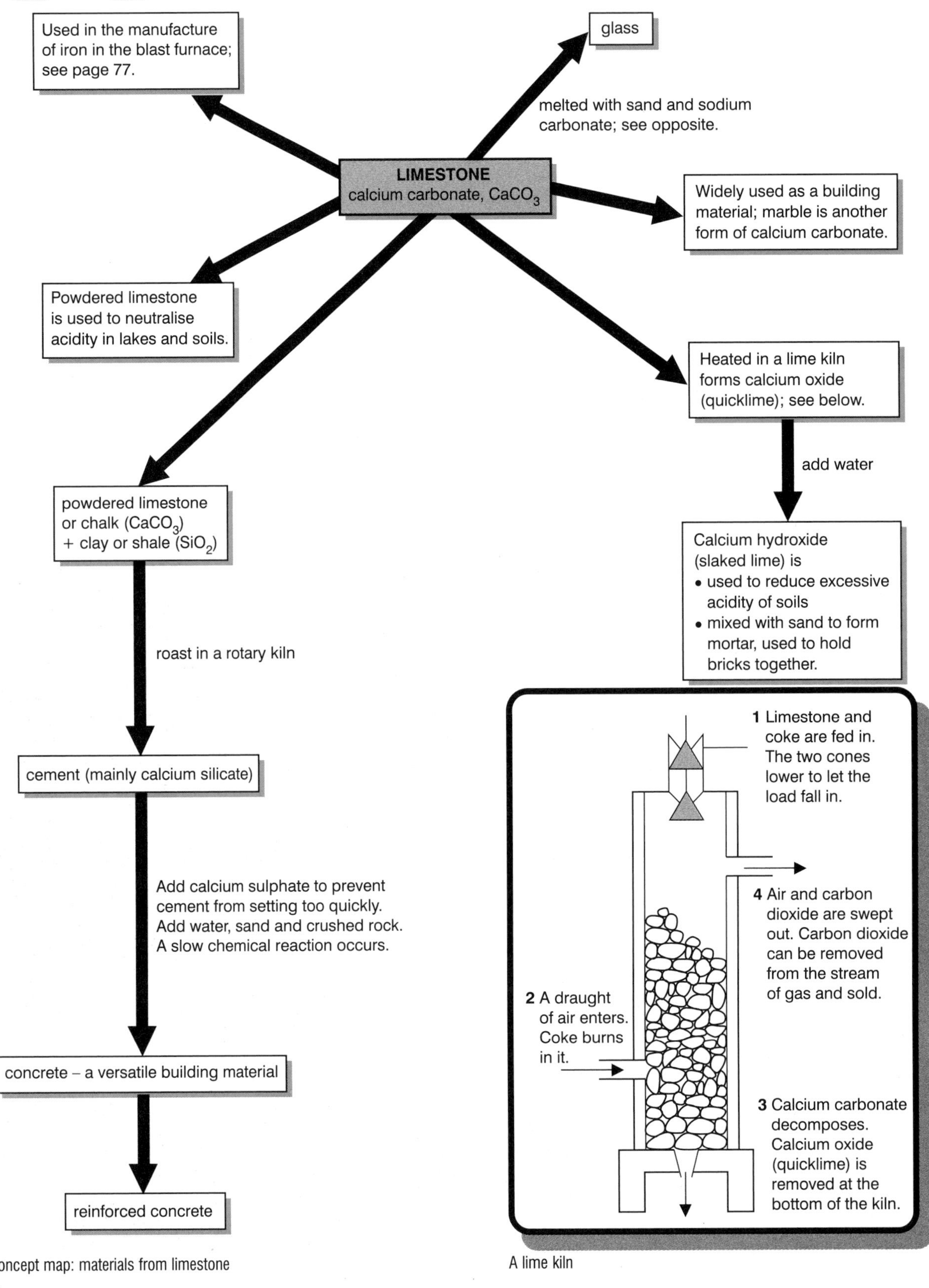

Used in the manufacture of iron in the blast furnace; see page 77.
glass
melted with sand and sodium carbonate; see opposite.
LIMESTONE
calcium carbonate, $CaCO_3$
Widely used as a building material; marble is another form of calcium carbonate.
Powdered limestone is used to neutralise acidity in lakes and soils.
Heated in a lime kiln forms calcium oxide (quicklime); see below.
add water
Calcium hydroxide (slaked lime) is
• used to reduce excessive acidity of soils
• mixed with sand to form mortar, used to hold bricks together.
powdered limestone or chalk ($CaCO_3$) + clay or shale (SiO_2)
roast in a rotary kiln
cement (mainly calcium silicate)
Add calcium sulphate to prevent cement from setting too quickly. Add water, sand and crushed rock. A slow chemical reaction occurs.
concrete – a versatile building material
reinforced concrete
1 Limestone and coke are fed in. The two cones lower to let the load fall in.
4 Air and carbon dioxide are swept out. Carbon dioxide can be removed from the stream of gas and sold.
2 A draught of air enters. Coke burns in it.
3 Calcium carbonate decomposes. Calcium oxide (quicklime) is removed at the bottom of the kiln.

Concept map: materials from limestone

A lime kiln

Silica

The concept map below shows the uses of silicon(IV) oxide (silica).

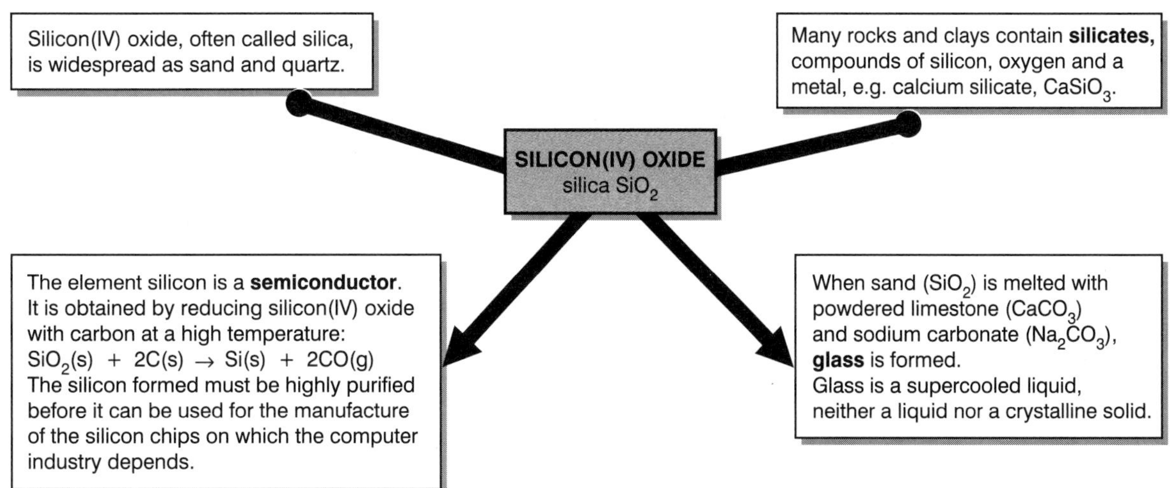

Silicon(IV) oxide, often called silica, is widespread as sand and quartz.
Many rocks and clays contain **silicates,** compounds of silicon, oxygen and a metal, e.g. calcium silicate, $CaSiO_3$.
SILICON(IV) OXIDE silica SiO_2
The element silicon is a **semiconductor**. It is obtained by reducing silicon(IV) oxide with carbon at a high temperature:
$SiO_2(s) + 2C(s) \rightarrow Si(s) + 2CO(g)$
The silicon formed must be highly purified before it can be used for the manufacture of the silicon chips on which the computer industry depends.
When sand (SiO_2) is melted with powdered limestone ($CaCO_3$) and sodium carbonate (Na_2CO_3), **glass** is formed.
Glass is a supercooled liquid, neither a liquid nor a crystalline solid.

Concept map: silica

round-up

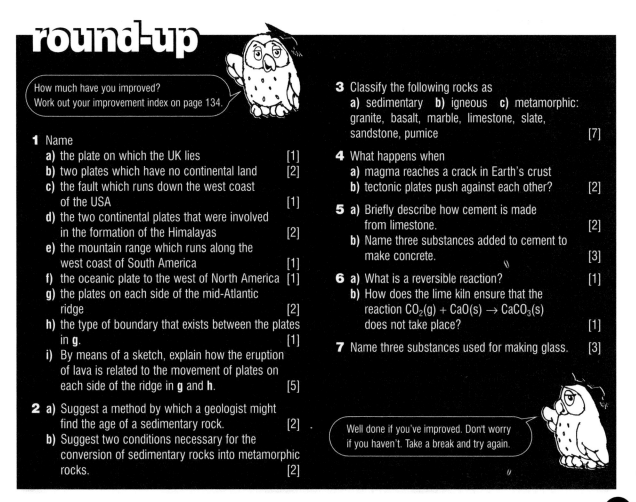

How much have you improved?
Work out your improvement index on page 134.

1 Name
- **a)** the plate on which the UK lies [1]
- **b)** two plates which have no continental land [2]
- **c)** the fault which runs down the west coast of the USA [1]
- **d)** the two continental plates that were involved in the formation of the Himalayas [2]
- **e)** the mountain range which runs along the west coast of South America [1]
- **f)** the oceanic plate to the west of North America [1]
- **g)** the plates on each side of the mid-Atlantic ridge [2]
- **h)** the type of boundary that exists between the plates in **g**. [1]
- **i)** By means of a sketch, explain how the eruption of lava is related to the movement of plates on each side of the ridge in **g** and **h**. [5]

2 **a)** Suggest a method by which a geologist might find the age of a sedimentary rock. [2]
- **b)** Suggest two conditions necessary for the conversion of sedimentary rocks into metamorphic rocks. [2]

3 Classify the following rocks as **a)** sedimentary **b)** igneous **c)** metamorphic: granite, basalt, marble, limestone, slate, sandstone, pumice [7]

4 What happens when
- **a)** magma reaches a crack in Earth's crust
- **b)** tectonic plates push against each other? [2]

5 **a)** Briefly describe how cement is made from limestone. [2]
- **b)** Name three substances added to cement to make concrete. [3]

6 **a)** What is a reversible reaction? [1]
- **b)** How does the lime kiln ensure that the reaction $CO_2(g) + CaO(s) \rightarrow CaCO_3(s)$ does not take place? [1]

7 Name three substances used for making glass. [3]

Well done if you've improved. Don't worry if you haven't. Take a break and try again.

Metals and alloys 12

preview

At the end of this topic you will:

- **understand the nature of the metallic bond**
- **be familiar with the chemical reactions of metals**
- **use the reactivity series to make predictions about metals and their compounds and methods used for extracting metals**
- **know methods of preventing the rusting of iron.**

MIND MAP
Page 152.
How much do you already know?
Work out your score on page 134.

Test yourself

1 List three characteristics of metals that are explained by the metallic bond. [3]

2 Name three metals that burn in air to form oxides. [3]

3 Name two metals that do not react when heated in air. [2]

4 Name three metals that react with cold water and say what products are formed. [5]

5 What is formed when a metal reacts with hydrochloric acid? [2]

6 In which groups of the periodic table do you find **a)** sodium **b)** magnesium **c)** transition metals? [3]

7 What method is used to extract very reactive metals from their ores? [2]

8 How is iron extracted from its ore? [3]

9 Name two metals which become coated with a film of oxide on exposure to the air. [2]

12.1 The metallic bond

A block of metal consists of positive metal ions and free electrons, as shown in the diagram.

The presence of free electrons explains how metals can conduct electricity. Electrons can be supplied at one end of a piece of metal and removed at the other end. The nature of the metallic bond also explains how metals can change their shape without breaking.

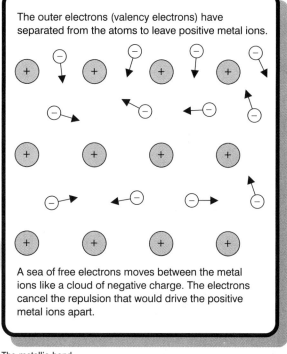

The outer electrons (valency electrons) have separated from the atoms to leave positive metal ions.

A sea of free electrons moves between the metal ions like a cloud of negative charge. The electrons cancel the repulsion that would drive the positive metal ions apart.

The metallic bond

12.2 Reactions of metals

Most metals react slowly with air to form a surface film of metal oxide. This reaction is called **tarnishing**. Gold and platinum do not tarnish in air. Aluminium rapidly forms a surface layer of aluminium oxide and only shows its true reactivity if this layer is removed. The table on the opposite page shows some of the reactions of metals.

metal	reaction when heated in oxygen	reaction with cold water	reaction with dilute hydrochloric acid
potassium sodium lithium	burn to form the oxides	displace hydrogen; form alkaline hydroxides.	react dangerously fast to form hydrogen and the metal chloride
calcium	burn to form the oxides	displace hydrogen; form alkaline hydroxides.	displace hydrogen; form metal chlorides
magnesium	burn to form the oxides	reacts slowly	displace hydrogen; form metal chlorides
aluminium zinc iron	burn to form the oxides	do not react, except for slow rusting of iron; all react with steam	displace hydrogen; form metal chlorides
tin lead	slowly form oxides without burning	do not react even with steam	react very slowly to form hydrogen and the metal chloride
copper	slowly form oxides without burning	do not react even with steam	do not react
silver gold platinum	do not react	do not react even with steam	do not react

Reactions of metals

Here are equations for some of the reactions mentioned in the table:

sodium + water → hydrogen + sodium hydroxide

$$2Na(s) + 2H_2O(l) \rightarrow H_2(g) + 2NaOH(aq)$$

(Sodium must be kept under oil to prevent it being attacked by water in the air.)

calcium + water → hydrogen + calcium hydroxide

$$Ca(s) + 2H_2O(l) \rightarrow H_2(g) + Ca(OH)_2(aq)$$

magnesium + water → hydrogen + magnesium hydroxide

$$Mg(s) + 2H_2O(l) \rightarrow H_2(g) + Mg(OH)_2(aq)$$

magnesium + steam → hydrogen + magnesium oxide

$$Mg(s) + H_2O(g) \rightarrow H_2(g) + MgO(s)$$

zinc + steam → hydrogen + zinc oxide

$$Zn(s) + H_2O(g) \rightarrow H_2(g) + ZnO(s)$$

iron + steam → hydrogen + tri-iron tetraoxide

$$3Fe(s) + 4H_2O(g) \rightarrow 4H_2(g) + Fe_3O_4(s)$$

zinc + hydrochloric acid → hydrogen + zinc chloride

$$Zn(s) + 2HCl(aq) \rightarrow H_2(g) + ZnCl_2(aq)$$

The metals can be placed in an order of reactivity which is called the **reactivity series**:

metal	symbol	↑ increase in reactivity; increase in the ease with which metals react to form ions	increase in the ease of discharge of metal ions in electrolysis ↓
potassium	K		
sodium	Na		
lithium	Li		
calcium	Ca		
magnesium	Mg		
aluminium	Al		
zinc	Zn		
iron	Fe		
tin	Sn		
lead	Pb		
copper	Cu		
silver	Ag		
gold	Au		
platinum	Pt		

Part of the reactivity series of metals

12.3 Metals in the periodic table

In Group 1 of the periodic table are the **alkali metals**, and in Group 2 are the **alkaline earths**. Aluminium is in Group 3. The less reactive metals tin and lead are in Group 4. The metals in the block between Group 2 and Group 3 are called the **transition metals**, e.g. iron, nickel, copper and zinc. For the differences between the physical and chemical properties of metallic and non-metallic elements, see page 14.

12.4 Making predictions

Competition between metals for oxygen

When aluminium is heated with iron(III) oxide, the two metals are in competition for oxygen. Aluminium wins because it is above iron in the reactivity series.

aluminium + iron(III) oxide → iron + aluminium oxide

$$2Al(s) + Fe_2O_3(s) \rightarrow 2Fe(s) + Al_2O_3(s)$$

The reaction that occurs is highly exothermic. It is called the **thermit reaction**. Since the iron forms in a molten state, it can be used to weld pieces of metal together.

Competition between metals to form ions

Metals high in the reactivity series form ions with ease. A metal which is higher in the reactivity series will displace a metal which is lower in the reactivity series from a salt. Examples are:

copper + silver nitrate solution (colourless solution) → silver (silver crystals, turn black in light) + copper(II) nitrate solution (blue solution)

$$Cu(s) + 2AgNO_3(aq) \rightarrow 2Ag(s) + Cu(NO_3)_2(aq)$$

or $$Cu(s) + 2Ag^+(aq) \rightarrow Cu^{2+}(aq) + 2Ag(s)$$

zinc + copper(II) sulphate (blue solution) → copper (reddish brown solid) + zinc sulphate (colourless solution)

$$Zn(s) + CuSO_4(aq) \rightarrow Cu(s) + ZnSO_4(aq)$$

or $$Zn(s) + Cu^{2+}(aq) \rightarrow Zn^{2+}(aq) + Cu(s)$$

Discharge of ions in electrolysis

When metal ions are discharged in electrolysis, the ions of metals high in the reactivity series are difficult to discharge, and the ions of metals low in the reactivity series are easy to discharge. For example:

- when a solution containing copper ions and iron ions is electrolysed, copper is formed at the cathode, while iron ions remain in solution
- when a solution containing copper ions and silver ions is electrolysed, silver is discharged at the cathode, while copper ions remain in solution.

Compounds and the reactivity series

The higher a metal is in the reactivity series,

- the more readily it forms compounds
- the more difficult it is to split up its compounds.

Oxides

★ Hydrogen will reduce the oxides of metals which are low in the reactivity series, e.g.

copper(II) oxide + hydrogen $\xrightarrow{\text{heat}}$ copper + water

$$CuO(s) + H_2(g) \rightarrow Cu(s) + H_2O(l)$$

★ Carbon, when heated, will reduce the oxides of metals which are low in the reactivity series, e.g.

lead(II) oxide + carbon $\xrightarrow{\text{heat}}$ lead + carbon monoxide

$$PbO(s) + C(s) \rightarrow Pb(s) + CO(g)$$

★ Carbon monoxide is used to reduce hot iron oxide to iron.

iron(III) oxide + carbon monoxide $\xrightarrow{\text{heat}}$ iron + carbon dioxide

$$Fe_2O_3(s) + 3CO(g) \rightarrow 2Fe(s) + 3CO_2(g)$$

★ The oxides of metals which are high in the reactivity series, e.g. aluminium, are not reduced by hydrogen or carbon or carbon monoxide.

★ Silver and mercury are very low in the reactivity series. Their oxides decompose when heated.

Other compounds

The position of the metal in the reactivity series ties in with the stability of its compounds to heat, as shown in the table on the opposite page.

cation	anion				
	oxide	**chloride**	**sulphate**	**carbonate**	**hydroxide**
potassium sodium	no decomposition	no decomposition	no decomposition		
calcium magnesium aluminium zinc iron lead			oxide + sulphur trioxide, $MO + SO_3$ some also give SO_2	oxide + carbon dioxide, $MO + CO_2$	oxide + water, $MO + H_2O$
copper silver	metal + oxygen		metal + O_2 + SO_3	metal + O_2 + CO_2	do not form hydroxides
gold	not formed				

Action of heat on compounds

12.5 Extracting metals

The method chosen for extracting a metal from its ore depends on the position of the metal in the reactivity series; see table opposite.

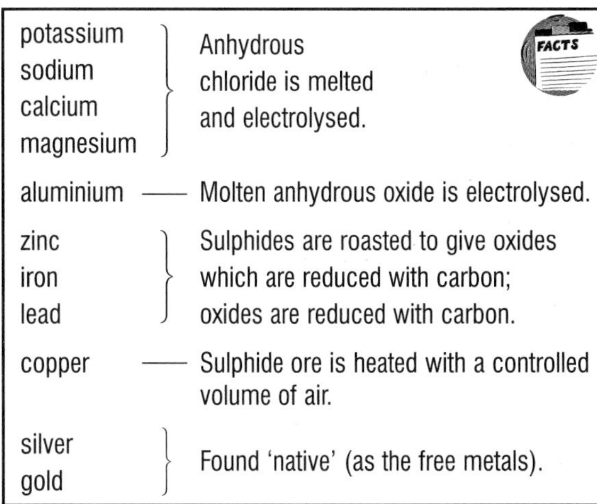

potassium sodium calcium magnesium	Anhydrous chloride is melted and electrolysed.
aluminium	Molten anhydrous oxide is electrolysed.
zinc iron lead	Sulphides are roasted to give oxides which are reduced with carbon; oxides are reduced with carbon.
copper	Sulphide ore is heated with a controlled volume of air.
silver gold	Found 'native' (as the free metals).

Methods used for the extraction of metals from their ores

Iron

The chief ores of iron are haematite, Fe_2O_3, magnetite, Fe_3O_4, and iron pyrites, FeS_2. The sulphide ore is roasted in air to convert it into an oxide. The oxide ores are reduced to iron in a blast furnace (see diagram below). The blast furnace is run continuously. The low cost of extraction and the plentiful raw materials make iron cheaper than other metals.

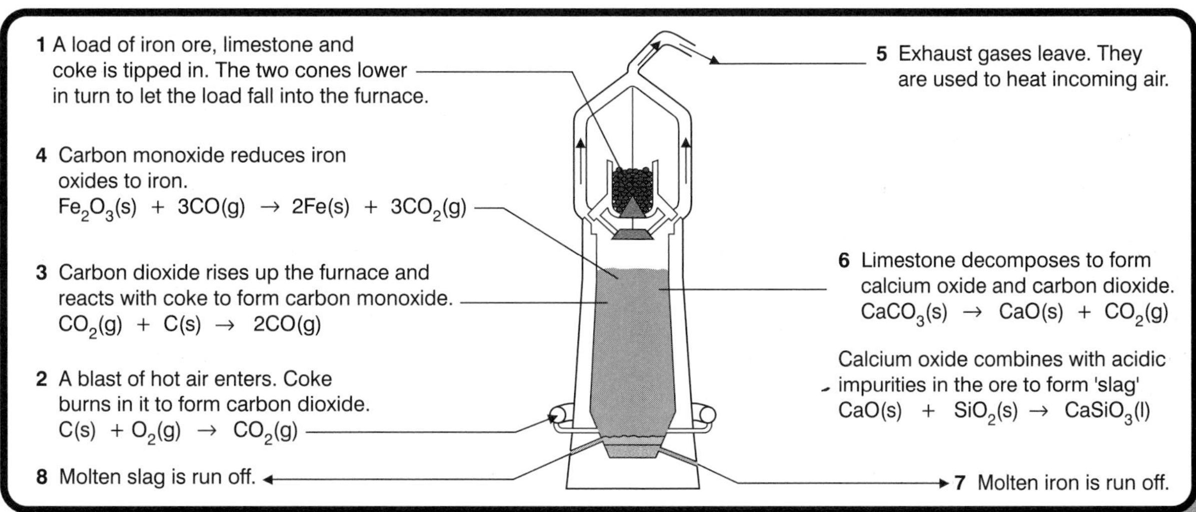

1 A load of iron ore, limestone and coke is tipped in. The two cones lower in turn to let the load fall into the furnace.
4 Carbon monoxide reduces iron oxides to iron.
$Fe_2O_3(s) + 3CO(g) \rightarrow 2Fe(s) + 3CO_2(g)$
3 Carbon dioxide rises up the furnace and reacts with coke to form carbon monoxide.
$CO_2(g) + C(s) \rightarrow 2CO(g)$
2 A blast of hot air enters. Coke burns in it to form carbon dioxide.
$C(s) + O_2(g) \rightarrow CO_2(g)$
8 Molten slag is run off.
5 Exhaust gases leave. They are used to heat incoming air.
6 Limestone decomposes to form calcium oxide and carbon dioxide.
$CaCO_3(s) \rightarrow CaO(s) + CO_2(g)$
Calcium oxide combines with acidic impurities in the ore to form 'slag'
$CaO(s) + SiO_2(s) \rightarrow CaSiO_3(l)$
7 Molten iron is run off.

A blast furnace

Titanium

Titanium is a transition metal which is sometimes described as the 'aerospace metal'. It has a low density, retains its strength at high temperatures and is resistant to corrosion. Titanium and its alloys are valuable in the manufacture of spacecraft and high-speed aircraft.

Titanium is mined as rutile, titanium(IV) oxide, TiO_2. Titanium(IV) oxide is more difficult to reduce than iron oxides, and carbon monoxide cannot be used. The **Kroll process** uses magnesium to reduce titanium(IV) chloride, $TiCl_4$. Magnesium, being higher than titanium in the reactivity series, can displace titanium from its compound.

The steps in the extraction are as follows.

1 Titanium(IV) oxide is mixed with coke and heated in a furnace, through which chlorine passes.

titanium(IV) oxide + chlorine + carbon → titanium(IV) choride + carbon monoxide

$$TiO_2(s) + 2Cl_2(g) + 2C(s) \rightarrow TiCl_4(g) + 2CO(g)$$

2 The titanium(IV) chloride is purified by fractional distillation.

3 The Kroll process: gaseous titanium(IV) chloride is passed into a reactor containing molten magnesium. Argon is passed through the reactor.

titanium(IV) choride + magnesium → titanium + magnesium choride

4 A spongy deposit of titanium forms on the walls of the reactor. A batch process is used because the reactor must be allowed to cool so that the deposit of titanium can be scraped off. The metal is distilled and melted to form ingots.

5 Magnesium chloride is run off from the reactor and electrolysed to give magnesium and chlorine for recycling.

12.6 Corrosion of metals

- ★ **Copper**: the green roofs you see on some buildings are of copper, which has corroded in the air to copper carbonate hydroxide, $Cu(OH)_2.CuCO_3$.
- ★ **Aluminium**: as soon as a fresh surface of aluminium meets the air, it is corroded to form a thin film of the oxide, which prevents air from reaching the metal below.
- ★ **Chromium** forms a protective oxide layer in the same way as aluminium. Stainless steel cutlery is made of a chromium–steel alloy (mixture).
- ★ **Nickel** forms a protective oxide layer as soon as a fresh surface of nickel meets the air. Nickel-plated steels are very useful.
- ★ **Lead** water pipes were used for centuries. However, water attacks lead slowly to form soluble lead compounds.
- ★ **Zinc** corrodes quickly in air to form a film of zinc carbonate. This protects the zinc beneath from further attack. Iron can be coated with zinc (**galvanised**) to protect it from rusting.

Rusting of iron and steel

The corrosion of iron and steel is called rusting. Rust has the formula $Fe_2O_3.nH_2O$, where n, the number of water molecules in the formula, varies.

The combination of reagents that attacks iron is water, air and acid. The carbon dioxide in the air provides the acidity. If the water contains salts, the speed of rusting is increased. In a warm climate, rusting is more rapid than at lower temperatures.

The rusting of iron is an expensive problem. The table on the opposite page lists some of the methods used to protect iron and steel against rusting.

method	where used	comment
1 a coat of paint	large objects, e.g. ships and bridges	If the paint is scratched, the iron beneath it starts to rust.
2 a film oil or grease	moving parts of machinery	The protective film must be renewed.
3 a coat of metal		
a) chromium plating	trim on cars, cycle handlebars, taps	Applied by electroplating, decorative as well as protective.
b) galvanising (zinc plating)	galvanised steel girders are used in buildings	Even if the layer of zinc is scratched, the iron underneath does not rust. Zinc cannot be used for food cans because zinc and its compounds are poisonous.
c) tin plating	food cans	If the layer of tin is scratched, the iron beneath it rusts.
4 stainless steel	cutlery, car accessories	Steels containing chromium (10–25%) or nickel (10–20%) do not rust.
5 sacrificial protection	ships	Bars of zinc attached to the hull of a ship corrode and protect the ship from rusting.
	underground pipes	Bags of magnesium scrap attached to underground iron pipes corrode in preference to the pipes. The scrap must be replaced from time to time.

Rust prevention

12.7 Conservation

The Earth's resources of metals are limited. It makes sense to collect scrap metals and recycle them. In addition, there is a saving in fuel resources because less energy is needed for recycling than for extracting metals from their ores. There is another reason for conserving metals: the impact which mining has on the environment. Before recycling, scrap metals must be collected, sorted and stored until there is enough to process.

12.8 Uses of metals and alloys

The strengths of metals and **alloys** (mixtures of metals) find them thousands of uses; the table overleaf lists just some of these.

12.9 Iron and steel

Cast iron

The iron that comes out of the blast furnace is called cast iron. It contains 3–4% carbon which lowers the melting point, making cast iron easier to melt and mould than pure iron. By casting, objects with complicated shapes can be made, such as the engine blocks of motor vehicles. The carbon content makes cast iron brittle.

Steel

Steel is made from iron by burning off carbon and other impurities in a stream of oxygen. A number of elements may be added to give different types of steel:

- chromium in stainless steels for cutlery, car accessories and tools
- cobalt steel in permanent magnets
- manganese in all steels to increase strength
- molybdenum steel for rifle barrels and propeller shafts
- nickel in stainless steel cutlery and industrial plants
- tungsten steel in high-speed cutting tools
- vanadium steel in springs.

metal/alloy	characteristics	uses
aluminium	low density good electrical conductor good thermal conductor reflector of light non-toxic resistant to corrosion	aircraft manufacture (Duralumin) overhead electrical cable saucepans, etc. car headlamps food packaging door frames, window frames, etc.
brass, an alloy of copper and zinc	golden colour, harder than copper, resists corrosion	ships' propellers, taps, screws, electrical fittings
bronze, an alloy of copper and tin	golden colour, hard, sonorous, resistant to corrosion	coins, medals, statues, springs, church bells
copper	good electrical conductor not corroded	electrical circuits water pipes and tanks
Duralumin, an alloy of aluminium	low density, stronger than aluminium	aircraft and spacecraft
gold	beautiful colour never tarnishes	jewellery, dentistry, electrical contacts
iron	hard, strong, inexpensive, rusts	construction, transport
lead	dense, unreactive, soft, not very strong	car batteries, divers' weights, roofing
magnesium	bright flame	flares and flash bulbs
mercury	liquid at room temperature	thermometers, dental amalgam for filling teeth
nickel	resists corrosion, strong, tough, hard	stainless steel
silver	beautiful colour and shine good electrical conductor good reflector of light	jewellery, silverware contacts in computers, etc. mirrors, dental amalgam
solder, alloy of tin and lead	low melting point	joining metals in an electrical circuit
steel, an iron alloy	strong	buildings, machinery, transport
tin	low in reactivity series	coating 'tin cans'
titanium	low in density, strong, very resistant to corrosion	high-altitude planes, nose-cones of spacecraft
zinc	high in reactivity series	protection of iron and steel by galvanising

The uses of some metals and alloys

12.10 Metals in chemical cells

Metals are composed of positive ions and a cloud of electrons. When a reactive metal such as zinc is put into water or a solution of an electrolyte, some zinc ions pass into solution. Electrons accumulate on the metal until the negative charge on the zinc becomes high enough to prevent any more Zn^{2+} ions from leaving the metal. Copper is low in the reactivity series and copper ions have little tendency to pass into solution.

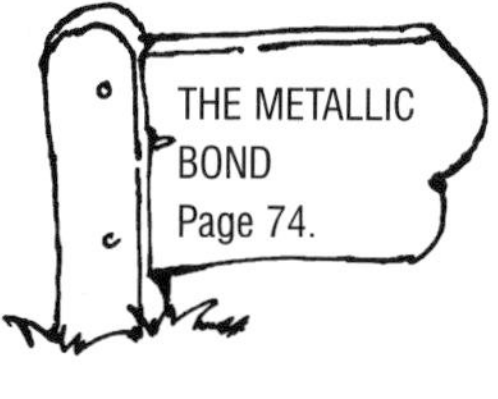

A strip of zinc and a strip of copper may be immersed in a solution and then connected, as shown below. Electrons flow through the external circuit from zinc, which is negatively charged, to copper, which has very little charge.

This kind of cell is called a **chemical cell**. The chemical reaction taking place inside the cell causes a current to flow through the external circuit. Many metals can be paired up in chemical cells like this. The direction of flow of electrons is from a metal higher in the reactivity series to a metal lower in the series. The wider apart the metals are in the reactivity series, the greater is the electromotive force (e.m.f.) of the cell.

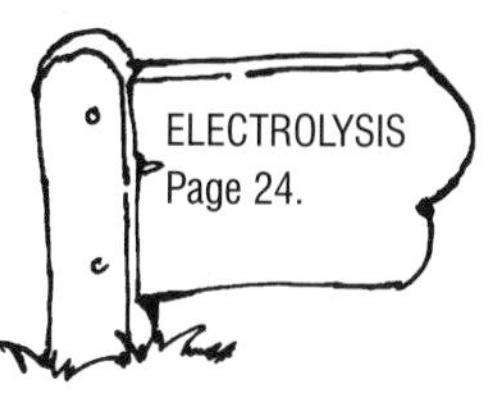

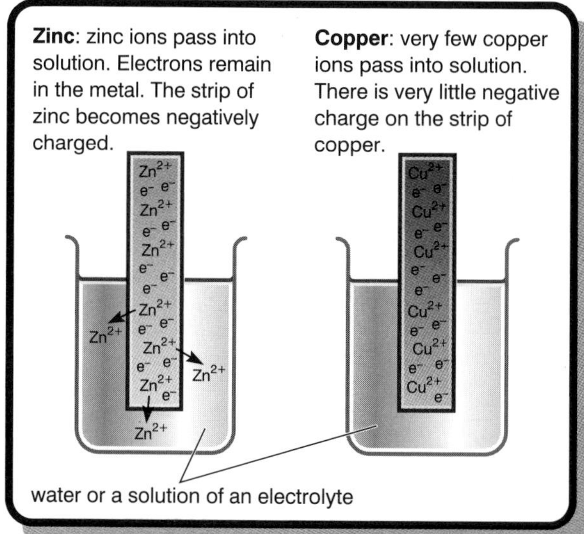

Zinc: zinc ions pass into solution. Electrons remain in the metal. The strip of zinc becomes negatively charged.
Copper: very few copper ions pass into solution. There is very little negative charge on the strip of copper.
water or a solution of an electrolyte

Zinc and copper

Dry cells

Dry cells are chemical cells used in batteries for torches, radios, etc. A dry cell has a damp paste instead of a liquid electrolyte, so it cannot leak.

- ★ The **zinc–carbon** dry cell has an e.m.f. of 1.5 V.
- ★ The **alkaline manganese** cell uses zinc and manganese(IV) oxide, and also has an e.m.f. of 1.5 V.
- ★ **Silver oxide** cells are the tiny 'batteries' used in electronic wristwatches and cameras.
- ★ The **nickel–cadmium** cell can be recharged when it goes 'flat'. This is done by connecting the cell to a source of direct current. The chemical reaction is reversed, and the cell has a new source of e.m.f.

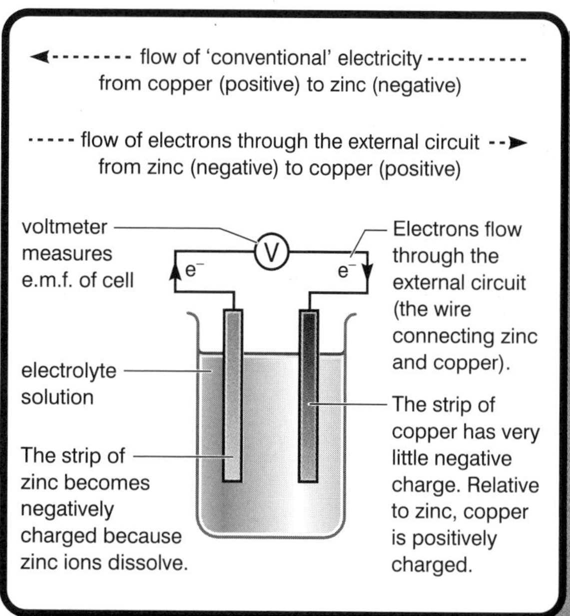

A zinc–copper chemical cell

12 round-up

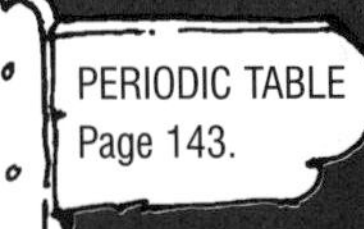

How much have you improved?
Work out your improvement index on pages 134–5.

1 Write equations for the reactions with oxygen of
a) sodium (to form Na_2O) [3]
b) magnesium [3]
c) zinc [3]
d) iron (to form Fe_3O_4) [3]
e) tin (to form SnO) [3]
f) lead (to form PbO) [3]
g) copper (to form CuO). [3]

2 **a)** Write equations for the reactions of
(i) magnesium and hydrochloric acid [4]
(ii) iron and hydrochloric acid (to form $FeCl_2$) [4]
(iii) tin and hydrochloric acid (to form $SnCl_2$). [4]
b) Write equations for the reactions between
(i) magnesium and sulphuric acid [4]
(ii) iron and sulphuric acid (to give $FeSO_4$). [4]

3 Copy and complete these word equations. If there is no reaction, write 'no reaction'. [8]
a) magnesium + sulphuric acid →
b) platinum + sulphuric acid →
c) silver + hydrochloric acid →
d) gold + hydrochloric acid →
e) zinc + sulphuric acid →
f) tin + water →

4 Why are copper and its alloys used as coinage metals in preference to iron? [3]

5 The following metals are listed in order of reactivity:
calcium > magnesium > iron > copper
Describe how the metals follow this order in their reactions with
a) water [4]
b) dilute hydrochloric acid. [4]

6 What would you see if you dropped a piece of zinc into a test tube of
a) copper(II) sulphate solution
b) lead(II) nitrate solution?
Write word equations and chemical equations for the reactions. [11]

7 A metal X displaces another metal Y from a solution of a salt of Y. X is displaced by a metal Z from a solution of a salt of X. List the metals in order of reactivity with the most reactive first. [2]

8 The following metals are listed in order of reactivity, with the most reactive first:
Na Mg Al Zn Fe Pb Cu Hg Au
List the metals which
a) occur as the free elements in the Earth's crust [1]
b) react at an observable speed with cold water [2]
c) react with steam but not with cold water [2]
d) react at an observable speed with dilute acids [4]
e) react dangerously fast with dilute acids [1]
f) displace lead from lead(II) nitrate solution. [4]

9 Suggest what method could be used to extract each of the metals A, B, C and D from a chloride ore or an oxide ore.
- Metal A reacts with cold water. [3]
- Metal B reacts only very, very slowly with water. [2]
- Metal C does not react with steam or with dilute hydrochloric acid. [2]
- Metal D when exposed to air immediately becomes coated with a layer of oxide. [3]

10 Predict the reaction of **a)** rubidium and cold water **b)** palladium and dilute hydrochloric acid. [5]

11 Copy and complete the following word equations. If no reaction occurs, write 'no reaction'.
a) copper + oxygen → [1]
b) aluminium + iron(III) oxide → [1]
c) iron + aluminium oxide → [1]
d) carbon monoxide + iron(III) oxide → [1]
e) carbon monoxide + aluminium oxide → [1]
f) zinc + copper(II) sulphate solution → [1]

12 List four different uses for aluminium. Say what property of aluminium makes it suitable for each use. [8]

13 What method of rust prevention is used on **a)** a bicycle chain **b)** bicycle handlebars **c)** steel girders **d)** cutlery **e)** parts of a ship above the waterline **f)** parts of a ship below the waterline **g)** food cans? [7]

14 List three savings which are made when metal objects are recycled. [3]

Reaction speeds 13

preview

At the end of this topic you will:

- **understand the factors which can change the speed of a chemical reaction.**

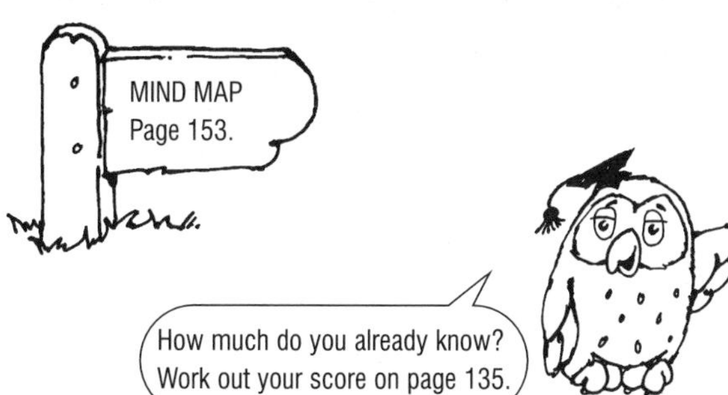

Test yourself

1 Which act faster to cure acid indigestion, indigestion tablets or indigestion powders? Explain your answer. [2]

2 a) Suggest three ways in which you could speed up the reaction between zinc and dilute sulphuric acid:

$Zn(s) + H_2SO_4(aq) \rightarrow H_2(g) + ZnSO_4(aq)$ [3]

b) Explain why each of these methods increases the speed of the reaction. [4]

3 Sketch an apparatus in which you could collect a gaseous product of a reaction and measure the rate at which it was formed. [5]

4 What is a catalyst? [2]

5 Why are catalysts important in industry? [2]

6 Name two reactions which depend on the absorption of light energy. [2]

13.1 Particle size

The reaction between a solid and a liquid is speeded up by using smaller particles of the solid reactant. The reason is that it is the atoms or ions at the surface of the solid that react, and the ratio of surface area:mass is greater for small particles than for large particles.

The diagram below shows an apparatus which you may have used to investigate the effect of particle size on the reaction:

calcium carbonate + hydrochloric acid → carbon dioxide + calcium chloride + water

$$CaCO_3(s) + 2HCl(aq) \rightarrow CO_2(g) + CaCl_2(aq) + H_2O(l)$$

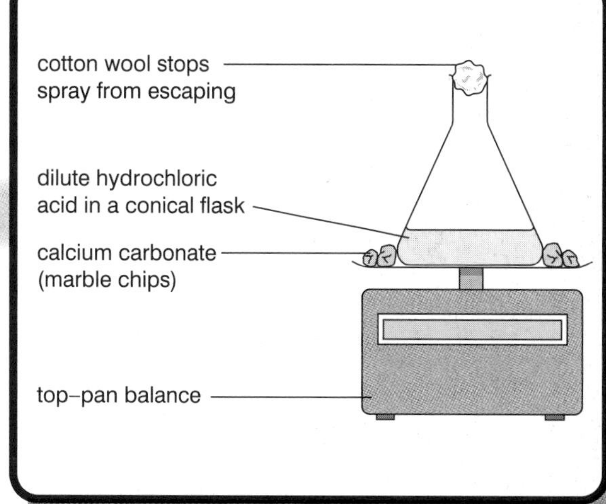

The effect of particle size on the speed of a reaction

As the reaction happens, carbon dioxide is given off and the mass of the reacting mixture decreases.

1 Note the mass of flask + acid + marble chips.
2 Add the marble chips to the acid, and start a stopwatch.
3 Note the mass after 10 seconds and then every 30 seconds for 5–10 minutes.
4 Plot the mass against time since the start of the reaction.
5 Repeat with the same mass of smaller chips.

13.2 Concentration

A precipitate of sulphur is formed in the reaction:

sodium thiosulphate + hydrochloric acid → sulphur + sulphur dioxide + sodium chloride + water

$$Na_2S_2O_3(aq) + 2HCl(aq) \rightarrow S(s) + SO_2(g) + 2NaCl(aq) + H_2O(l)$$

1 Watch the precipitate of sulphur appear.
2 Note the time when the precipitate is thick enough to block your view of a cross on a piece of paper.
3 Repeat for various concentrations of acid and for various concentrations of thiosulphate.

The experiment shows that, for this reaction,

- rate of reaction is proportional to concentration of thiosulphate
- rate of reaction is proportional to concentration of acid.

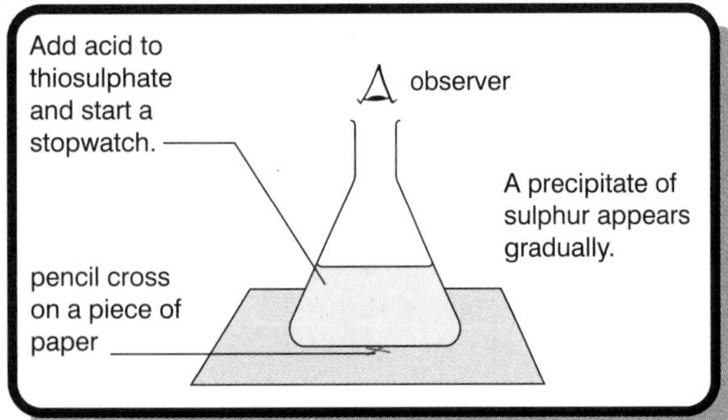

observer

The effect of concentration on the speed of a reaction

13.3 Pressure

An increase in pressure increases the rates of reactions between gases. As the molecules are pushed more closely together, they react more rapidly.

13.4 Temperature

The reaction between thiosulphate and acid can be used to study the effect of temperature on the rate of a reaction, as shown in the following graphs. This reaction goes twice as fast at 30°C as it does at 20°C. At higher temperatures, ions have more kinetic energy and collide more often and more vigorously, giving them a greater chance of reacting.

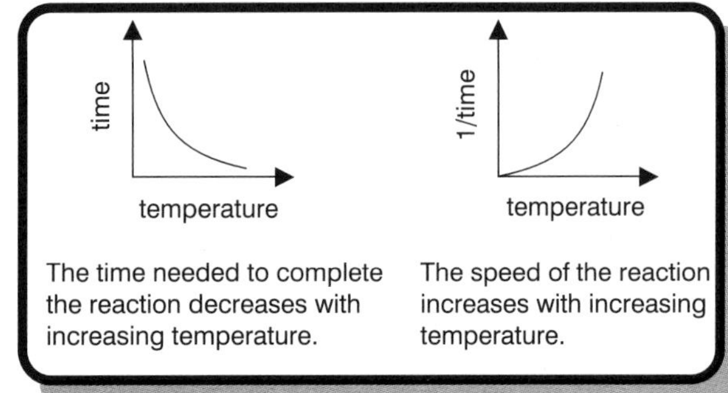

The time needed to complete the reaction decreases with increasing temperature.

The effect of temperature on the speed of a reaction

13.5 Light

Heat is not the only form of energy that speeds up chemical reactions. Light energy enables many reactions to take place, e.g. photosynthesis and photography.

13.6 Catalysts

Hydrogen peroxide decomposes to form oxygen and water:

hydrogen peroxide → oxygen + water

$$2H_2O_2(aq) \rightarrow O_2(g) + 2H_2O(l)$$

The decomposition takes place very slowly unless a **catalyst**, e.g. manganese(IV) oxide, is present. The rate at which the reaction takes place can be found by collecting the oxygen formed and measuring its volume at certain times after the start of the reaction, as shown in the diagram.

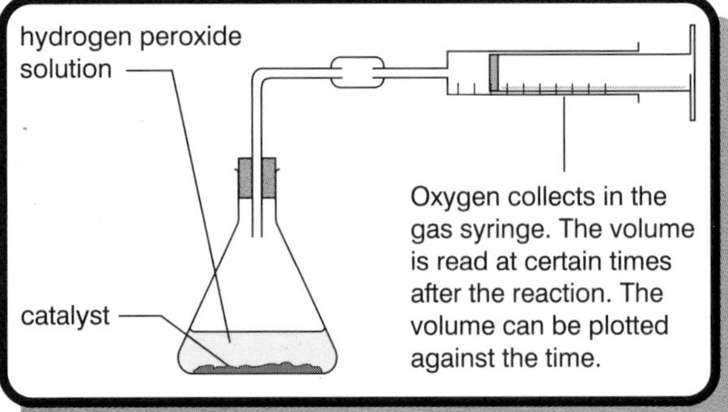

hydrogen peroxide solution
catalyst
Oxygen collects in the gas syringe. The volume is read at certain times after the reaction. The volume can be plotted against the time.

Collecting and measuring a gas

★ A catalyst is a substance which increases the rate of a chemical reaction without being used up in the reaction.

★ A catalyst will catalyse a certain reaction or group of reactions. Platinum catalyses certain oxidation reactions, and nickel catalyses some hydrogenation reactions.

★ Catalysts are very important in industry. They enable a manufacturer to make a product more rapidly or at a lower temperature.

13.7 Enzymes

Chemical reactions take place in the cells of living things. These reactions happen at reasonably fast rates at the temperatures which exist in plants and animals. They can do this because the cells contain powerful catalysts called **enzymes**.

Enzymes are proteins. They have large molecules which are twisted into complicated three-dimensional structures. The structures are damaged by temperatures above about 45°C. Here are some examples of enzyme-catalysed reactions:

- Enzymes in yeast catalyse the conversion of sugar into ethanol and carbon dioxide. The process is called **fermentation**. It is used to make ethanol (alcohol) by the fermentation of carbohydrates. It also produces bubbles of carbon dioxide which make bread rise.
- Enzymes in bacteria produce yoghurt from milk. They catalyse the conversion of lactose, the sugar in milk, into lactic acid.

13.8 How enzymes work

Enzymes are **specific**; they catalyse the reactions of only one substance or one group of substances. The substance that the enzyme enables to react is called the **substrate**. A molecule of the substrate has to fit into the contours of a region in the enzyme molecule called the **active site**. Only a substance that will fit the active site can be enabled to react by the enzyme; this is the reason why enzymes are specific. The fit between the molecules of substrate and enzyme has been described as 'like a lock and key'.

The digestive enzyme amylase catalyses the hydrolysis of starch into sugars. This reaction can be carried out in the laboratory without amylase by boiling a solution of starch with hydrochloric acid for an hour. Catalysed by amylase, the reaction takes place rapidly at body temperature. The diagram below shows how the enzyme manages to do this.

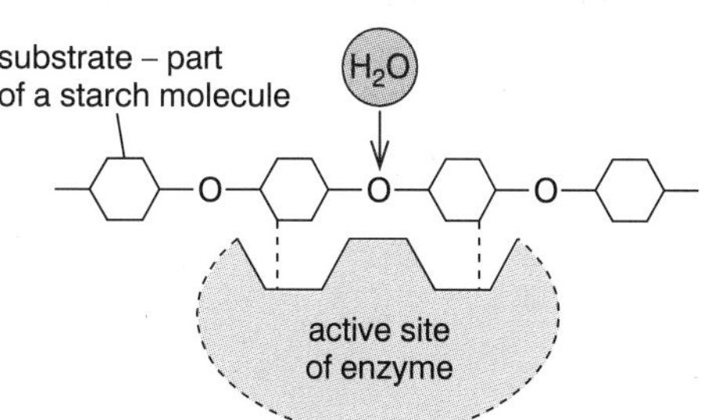

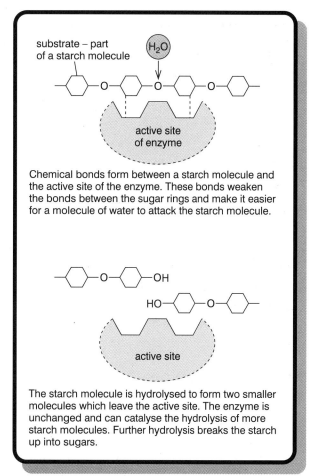

Chemical bonds form between a starch molecule and the active site of the enzyme. These bonds weaken the bonds between the sugar rings and make it easier for a molecule of water to attack the starch molecule.

The starch molecule is hydrolysed to form two smaller molecules which leave the active site. The enzyme is unchanged and can catalyse the hydrolysis of more starch molecules. Further hydrolysis breaks the starch up into sugars.

Enzyme catalysis of the hydrolysis of starch

round-up

How much have you improved?
Work out your improvement index on page 135.

1 The three graphs were obtained in experiments as described on page 83.

a) Why is there a decrease in mass? [1]

b) Which of the graphs relates to **(i)** small chips **(ii)** large chips **(iii)** medium-sized chips? [2]

c) Explain why there is a difference. [1]

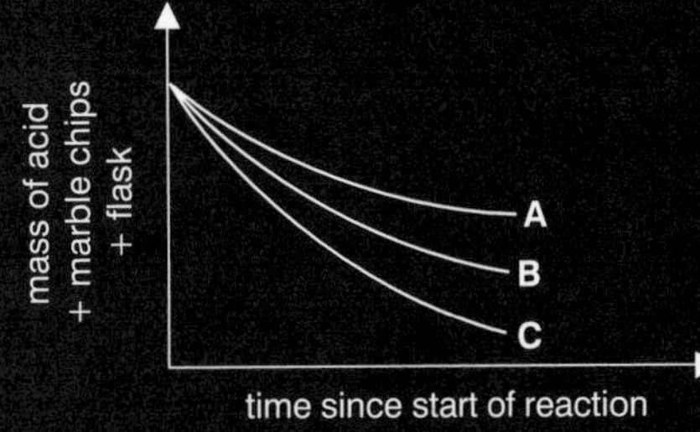

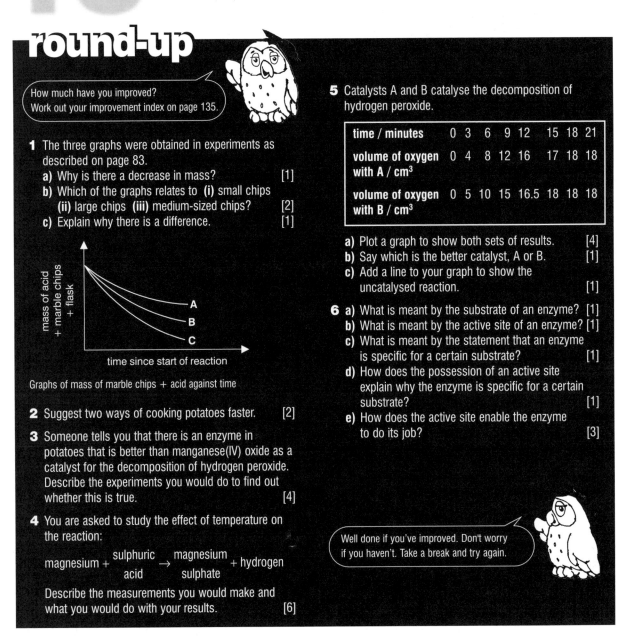

Graphs of mass of marble chips + acid against time

2 Suggest two ways of cooking potatoes faster. [2]

3 Someone tells you that there is an enzyme in potatoes that is better than manganese(IV) oxide as a catalyst for the decomposition of hydrogen peroxide. Describe the experiments you would do to find out whether this is true. [4]

4 You are asked to study the effect of temperature on the reaction:

magnesium + sulphuric acid → magnesium sulphate + hydrogen

Describe the measurements you would make and what you would do with your results. [6]

5 Catalysts A and B catalyse the decomposition of hydrogen peroxide.

time / minutes	0	3	6	9	12	15	18	21
volume of oxygen with A / cm^3	0	4	8	12	16	17	18	18
volume of oxygen with B / cm^3	0	5	10	15	16.5	18	18	18

a) Plot a graph to show both sets of results. [4]

b) Say which is the better catalyst, A or B. [1]

c) Add a line to your graph to show the uncatalysed reaction. [1]

6 a) What is meant by the substrate of an enzyme? [1]

b) What is meant by the active site of an enzyme? [1]

c) What is meant by the statement that an enzyme is specific for a certain substrate? [1]

d) How does the possession of an active site explain why the enzyme is specific for a certain substrate? [1]

e) How does the active site enable the enzyme to do its job? [3]

Well done if you've improved. Don't worry if you haven't. Take a break and try again.

Copy and complete the Mind Map to revise this topic.

Tackling chemical calculations

14

preview

At the end of this topic you will be able to:

- calculate the relative molecular mass and molar mass of a compound
- understand 'the mole'
- calculate the empirical formula and molecular formula of a compound
- use the equation for a reaction to calculate the masses of solids that react.

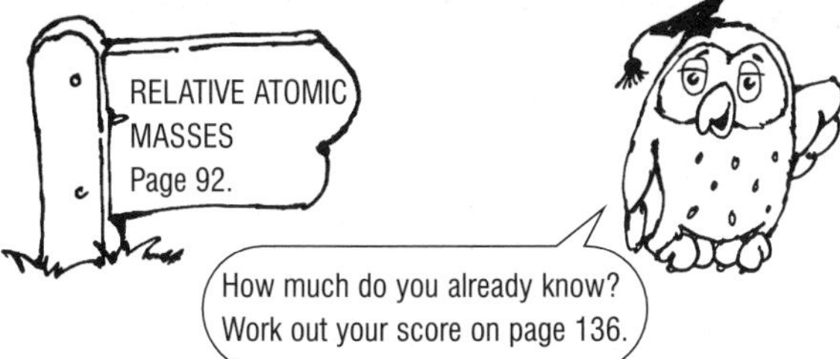

RELATIVE ATOMIC MASSES Page 92.
How much do you already know? Work out your score on page 136.

Test yourself

1 State the relative molecular masses of **a)** SO_2 **b)** SO_3 **c)** H_2SO_4 **d)** CH_3CO_2H **e)** $CuSO_4.5H_2O$. [5]

2 State the amount in moles of **a)** sodium in 46 g of sodium **b)** sulphur atoms in 64 g of sulphur **c)** S_8 molecules in 64 g of sulphur. [3]

3 State the mass of **a)** mercury in 0.100 mol of mercury **b)** sulphuric acid in 0.25 mol of H_2SO_4 **c)** magnesium oxide in 3.0 mol of MgO. [3]

4 Calculate the empirical formulas of
a) the compound containing 55.5% mercury and 44.5% bromine by mass [1]
b) the compound formed from 14.9 g of copper and 17.7 g of chlorine [1]
c) the compound formed when 0.69 g of sodium forms 0.93 g of an oxide. [1]

5 Calculate the percentage by mass of sulphur in
a) SO_2 **b)** SO_3 **c)** H_2SO_4. [3]

6 When a mixture of 8 g of iron and 4 g of sulphur is heated, the elements react to form iron(II) sulphide, FeS. How much iron will be left over at the end of the reaction? [1]

7 a) Calculate the mass of carbon dioxide formed by the action of acid on 15 g of calcium carbonate in the reaction [1]

$$CaCO_3(s) + 2HCl(aq) \rightarrow CO_2(g) + CaCl_2(aq) + H_2O(l)$$

b) State the volume at room temperature and pressure (rtp) of the carbon dioxide formed. [1]

8 A sulphuric acid plant uses 2500 tonnes of sulphur dioxide each day.
a) What mass of sulphur must be burned to produce this quantity of sulphur dioxide? [1]
b) What is the volume at rtp of this mass of sulphur dioxide? [1]

9 A company buys 100 kg of $Na_2CO_3.10H_2O$ at 30p/kg with the intention of selling it as bath salts. While standing in the warehouse, the bag punctures, and the crystals lose some of their water of crystallisation to form $Na_2CO_3.H_2O$. The company sells this powder at 50p/kg. Does the company make a profit or a loss? [2]

14.1 Some definitions

Relative atomic mass

Relative atomic mass A_r of element =

$$\frac{\text{mass of one atom of the element}}{\frac{1}{12}\text{ mass of one atom of carbon-12}}$$

Relative molecular mass

Relative molecular mass M_r of compound =

$$\frac{\text{mass of one molecule or formula unit}}{\frac{1}{12}\text{ mass of one atom of carbon-12}}$$

The relative molecular mass M_r of a compound is the sum of the relative atomic masses of all the atoms in a molecule of the compound. For sulphuric acid, H_2SO_4,

$$M_r = 2(A_r\ H) + 1(A_r\ S) + 4(A_r\ O) = 2 + 32 + 64 = 98$$

The mole

The amount of an element that contains 6.022×10^{23} atoms (the same number of atoms as 12 g of carbon-12) is called **one mole** (symbol mol) of that element.

Take the relative atomic mass expressed in grams of any element:

12 g of carbon	24 g of magnesium	56 g of iron
40 g of calcium	108 g of silver	238 g of uranium

All these masses contain the same number of atoms: 6.022×10^{23} atoms.

The ratio 6.022×10^{23}/mol is called the **Avogadro constant**. Each of these masses represents one mole (1 mol) of the element. One mole of sulphuric acid contains 6.022×10^{23} molecules of H_2SO_4, that is, 98 g of H_2SO_4 (the molar mass in grams). To write 'a mole of nitrogen' is imprecise: one mole of nitrogen atoms, N, has a mass of 14 g; one mole of nitrogen molecules, N_2, has a mass of 28 g.

Molar mass

The molar mass of a substance, symbol M, is defined by the equation:

$$\text{amount (in moles) of substance} = \frac{\text{mass of substance}}{\text{molar mass of substance}}$$

The molar mass of carbon is 12 g/mol; that is the relative atomic mass expressed in grams per mole. The molar mass of sulphuric acid, H_2SO_4, is 98 g/mol. Notice the units: relative molecular mass has no unit; molar mass has the unit g/mol.

Make sure you understand each of the terms in the Mind Map:

Example 1

What is the amount of calcium present in 120 g of calcium?

A_r of calcium = 40; molar mass of calcium = 40 g/mol

$$\text{amount of calcium} = \frac{\text{mass of calcium}}{\text{molar mass of calcium}} = \frac{120\text{ g}}{40\text{ g/mol}} = 3.0\text{ mol}$$

The amount of calcium is 3.0 mol.

Example 2

If you need 2.25 mol of magnesium carbonate, what mass of the substance do you have to weigh out?

relative molecular mass of $MgCO_3$ = $24 + 12 + (3 \times 16)$ = 84

molar mass of $MgCO_3$ = 84 g/mol

$$\text{amount of substance} = \frac{\text{mass of substance}}{\text{molar mass of substance}}$$

$$2.25\text{ mol} = \frac{\text{mass}}{84\text{ g/mol}}$$

$$\text{mass} = 84\text{ g/mol} \times 2.25\text{ mol} = 189\text{ g}$$

You need to weigh out 189 g of magnesium carbonate.

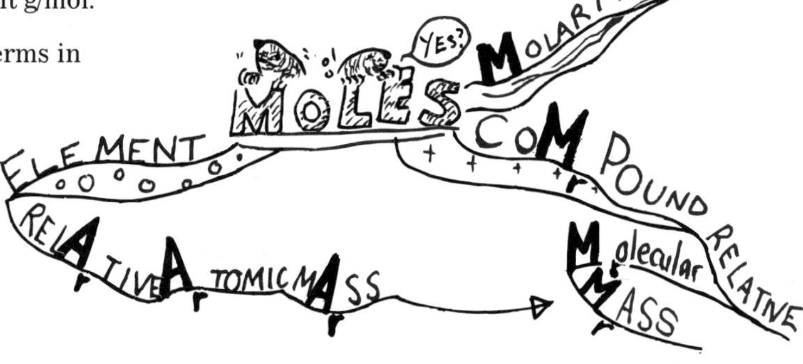

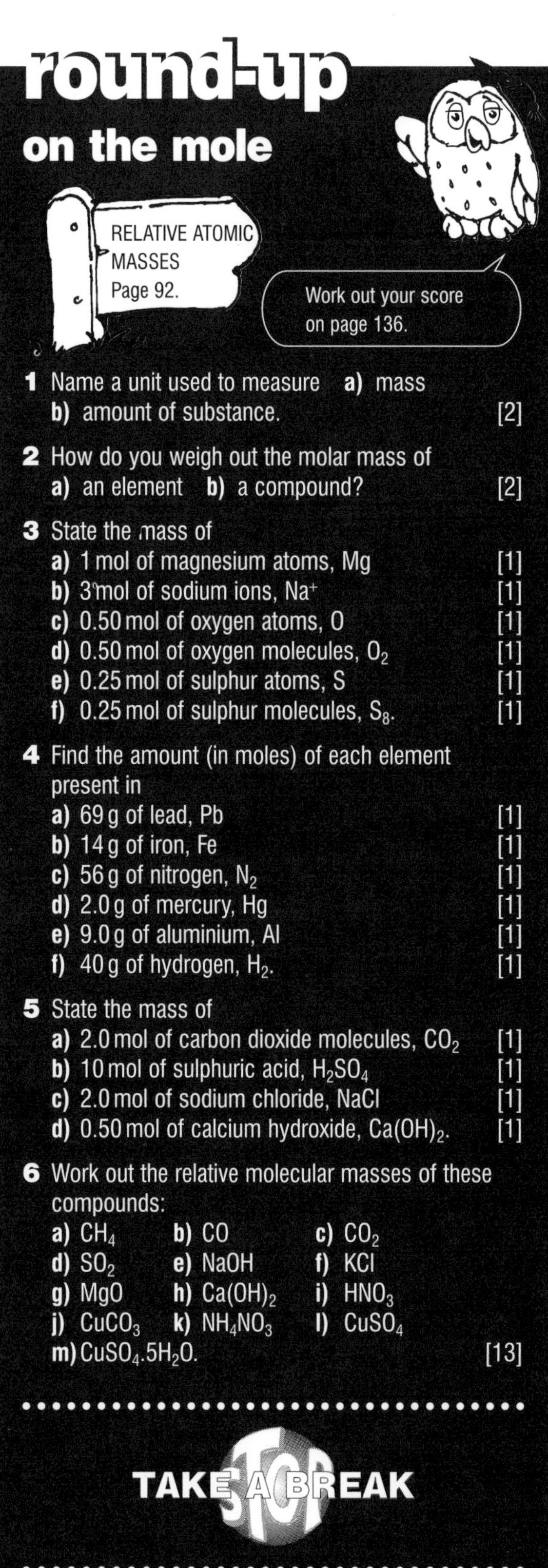

round-up on the mole

RELATIVE ATOMIC MASSES Page 92.

Work out your score on page 136.

1 Name a unit used to measure **a)** mass **b)** amount of substance. [2]

2 How do you weigh out the molar mass of **a)** an element **b)** a compound? [2]

3 State the mass of
- **a)** 1 mol of magnesium atoms, Mg [1]
- **b)** 3 mol of sodium ions, Na^+ [1]
- **c)** 0.50 mol of oxygen atoms, O [1]
- **d)** 0.50 mol of oxygen molecules, O_2 [1]
- **e)** 0.25 mol of sulphur atoms, S [1]
- **f)** 0.25 mol of sulphur molecules, S_8. [1]

4 Find the amount (in moles) of each element present in
- **a)** 69 g of lead, Pb [1]
- **b)** 14 g of iron, Fe [1]
- **c)** 56 g of nitrogen, N_2 [1]
- **d)** 2.0 g of mercury, Hg [1]
- **e)** 9.0 g of aluminium, Al [1]
- **f)** 40 g of hydrogen, H_2. [1]

5 State the mass of
- **a)** 2.0 mol of carbon dioxide molecules, CO_2 [1]
- **b)** 10 mol of sulphuric acid, H_2SO_4 [1]
- **c)** 2.0 mol of sodium chloride, NaCl [1]
- **d)** 0.50 mol of calcium hydroxide, $Ca(OH)_2$. [1]

6 Work out the relative molecular masses of these compounds:
a) CH_4 **b)** CO **c)** CO_2
d) SO_2 **e)** NaOH **f)** KCl
g) MgO **h)** $Ca(OH)_2$ **i)** HNO_3
j) $CuCO_3$ **k)** NH_4NO_3 **l)** $CuSO_4$
m) $CuSO_4.5H_2O$. [13]

TAKE A BREAK

14.2 Formulas

Molecular formula

The molecular formula of a compound shows the elements present and how many atoms of each element are present in a molecule or formula unit of the compound. For example, the molecular formula of ethanoic acid is $C_2H_4O_2$.

Empirical formula

The empirical formula of a compound shows the elements present and the **ratio** of the numbers of atoms of each element present in a molecule or formula unit of the compound. For example, the empirical formula of ethanoic acid is CH_2O.
The empirical formula is calculated from the composition by mass of the compound. It is also possible to find the percentage composition by mass of the compound if its empirical formula is known.

Calculation of empirical formula

3.72 g of phosphorus react with 4.80 g of oxygen to form an oxide. What is the empirical formula of the oxide?

	phosphorus		oxygen
mass	3.72 g		4.80 g
A_r	31		16
amount (moles)	$\frac{3.72}{31}$		$\frac{4.80}{16}$
	= 0.12		0.30
ratio of amounts	= 1	to	2.5
ratio of numbers of atoms	= 2	to	5

Empirical formula is P_2O_5.

Calculation of percentage composition

Find the percentages by mass of carbon, hydrogen and oxygen in propanol, C_3H_7OH.

The empirical formula is C_3H_8O.

$M_r = (3 \times 12) + 8 + 16 = 60$

$$\text{percentage of carbon} = \frac{A_r(C) \times \text{no. of C atoms}}{M_r(C_3H_8O)} \times 100\%$$

$$= \frac{(12 \times 3)}{60} \times 100\% = 60.0\%$$

$$\text{percentage of hydrogen} = \frac{A_r(\text{H}) \times \text{no. of H atoms}}{M_r(C_3H_8O)} \times 100\%$$

$$= \frac{(1 \times 8)}{60} \times 100\% = 13.3\%$$

$$\text{percentage of oxygen} = \frac{A_r(\text{O}) \times \text{no. of O atoms}}{M_r(C_3H_8O)} \times 100\%$$

$$= \frac{(16 \times 1)}{60} \times 100\% = 26.7\%$$

You can check on your calculation by adding up the percentages:

carbon 60.0% + hydrogen 13.3% + oxygen 26.7% = 100%

Calculation of molecular formula

The molecular formula is a multiple of the empirical formula:

molecular formula = (empirical formula)$_n$

Therefore relative molecular mass = n × relative empirical formula mass.

For ethanoic acid:

empirical formula = CH_2O

relative empirical formula mass = (12 + 2 + 16) = 30

The relative molecular mass of ethanoic acid is found by experiment to be 60, therefore

molecular formula = 2 × empirical formula = $C_2H_4O_2$.

Calculation of molecular formula of a hydrate

What is the formula of the hydrate of barium chloride that contains 85.2% by mass of $BaCl_2$ and 14.8% by mass of water?

	$BaCl_2$		H_2O
mass	85.2%		14.8%
M_r	137 + (2 × 35.5) = 208		2 + 16 = 18
amount (moles) =	$\frac{85.2}{208}$		$\frac{14.8}{18}$
=	0.41		0.82
ratio of amounts =	1	to	2

Empirical formula is $BaCl_2.2H_2O$.

round-up on formulas

1 Which of the following shows the mass of each element present in one mole of aluminium oxide, Al_2O_3? [1]

	mass of aluminium / g	mass of oxygen / g
A	2	3
B	27	16
C	54	32
D	54	48

2 Calculate the empirical formulas of the following compounds. [5]

A contains 0.72 g of magnesium and 0.28 g of nitrogen.
B contains 1.68 g of iron and 0.64 g of oxygen.
C contains 3.5 g of silicon and 4.0 g of oxygen.
D contains 20.0% magnesium, 26.6% sulphurand 53.3% oxygen.
E contains 60.0% carbon, 13.3% hydrogen and 26.7% oxygen.

3 Find the percentage by mass of

a) carbon and hydrogen in ethane, C_2H_6 [2]
b) sulphur and oxygen in sulphur trioxide, SO_3 [2]
c) nitrogen, hydrogen and oxygen in ammonium nitrate, NH_4NO_3 [3]
d) calcium and bromine in calcium bromide, $CaBr_2$. [2]

4 Calculate the empirical formulas of these hydrates:

a) copper(II) sulphate crystals which contain 63.9% $CuSO_4$ and 36.1% H_2O
b) magnesium sulphate crystals which contain 48.8% $MgSO_4$ and 51.2% H_2O. [4]

14.3 Masses of reacting solids

The equation for a chemical reaction enables us to calculate the masses of solids that react together, and the masses of solid products that are formed.

Example 1

What mass of copper(II) oxide is formed by the complete oxidation of 3.175 g of copper?

Equation: $2Cu(s) + O_2(g) \rightarrow 2CuO(s)$

The equation shows that 2 mol of copper form 2 mol of copper(II) oxide; that is, 1 mol of copper forms 1 mol of copper(II) oxide.

Putting in the values $A_r(Cu) = 63.5$, $A_r(O) = 16$, $M_r(CuO) = 79.5$:

63.5 g of copper form 79.5 g of copper(II) oxide

3.175 g of copper gives $(\frac{3.175}{63.5}) \times 79.5 = 3.975$ g of copper(II) oxide

Example 2

What mass of calcium carbonate must be decomposed to give 50 tonnes of calcium oxide? (1 tonne = 1×10^3 kg = 1×10^6 g)

Equation: $CaCO_3(s) \rightarrow CaO(s) + CO_2(g)$

Putting in the values $A_r(Ca) = 40$, $A_r(C) = 12$, $A_r(O) = 16$:

M_r of $CaCO_3 = 40 + 12 + (3 \times 16) = 100$

M_r of $CaO = 40 + 16 = 56$

Therefore 56 g of CaO are formed from 100 g of $CaCO_3$.

50 tonnes of CaO are formed from $(50 \times 10^6/56) \times$ 100 g of $CaCO_3$ = 89 tonnes of $CaCO_3$

round-up on reacting masses

RELATIVE ATOMIC MASSES Page 92.

Work out your score on page 136.

1 Find the mass of sodium hydroxide needed to neutralise a solution containing 7.3 g of hydrogen chloride in the reaction:

$NaOH(aq) + HCl(aq) \rightarrow NaCl(aq) + H_2O(l)$ [1]

2 Find the mass of sodium sulphate formed when a solution containing 49 g of sulphuric acid is neutralised by the reaction:

$H_2SO_4(aq) + 2NaOH(aq) \rightarrow Na_2SO_4(aq) + 2H_2O(l)$ [1]

3 An anti-acid tablet contains 0.10 g of magnesium hydrogencarbonate, $Mg(HCO_3)_2$. What mass of stomach acid, HCl, will it neutralise? [1]

4 Wine is made by fermenting the sugar in grapes:

$C_6H_{12}O_6(aq) \rightarrow 2C_2H_6O(aq) + 2CO_2(g)$

sucrose — ethanol — carbon dioxide

What mass of ethanol is obtained from 6.00 kg of sucrose? [1]

5 Aspirin, $C_9H_8O_4$, is made by the reaction:

salicylic acid + ethanoic anhydride → aspirin + ethanoic acid

$C_7H_6O_3 + C_4H_6O_3 \rightarrow C_9H_8O_4 + C_2H_4O_2$

What mass of salicylic acid, $C_7H_6O_3$, is needed to make one aspirin tablet, which contains 0.33 g of aspirin? [1]

TAKE A BREAK

14.4 Reacting volumes of gases

The **gas molar volume** is 24.0 dm^3/mol at rtp. This means that one mole of any gas occupies a volume of 24.0 dm^3 at rtp (room temperature and one atmosphere pressure). Calculations on the reacting volumes of gases use this fact.

Example 1

What volume of oxygen is required for the complete combustion of 1.0 dm^3 of butane gas?

Equation: $2C_4H_{10}(g) + 13O_2(g) \rightarrow 8CO_2(g) + 10H_2O(g)$

- 13 mol of oxygen are needed for the complete combustion of 2 mol of butane
- $13 \times 24\,dm^3$ of oxygen are needed for the complete combustion of $2 \times 24\,dm^3$ of butane
- 13 volumes of oxygen are needed for the complete combustion of 2 volumes of butane
- 6.5 dm^3 of oxygen are needed for the complete combustion of 1.0 dm^3 of butane.

element	symbol	relative atomic mass
aluminium	Al	27
bromine	Br	80
cadmium	Cd	112
calcium	Ca	40
carbon	C	12
chlorine	Cl	35.5
copper	Cu	63.5
hydrogen	H	1
iron	Fe	56
lead	Pb	207
magnesium	Mg	24
mercury	Hg	200
nickel	Ni	59
nitrogen	N	14
oxygen	O	16
phosphorus	P	31
potassium	K	39
silicon	Si	28
silver	Ag	108
sodium	Na	23
sulphur	S	64
tin	Sn	119

Table of selected relative atomic masses

Example 2

What volume of carbon dioxide is formed by the thermal decomposition of 1.00 kg of calcium carbonate?

Equation: $CaCO_3(s) \rightarrow CaO(s) + CO_2(g)$

M_r of $CaCO_3$ = 100 g/mol (see page 91)

$$\text{amount of } CaCO_3 = \frac{\text{mass}}{\text{molar mass}} = \frac{1000\,g}{100\,g/mol} = 10.0\,mol$$

since 1 mol of $CaCO_3$ forms 1 mol of CO_2,
amount of CO_2 = 10.0 mol

volume of CO_2 = amount × gas molar volume
= 10.0 mol × 24.0 dm^3/mol = 240 dm^3

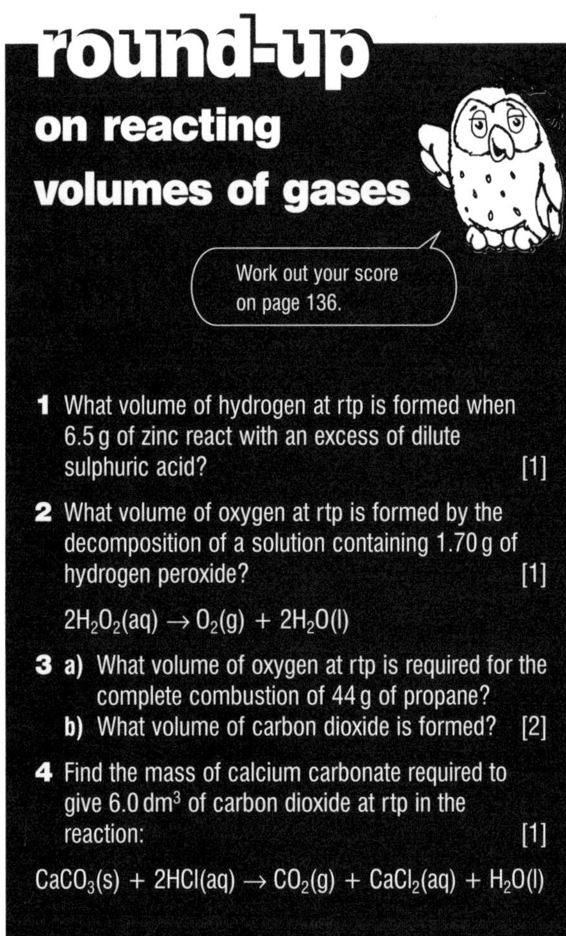

round-up on reacting volumes of gases

Work out your score on page 136.

1 What volume of hydrogen at rtp is formed when 6.5 g of zinc react with an excess of dilute sulphuric acid? [1]

2 What volume of oxygen at rtp is formed by the decomposition of a solution containing 1.70 g of hydrogen peroxide? [1]

$2H_2O_2(aq) \rightarrow O_2(g) + 2H_2O(l)$

3 a) What volume of oxygen at rtp is required for the complete combustion of 44 g of propane?

b) What volume of carbon dioxide is formed? [2]

4 Find the mass of calcium carbonate required to give 6.0 dm^3 of carbon dioxide at rtp in the reaction: [1]

$CaCO_3(s) + 2HCl(aq) \rightarrow CO_2(g) + CaCl_2(aq) + H_2O(l)$

14.5 Electrolysis calculations

In the electrolysis of silver nitrate solution, the cathode process is

$Ag^+(aq) + e^- \rightarrow Ag(s)$

- 1 mol of silver ions accept 1 mol of electrons to form 1 mol of silver atoms.
- 1 mol of silver deposited increases the mass of the cathode by 108 g ($A_r(Ag) = 108$).

Measurements show that to deposit 108 g of silver requires the passage of 96 500 coulombs (96 500 C) of electric charge.

$$\underset{\text{(in coulombs)}}{\text{charge}} = \underset{\text{(in amperes)}}{\text{current}} \times \underset{\text{(in seconds)}}{\text{time}}$$

This quantity of electric charge is the charge on one mole of electrons. The value 96 500 C/mol is called the **Faraday constant**.

In the deposition of copper in electrolysis, the cathode process is

$Cu^{2+}(aq) + 2e^- \rightarrow Cu(s)$

- 1 mol of copper ions needs 2 mol of electrons for discharge
- 1 mol of copper ions needs 2 × 96 500 C of electric charge for discharge.

In the electrolysis of gold(III) salts, the cathode process is

$Au^{3+}(aq) + 3e^- \rightarrow Au(s)$

- 1 mol of gold ions needs 3 mol of electrons for discharge
- 1 mol of gold ions needs 3 × 96 500 C of electric charge for discharge.

The equation below shows how to calculate the number of moles of a substance discharged when you know how much charge has passed.

Example 1

A current of 10.0 milliamps (mA) passes for 4.00 hours through a solution of silver nitrate, a solution of copper(II) sulphate and a solution of gold(III) nitrate connected in series. What mass of metal is deposited in each?

$$\underset{\text{(in coulombs)}}{\text{charge}} = \underset{\text{(in amperes)}}{\text{current}} \times \underset{\text{(in seconds)}}{\text{time}}$$

$$= 0.010 \times 4.00 \times 60 \times 60 = 144\,\text{C}$$

$$= \frac{144}{96\,500} \text{ mol of electrons}$$

Equations:

$Ag^+(aq) + e^- \rightarrow Ag(s)$

$Cu^{2+}(aq) + 2e^- \rightarrow Cu(s)$

$Au^{3+}(aq) + 3e^- \rightarrow Au(s)$

1 mol of electrons deposits 1 mol of silver

therefore $\frac{144}{96\,500}$ mol of electrons deposit

$\frac{144}{96\,500}$ mol of silver

$= \frac{144 \times 108}{96\,500}$ g of silver = **0.161g of silver**

1 mol of electrons deposits $\frac{1}{2}$ mol of copper

therefore $\frac{144}{96\,500}$ mol of electrons deposit

$\frac{1}{2} \times \frac{144}{96\,500}$ mol of copper

$= \frac{1}{2} \times \frac{144 \times 63.5}{96\,500}$ g of copper = **0.0474 g of copper**

1 mol of electrons deposits $\frac{1}{3}$ mol of gold

therefore $\frac{144}{96\,500}$ mol of electrons deposit

$\frac{1}{3} \times \frac{144}{96\,500}$ mol of gold

$= \frac{1}{3} \times \frac{144 \times 197}{96\,500}$ g of gold = **0.0980 g of gold**

$$\text{number of moles of element discharged} = \frac{\text{number of moles of electrons}}{\text{number of charges on one ion of the element}}$$

$$= \frac{\text{number of coulombs}/96\,500}{\text{number of charges on one ion of the element}}$$

Example 2

A metal of relative atomic mass 27 is deposited by electrolysis. If 0.201 g of the metal is deposited when 0.200 A flows for 3.00 hours, what is the charge on an ion of this element?

charge = current × time (s)

= 0.200 × 3.00 × 60 × 60

= 2160 C

If 2160 C deposit 0.201 g of the metal, then

$$96\,500 \text{ C deposit } 0.201 \times \frac{96\,500}{2160} \text{ g} = 8.98 \text{ g}$$

Since 8.98 g of metal are deposited by 1 mol of electrons, 27.0 g (1 mol) of metal would be deposited by

$$\frac{27}{8.98} \text{ mol of electrons} = 3 \text{ mol of electrons}$$

The charge on the metal ions is **+3**.

Calculating the volume of gas evolved during electrolysis

Hydrogen: when hydrogen ions are discharged at the cathode, the following reactions take place.

$H^+(aq) + e^- \rightarrow H(g)$

followed by $2H(g) \rightarrow H_2(g)$

The evolution of 1 mol of hydrogen, H_2 (24 dm^3 at rtp) needs 2 mol of electrons (2 × 96 500 C of charge).

Chlorine: when chlorine is evolved at the anode, the following reactions take place.

$Cl^-(aq) \rightarrow Cl(g) + e^-$

followed by $2Cl(g) \rightarrow Cl_2(g)$

The evolution of 1 mol of chlorine, Cl_2 (24 dm^3 at rtp) needs 2 mol of electrons (2 × 96 500 C of charge).

Oxygen: when oxygen is evolved at the anode, the following reactions take place.

$OH^-(aq) \rightarrow OH(g) + e^-$

followed by $4OH(g) \rightarrow O_2(g) + 2H_2O(l)$

So 4 mol of electrons must pass with the evolution of 1 mol of oxygen (24 dm^3 at rtp).

Example 3

Name the gases formed at each electrode when 15.0 mA of current pass for 6.00 hours through a solution of sulphuric acid, and calculate their volumes at rtp.

At the cathode hydrogen is evolved, and 2 mol of electrons discharge 1 mol of H_2.

At the anode oxygen is evolved, and 4 mol of electrons discharge 1 mol of O_2.

charge = current × time
$= 15.0 \times 10^{-3} \times 6.00 \times 60 \times 60 = 324 \text{ C}$

$$\text{number of mol of electrons} = \frac{324 \text{ C}}{96\,500 \text{ C/mol}}$$

$= 3.36 \times 10^{-3}$ mol

amount of hydrogen discharged
$= \frac{1}{2} \times 3.36 \times 10^{-3}$ mol

volume of hydrogen $= 1.68 \times 10^{-3} \times 24.0 \text{ dm}^3$
= **40.3 cm^3** at rtp

amount of oxygen $= \frac{1}{4} \times 3.36 \times 10^{-3}$ mol
$= 0.84 \times 10^{-3}$ mol

volume of oxygen $= 0.84 \times 10^{-3} \times 24.0 \text{ dm}^3$
= **20.2 cm^3** at rtp

(Now do the next Round-up.)

14.6 Concentration of solution

One way of describing the concentration of a solution is to state the mass of solute present per cubic decimetre of solution: the number of grams per cubic decimetre, g/dm^3.

Another way, which is more convenient in chemistry, is to state the amount in *moles* of a solute present per cubic decimetre of solution.

$$\text{concentration in moles per litre} = \frac{\text{amount of solute in moles}}{\text{volume of solution in dm}^3}$$

Rearranging,

$$\text{amount of solute (mol)} = \text{volume of solution (dm}^3) \times \text{concentration (mol/dm}^3)$$

round-up
on electrolysis

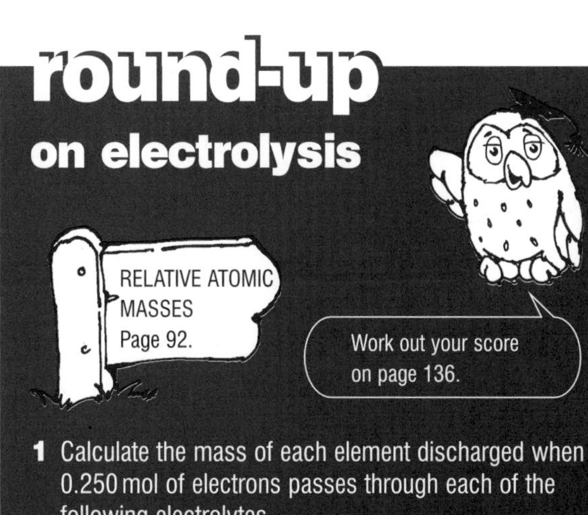

1 Calculate the mass of each element discharged when 0.250 mol of electrons passes through each of the following electrolytes.
a) lead from lead(II) nitrate solution
b) bromine from potassium bromide solution
c) silver from silver nitrate solution
d) aluminium from its molten oxide [4]

2 A current passes through two cells in series. The first cell contains a solution of silver nitrate and the second a solution of lead(II) nitrate. In the first, 0.540 g of silver is deposited. What mass of lead is deposited in the second? [1]

3 Which one of the following requires the largest quantity of electricity for discharge at an electrode?
A 1 mol of Ni^{2+} ions **B** 2 mol of Fe^{3+} ions
C 3 mol of Ag^{+} ions **D** 4 mol of Cl^{-} ions
E 5 mol of OH^{-} ions [1]

4 When a current passes through a solution of copper(II) sulphate, 0.635 g of copper is deposited on the cathode. What volume of oxygen (at rtp) is evolved at the anode? [1]

5 A current passes through two cells in series. In the first, 0.2160 g of silver is deposited. In the second, 0.112 g of cadmium is deposited. Use this information to calculate the charge on the cadmium ion. [1]

6 A current of 2.01 A passed for 8.00 minutes through aqueous nickel sulphate. The mass of the cathode increased by 0.295 g .
a) How many coulombs of electricity passed during the experiment? [1]
b) How many moles of electrons carry this charge? [1]
c) How many moles of nickel were deposited? [1]
d) How many moles of electrons were needed to discharge one mole of nickel ions? [1]
e) Write an equation for the cathode reaction. [2]

7 A student electrolysed a solution of silver nitrate in series with a solution of sulphuric acid. A steady current passed for 30 minutes, and 24 cm^3 of hydrogen collected at the cathode of the sulphuric acid cell.
a) What is the volume of oxygen evolved at the anode? Choose from **A–E** below.
A 6 cm^3 **B** 12 cm^3 **C** 24 cm^3 **D** 32 cm^3
E 48 cm^3 [1]
b) If the student doubled the current and passed it for 15 minutes, what would be the volume of hydrogen evolved? Choose from **A–E** below.
A 6 cm^3 **B** 12 cm^3 **C** 24 cm^3 **D** 48 cm^3
E 96 cm^3 [1]
c) What is the mass of silver deposited on the cathode of the silver nitrate cell? Choose from **A–E** below.
A 0.108 g **B** 0.216 g **C** 0.0270 g **D** 0.0540 g
E 0.0135 g [1]

8 A current of 0.010 A passed for 5.00 hours through a solution of a salt of the metal M. The metal M has a relative atomic mass of 52. The mass of M deposited on the cathode was 0.0324 g. What is the charge on an ion of M? [3]

Example 1

Calculate the amount in moles of solute present in 250 cm^3 of a solution of hydrochloric acid which has a concentration of 2.0 mol/dm^3.

$$\underset{(\text{mol})}{\text{amount}} = \underset{(\text{dm}^3)}{\text{volume}} \times \underset{(\text{mol/dm}^3)}{\text{concentration}}$$

amount of solute, HCl = $250 \times 10^{-3}\,dm^3 \times 2.0\,mol/dm^3$
= **0.50 mol**

Note: when you are given the volume in cubic centimetres (cm^3), you have to change it into cubic decimetres (dm^3). This makes the units come right.

Example 2

What mass of sodium carbonate must be dissolved in 1 dm^3 of water to give a solution of concentration 1.5 M (a 1.5 M solution)?

M means mol/dm^3, so a 2 M solution means a solution of concentration 2 mol/dm^3

$$\underset{\text{(mol)}}{\text{amount}} = \underset{(dm^3)}{\text{volume}} \times \underset{(mol/dm^3)}{\text{concentration}}$$

$= 1.00\,dm^3 \times 1.5\,mol/dm^3$

$= 1.5\,mol$

M_r of sodium carbonate, Na_2CO_3 $= (2 \times 23) + 12 + (3 \times 16)$

$= 106\,g/mol$

mass of sodium carbonate $= 1.5\,mol \times 106\,g/mol =$ **159 g**

(Now do the next Round-up.)

14.7 Titration

Example 1

In a titration of hydrochloric acid against sodium hydroxide solution, 15.0 cm^3 of hydrochloric acid neutralise 25.0 cm^3 of a 0.100 mol/dm^3 solution of sodium hydroxide. What is the concentration of the hydrochloric acid?

1 First write the equation for the reaction:

hydrochloric acid + sodium hydroxide → sodium chloride + water

$HCl(aq) + NaOH(aq) \rightarrow NaCl(aq) + H_2O(l)$

The equation tells you that 1 mol of HCl neutralises 1 mol of NaOH.

2 Now work out the amount in moles of base. You must start with the base because you know its concentration, and you do not know the concentration of the acid.

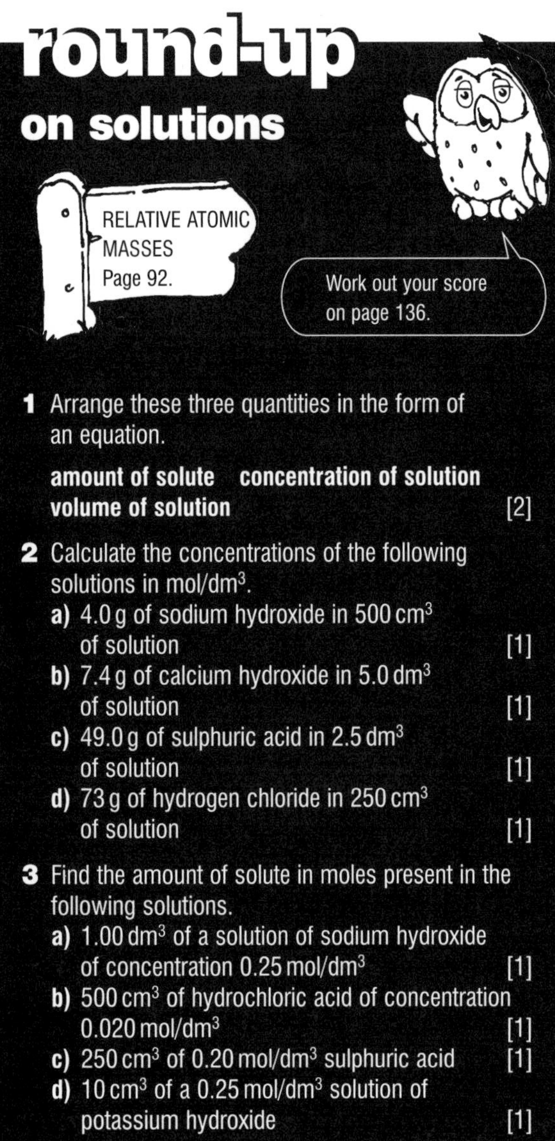

round-up on solutions

1 Arrange these three quantities in the form of an equation.

amount of solute **concentration of solution** **volume of solution** [2]

2 Calculate the concentrations of the following solutions in mol/dm^3.

a) 4.0 g of sodium hydroxide in 500 cm^3 of solution [1]

b) 7.4 g of calcium hydroxide in 5.0 dm^3 of solution [1]

c) 49.0 g of sulphuric acid in 2.5 dm^3 of solution [1]

d) 73 g of hydrogen chloride in 250 cm^3 of solution [1]

3 Find the amount of solute in moles present in the following solutions.

a) 1.00 dm^3 of a solution of sodium hydroxide of concentration 0.25 mol/dm^3 [1]

b) 500 cm^3 of hydrochloric acid of concentration 0.020 mol/dm^3 [1]

c) 250 cm^3 of 0.20 mol/dm^3 sulphuric acid [1]

d) 10 cm^3 of a 0.25 mol/dm^3 solution of potassium hydroxide [1]

$$\underset{\text{(mol)}}{\text{amount}} = \underset{(dm^3)}{\text{volume}} \times \underset{(mol/dm^3)}{\text{concentration}}$$

$$\underset{\text{(mol)}}{\text{amount of NaOH}} = \underset{(25.0\,cm^3)}{\text{volume}} \times \underset{(0.100\,mol/dm^3)}{\text{concentration}}$$

$= 25.0 \times 10^{-3}\,dm^3 \times 0.100\,mol/dm^3 = 2.50 \times 10^{-3}\,mol$

3 Now work out the concentration of the acid.

amount (mol) of HCl = amount (mol) of NaOH

$= 2.50 \times 10^{-3}\,mol$

$$\underset{\text{of HCl}}{\text{amount (mol)}} = \underset{\text{HCl(aq)}}{\text{volume of}} \times \underset{\text{of HCl(aq)}}{\text{concentration}}$$

Therefore, if c mol/dm³ is the concentration of HCl,

$$2.50 \times 10^{-3}\,\text{mol} = 15.0 \times 10^{-3}\ \text{dm}^3 \times c\ \text{mol/dm}^3$$

$$c\ \text{mol/dm}^3 = \frac{2.50 \times 10^{-3}\,\text{mol}}{15.0 \times 10\,\text{dm}^3}$$

$$= \mathbf{0.167\ mol/dm^3}$$

Example 2

In a titration, 25.0 cm³ of sulphuric acid of concentration 0.150 mol/dm³ neutralised 31.2 cm³ of potassium hydroxide solution. Find the concentration of the potassium hydroxide solution.

1 First write the equation:

$$\text{sulphuric acid} + \text{potassium hydroxide} \rightarrow \text{potassium sulphate} + \text{water}$$

$$H_2SO_4(aq) + 2KOH(aq) \rightarrow K_2SO_4(aq) + 2H_2O(l)$$

The equation tells you that 1 mol of H_2SO_4 neutralises 2 mol of KOH.

2 Now work out the amount of acid in moles. You must start with the acid because you do not know the concentration of the base.

$$\text{amount of acid (mol)} = \text{volume }(25.0\,\text{cm}^3) \times \text{concentration }(0.150\,\text{mol/dm}^3)$$

$$= 25.0 \times 10^{-3}\,\text{dm}^3 \times 0.150\,\text{mol/dm}^3 = 3.75 \times 10^{-3}\,\text{mol}$$

3 Now work out the concentration of base.

$$\text{amount (mol) of KOH} = 2 \times \text{amount (mol) of } H_2SO_4$$
$$= 7.50 \times 10^{-3}\,\text{mol}$$

$$\text{amount (mol) of KOH} = \text{volume of KOH(aq)} \times \text{concentration of KOH(aq)}$$

Therefore, if c mol/dm³ is the concentration of KOH,

$$c\,\text{mol/dm}^3 = \frac{7.50 \times 10^{-3}\,\text{mol}}{31.2 \times 10^{-3}\,\text{dm}^3}$$

$$= \mathbf{0.240\ mol/dm^3}$$

round-up on titration

1 25.0 cm³ of sodium hydroxide solution are neutralised by 15.0 cm³ of a solution of hydrochloric acid of concentration 0.25 mol/dm³. Find the concentration of the sodium hydroxide solution. [1]

2 A solution of sodium hydroxide contains 10 g/dm³ of solute.

a) What is the concentration of the solution in mol/dm³? [1]

b) What volume of this solution would be needed to neutralise 25.0 cm³ of 0.10 mol/dm³ hydrochloric acid? [1]

3 Year Ten decide to test some antacid indigestion tablets. They dissolve the tablets and titrate the alkali in them against a standard acid. Their results are shown in the table.

brand	price of 100 tablets/ £	volume of 0.01 mol/dm³ acid required to neutralise one tablet
Stoppo	0.76	2.8 cm³
Settlo	0.87	3.0 cm³
Alko	1.08	3.3 cm³
Baso	1.30	3.6 cm³

a) Which antacid tablets offer the best value for money? [1]

b) What other factors would you consider before choosing a brand? [2]

4 A tanker of acid is emptied into a water supply by mistake. A chemist titrates the water and finds that 10.0 dm³ of water are needed to neutralise 10.0 cm³ of a 0.010 mol/dm³ solution of sodium hydroxide. What is the concentration of hydrogen ions in the water? [2]

Well done if you've improved. Don't worry if you haven't. Take a break and try again.

15

Fuels

preview

At the end of this topic you will:

- **know about fossil fuels: coal, oil and natural gas**
- **know about the alkane hydrocarbons**
- **understand energy diagrams and heat of reaction.**

MIND MAP
Page 154.
How much do you already know? Work out your score on page 137.

Test yourself

1 Why are coal and oil called 'fossil fuels'? [3]

2 What is most of the world's coal used for? [1]

3 Crude oil can be separated into useful fuels and other substances.
a) Name the process which is used. [1]
b) Name four fuels obtained from crude oil. [4]
c) Name two other useful substances separated from crude oil. [2]

4 Name the compounds with formulas **a)** CH_4 **b)** C_2H_6 **c)** C_3H_8 **d)** and name the series to which they belong. [4]

5 Explain what is meant by 'cracking'. [4]

6 Divide the following list of reactions into
a) exothermic reactions **b)** endothermic reactions: [4]
photosynthesis, combustion, cracking of hydrocarbons, respiration.

15.1 Fossil fuels

Coal

Coal is one of the fuels we describe as **fossil fuels.** It was formed from dead plant material decaying slowly over millions of years under the pressure of deposits of mud and sand. Coal is a complicated mixture of carbon, hydrocarbons and other compounds. Much of the coal used in the world is burned in power stations. The main combustion products are carbon dioxide and water.

Petroleum oil and natural gas

Petroleum oil (usually called simply oil) and natural gas are fossil fuels: they are the remains of sea animals which lived millions of years ago. Decaying slowly under the pressure of layers of mud and silt, the organic part of the creatures' bodies turned into a mixture of hydrocarbons: petroleum oil. The sediment on top of the decaying matter became compressed to form rock, so oil is held in porous oil-bearing rock. Natural gas is always formed in the same deposits as oil.

The economic importance of oil

Industrialised countries depend on fossil fuels for transport, for power stations and for manufacturing industries. The petrochemicals industry makes a vast number of important chemicals from oil including fertilisers, herbicides, insecticides and the raw materials needed by the pharmaceutical industry. When we have used the Earth's deposits of coal, oil and gas, there will be no more forthcoming. The economies of all industrial countries will depend on alternative energy sources.

15.2 Fuels from petroleum

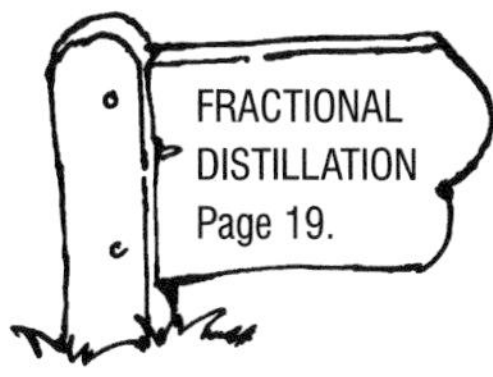

Fractional distillation

Crude oil is separated by fractional distillation into a number of important fuels. Each fraction is collected over a certain boiling point range. Each fraction is a mixture of hydrocarbons (compounds which consist of hydrogen and carbon only). The use that is made of each fraction depends on these factors, all of which increase with the size of the molecules:

- its boiling point range: the higher the boiling point range, the more difficult it is to vaporise in a vehicle engine.
- its viscosity: the more viscous a fraction is, the less easily it flows.
- its ignition temperature: the less easily a fraction ignites, the less flammable it is.

below 25 °C — **Petroleum gases** are liquefied under pressure, and sold in cylinders as 'bottled gas' for use in gas cookers.

40–75 °C — **Petrol** (gasoline) vaporises easily at the temperature of vehicle engines.

75–150 °C — **Naphtha** is used in the manufacture of plastics, fabrics, medicines, agricultural chemicals, etc.

150–260 °C — **Kerosene** needs a higher temperature for combustion. It is used as aviation fuel.

260–340 °C — **Diesel oil** is used in the diesel engine which has a special fuel injection system to allow this fuel to burn. It is used in buses, lorries, etc.

vapour of crude oil →

340–500 °C — **Lubricating oil** is used as a lubricant to reduce engine wear.

>500 °C — **Fuel oil** is a viscous liquid with a high ignition temperature. It is used in ships, heating plants and power stations. To help it to ignite, fuel oil must be sprayed into the combustion chambers as a fine mist.

Bitumen is left as a residue at the bottom of the distillation column. It is used to waterproof roofs and pipes and to tar roads.

Petroleum fractions and their uses

Cracking

We use more naphtha, petrol and kerosene than heavy fuel oil. The technique called **cracking** is used to convert the high boiling point range fractions into the lower boiling point range fractions petrol and kerosene.

vapour of hydrocarbon with large molecules and high boiling point $\xrightarrow[\text{e.g. } Al_2O_3 \text{ or } SiO_2]{\textit{cracking}\text{ passed over a heated catalyst}}$ mixture of hydrocarbons with smaller molecules and low boiling point, and hydrogen. The mixture is separated by fractional distillation.

15.3 Alkanes

Most of the hydrocarbons in crude oil belong to the **homologous series** called **alkanes**; they are shown in the table. A homologous series is a set of compounds with similar chemical properties in which one member of the series differs from the next by a $-CH_2-$ group. Physical properties such as boiling point vary gradually as the size of the molecules increases.

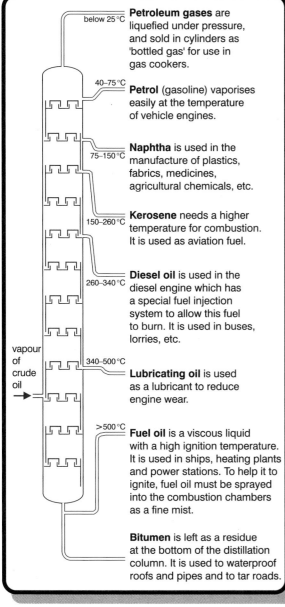

The alkanes	
name	**formula**
methane	CH_4
ethane	C_2H_6
propane	C_3H_8
butane	C_4H_{10}
pentane	C_5H_{12}
hexane	C_6H_{14}
general formula	C_nH_{2n+2}

Here are the structural formulas for the first three alkanes:

```
      H              H   H               H   H   H
      |              |   |               |   |   |
   H—C—H         H—C—C—H          H—C—C—C—H
      |              |   |               |   |   |
      H              H   H               H   H   H
   methane           ethane              propane
```

Alkanes do not take part in many chemical reactions. Their important reaction is combustion.

Alkanes contain only single bonds between carbon atoms. Such hydrocarbons are called **saturated hydrocarbons**. This is in contrast to the alkenes, which contain double bonds and are **unsaturated hydrocarbons**.

15.4 Energy and chemical reactions

Exothermic reactions

1 **Combustion**: the combustion of hydrocarbons is an exothermic reaction – heat is given out.

methane + oxygen → carbon dioxide + water; heat is given out

$CH_4(g) + 2O_2(g) \rightarrow CO_2(g) + 2H_2O(l)$

octane + oxygen → carbon dioxide + water; heat is given out

★ An oxidation reaction in which heat is given out is **combustion**.

★ Combustion accompanied by a flame is **burning**.

★ A substance which is oxidised with the release of energy is a **fuel**.

2 **Respiration**: our bodies obtain energy from the oxidation of foods, e.g. glucose, in cells. This process is called **cellular respiration**.

glucose + oxygen → carbon dioxide + water; energy is given out

$C_6H_{12}O_6(aq) + 6O_2(g) \rightarrow 6CO_2(g) + 6H_2O(l)$

3 **Neutralisation**

hydrogen ion + hydroxide ion → water; heat is given out

$H^+(aq) + OH^-(aq) \rightarrow H_2O(l)$

Endothermic reactions

1 **Photosynthesis**: plants convert carbon dioxide and water into sugars in the process of photosynthesis.

carbon dioxide + water $\xrightarrow{\text{catalysed by chlorophyll}}$ glucose + oxygen; energy of sunlight is taken in

$6CO_2(g) + 6H_2O(l) \rightarrow C_6H_{12}O_6(aq) + 6O_2(g)$

2 **Thermal decomposition**; for example the cracking of hydrocarbons and the decomposition of calcium carbonate:

calcium carbonate $\xrightarrow{\text{heat}}$ calcium oxide + carbon dioxide; heat is taken in

$CaCO_3(s) \rightarrow CaO(s) + CO_2(g)$

15.5 Heat of reaction

The atoms, ions or molecules in a substance are held together by chemical bonds. Energy must be supplied if these chemical bonds are to be broken. When bonds are created, energy is given out. The reactants and the products possess different amounts of energy because they have different chemical bonds; see diagram below.

In the reaction shown, the energy taken in is less than the energy given out: this reaction is exothermic.

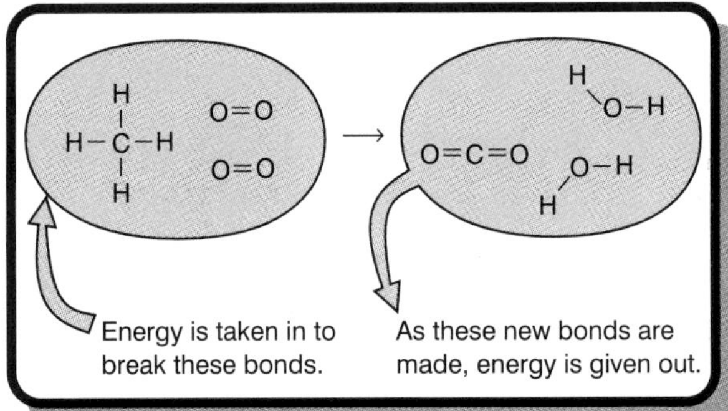
H
H–C–H
H
O=O
O=O
O=C=O
H
O–H
O–H
H
Energy is taken in to break these bonds.
As these new bonds are made, energy is given out.

Bonds broken and made when methane burns

The graphs below are energy diagrams, in which:

- H = energy content of a substance
- ΔH = heat of reaction = heat taken in or given out during a reaction
- ΔH = energy of products – energy of reactants
- In an **exothermic reaction**, the products of the reaction contain less energy than the reactants. When the reactants change into the products, they get rid of their extra energy by giving out heat to the surroundings.
- In an **endothermic reaction**, the reactants have to climb to a higher energy level to change into the products. To do this, they take energy from the surroundings: they cool the surroundings.

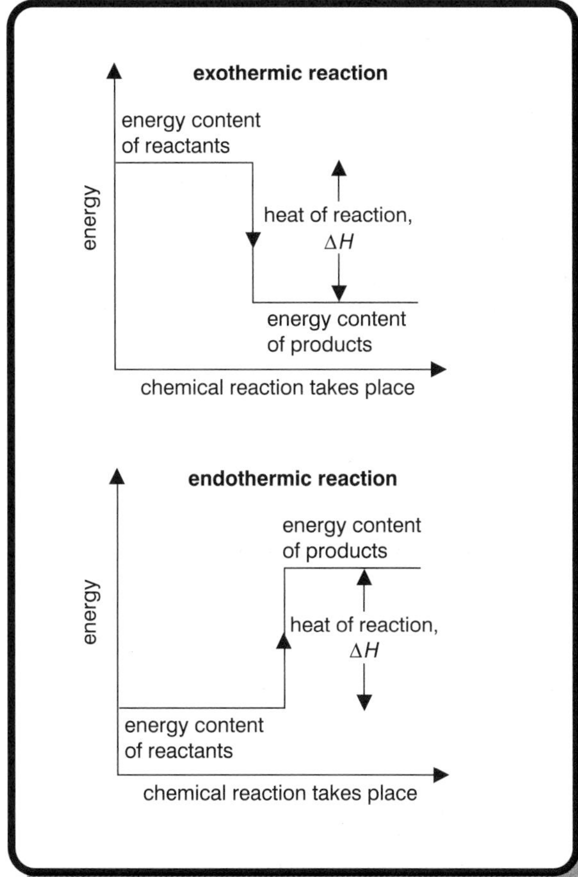

Energy diagrams for an exothermic reaction and an endothermic reaction

15.6 Activation energy

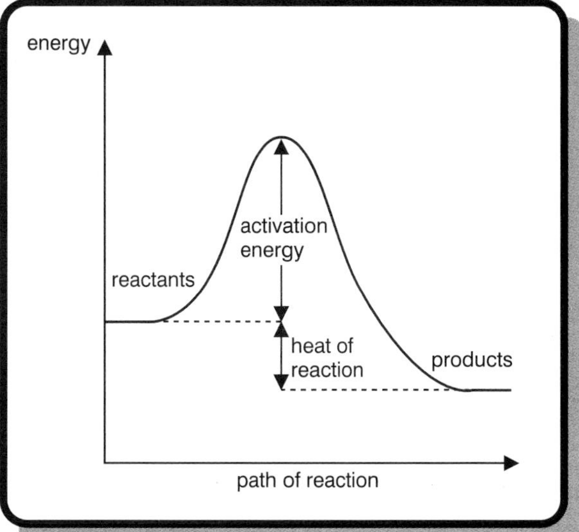

Activation energy

The graph shows an **energy profile** for an exothermic reaction. The products possess less energy than the reactants, but the reactants cannot just slide down an energy hill to form the products. There is an energy barrier which the reactants must climb before they can be converted into the products. The energy barrier is called the **activation energy** or the **energy of activation**. Reactant molecules which collide with energy equal to the activation energy are converted into the products. A catalyst alters the speed of a reaction by altering the activation energy.

CATALYSTS Pages 84–5.

15.7 Using bond energy values

It is possible to measure exactly how much energy it takes to break different chemical bonds. To break 1 mol of C—C bonds requires 348 kJ; the **bond energy** of the C—C bond is 348 kJ/mol. To break a chemical bond, energy must be supplied, so all bond energies are positive. Energy is given out when new bonds are made. This energy change has a negative value. Some bond energies are shown in the following table (overleaf).

Bond energy values

bond	bond energy / kJ/mol
H—H	436
O═O	496
C—C	348
C═C	612
C—H	412
C—O	360
C═O	743
H—O	463

We can use bond energy values to calculate a value for the heat of reaction.

Example

Use bond energies to calculate ΔH for the reaction:

$CH_4(g) + 2O_2(g) \rightarrow CO_2(g) + 2H_2O(l)$

First, show the bonds that are broken and the bonds that are made.

```
    H
    |
H—C—H  +  2O═O  ⟶  O═C═O  +  2H—O—H
    |
    H
```

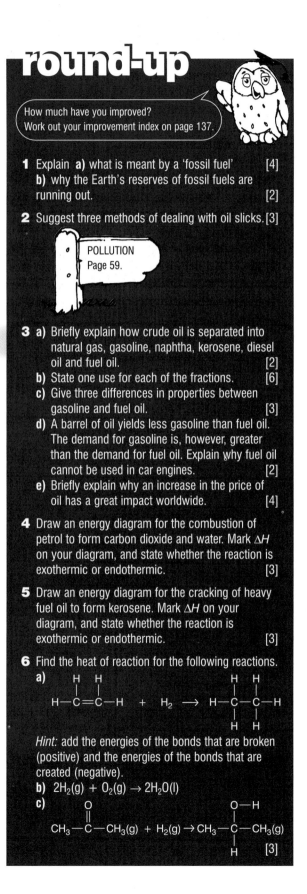

Next, list the bonds that are broken and the bonds that are made along with their bond energies.

bonds broken:

4(C—H) bonds; energy = 4 × 412 = 1648 kJ/mol

2(O═O) bonds; energy = 2 × 496 = 992 kJ/mol

total energy required = +2640 kJ/mol

bonds made:

2(C═O) bonds; energy = –2 × 743 = –1486 kJ/mol

2(H—O) bonds; energy = –4 × 463 = –1852 kJ/mol

total energy change = –3338 kJ/mol

heat of reaction =
energy required to break old bonds +
energy change when new bonds are made

= +2640 – 3338 = **–698 kJ/mol**

round-up

How much have you improved?
Work out your improvement index on page 137.

1 Explain **a)** what is meant by a 'fossil fuel' [4]
b) why the Earth's reserves of fossil fuels are running out. [2]

2 Suggest three methods of dealing with oil slicks. [3]

3 a) Briefly explain how crude oil is separated into natural gas, gasoline, naphtha, kerosene, diesel oil and fuel oil. [2]
b) State one use for each of the fractions. [6]
c) Give three differences in properties between gasoline and fuel oil. [3]
d) A barrel of oil yields less gasoline than fuel oil. The demand for gasoline is, however, greater than the demand for fuel oil. Explain why fuel oil cannot be used in car engines. [2]
e) Briefly explain why an increase in the price of oil has a great impact worldwide. [4]

4 Draw an energy diagram for the combustion of petrol to form carbon dioxide and water. Mark ΔH on your diagram, and state whether the reaction is exothermic or endothermic. [3]

5 Draw an energy diagram for the cracking of heavy fuel oil to form kerosene. Mark ΔH on your diagram, and state whether the reaction is exothermic or endothermic. [3]

6 Find the heat of reaction for the following reactions.

a)

```
  H  H                   H  H
  |  |                   |  |
H—C═C—H  +  H₂  ⟶  H—C—C—H
                         |  |
                         H  H
```

Hint: add the energies of the bonds that are broken (positive) and the energies of the bonds that are created (negative).

b) $2H_2(g) + O_2(g) \rightarrow 2H_2O(l)$

c)

```
       O                      O—H
       ‖                      |
CH₃—C—CH₃(g) + H₂(g) → CH₃—C—CH₃(g)
                              |
                              H
```

[3]

Alkenes and plastics

16

preview

At the end of this topic you will:

- **know the general formula and reactions of alkenes**
- **understand the differences between thermoplastic and thermosetting plastics**
- **know the names and uses of some poly(alkenes)**
- **appreciate the difficulties of disposing of plastics waste.**

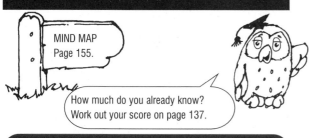

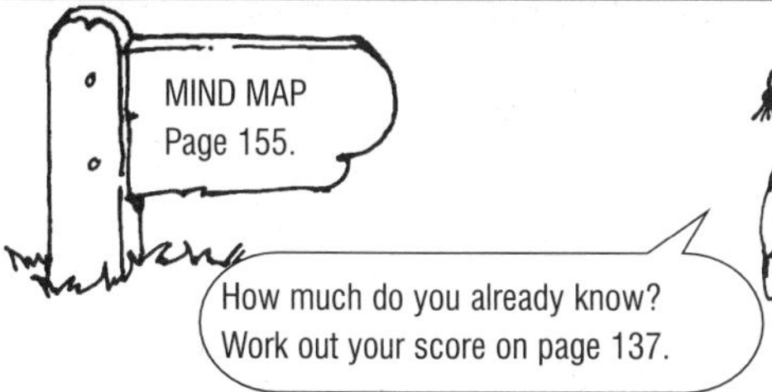

MIND MAP
Page 155.
How much do you already know?
Work out your score on page 137.

Test yourself

1 Draw the functional group of an alkene. Say in what type of reactions this functional group takes part. [2]

2 Unlike alkanes, alkenes are not used as fuels. Why is this? [2]

3 Why does ethene decolorise a solution of bromine? Give the formula of the product. [1]

4 **a)** What is hydration? [1]
b) What important compound is formed by the hydration of ethene? Give its name and formula. [1]

5 **a)** What is hydrogenation? [1]
b) What is the industrial importance of hydrogenation? [1]

6 Explain what is meant by addition polymerisation. [2]

7 Name two sets of plastics which differ in their reaction to heat. Describe the difference in behaviour. [4]

8 By what types of process are the two different kinds of plastics moulded? [2]

16.1 Alkenes

The alkenes are a homologous series of hydrocarbons, as shown in the table.

The alkenes	
name	**formula**
ethene	C_2H_4
propene	C_3H_6
butene	C_4H_8
general formula	C_nH_{2n}

The double bond (see page 31) between the carbon atoms is the **functional group** of alkenes, and is responsible for their reactions. Alkenes are described as **unsaturated hydrocarbons**. They will react with hydrogen in an **addition reaction** to form saturated hydrocarbons (alkanes).

ethene + hydrogen → ethane

$$\begin{array}{c} \quad H \\ \quad | \\ H-C \\ \quad \| \\ H-C \\ \quad | \\ \quad H \end{array} \; + \; \begin{array}{c} H \\ | \\ H \end{array} \; \longrightarrow \; \begin{array}{c} H \\ | \\ H-C-H \\ | \\ H-C-H \\ | \\ H \end{array}$$

16.2 Reactions of alkenes

Alkenes are not used as fuels because they are an important source of other compounds. The double bond makes them chemically reactive, and they are starting materials in the manufacture of plastics, fibres, solvents and other chemicals.

Addition reactions

1 **Halogens add** to alkenes. A solution of bromine in an organic solvent is brown. If an alkene is bubbled through such a bromine solution, the solution loses its colour. Bromine has added to the alkene to form a colourless compound, for example:

ethene + bromine → 1, 2-dibromoethane

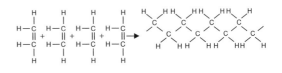

```
    H                          H
    |                          |
H — C          Br          H — C — Br
    ||    +    |     →         |
H — C          Br          H — C — Br
    |                          |
    H                          H
```

The decolorisation of a bromine solution is used to distinguish between an alkene and an alkane. Chlorine adds to alkenes in a similar way.

2 **Hydration**: a molecule of water will add across the double bond. Addition of water is called **hydration**.

ethene + water → ethanol

```
    H                          H
    |                          |
H — C          H           H — C — H
    ||    +    |     →         |
H — C          O — H       H — C — O — H
    |                          |
    H                          H
```

Ethene and steam are passed over a heated catalyst under pressure. The product is ethanol, an important industrial solvent.

3 **Hydrogenation**: animal fats, such as butter, are saturated compounds and are solid. Vegetable oils, such as sunflower seed oil, are unsaturated compounds and are liquid. An unsaturated vegetable oil can be converted into a saturated fat by hydrogenation (the addition of hydrogen):

$$\text{vegetable oil (unsaturated)} + \text{hydrogen} \xrightarrow{\text{pass over heated nickel catalyst}} \text{solid fat (saturated)}$$

The solid fat produced is sold as margarine.

4 **Addition polymerisation**: in this reaction, many molecules of the **monomer**, e.g. ethene, join together (**polymerise**) to form the **polymer**, e.g. poly(ethene).

```
    H       H       H       H
    |       |       |       |
H — C   H — C   H — C   H — C
    || +    || +    || +    ||  →   (chain of C atoms, each bearing two H atoms)
H — C   H — C   H — C   H — C
    |       |       |       |
    H       H       H       H
```

The conditions needed are:

$$\text{ethene} \xrightarrow{\text{pass at high pressure over a heated catalyst}} \text{poly(ethene)}$$

$$nCH_2{=}CH_2 \longrightarrow (\text{–}CH_2\text{–}CH_2\text{–})_n$$

In poly(ethene), n is between 30 000 and 40 000. Poly(ethene) is used for making plastic bags, for kitchenware (buckets, bowls, etc.), for laboratory tubing and for toys. It is flexible and difficult to break. Polymers of alkenes are called poly(alkenes).

16.3 Uses of plastics

Plastics are
- strong
- low in density
- good insulators of heat and electricity
- resistant to attack by chemicals
- smooth
- able to be moulded into different shapes.

There are two kinds of plastics, **thermoplastics** and **thermosetting plastics**. The difference is shown in the diagram below.

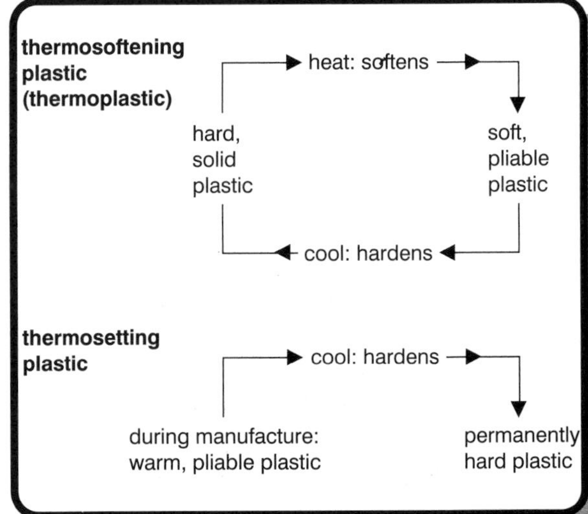

The reason for the difference in behaviour is a difference in structure, as shown.

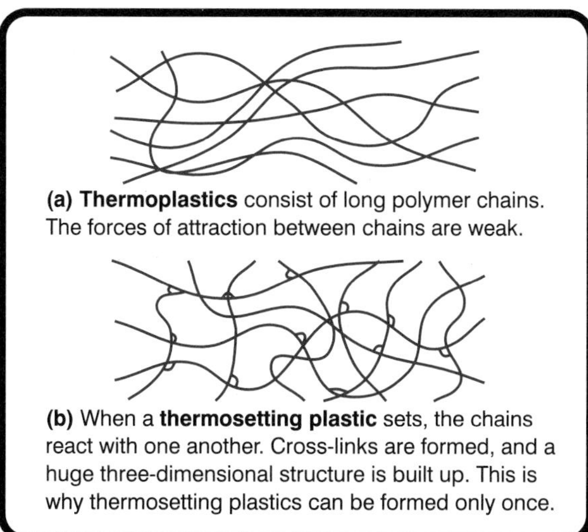

(a) Thermoplastics consist of long polymer chains. The forces of attraction between chains are weak.

(b) When a **thermosetting plastic** sets, the chains react with one another. Cross-links are formed, and a huge three-dimensional structure is built up. This is why thermosetting plastics can be formed only once.

The structure of **(a)** a thermosoftening plastic
(b) a thermosetting plastic

Moulding of thermoplastics can be a **continuous process**: solid granules of the plastic are fed into one end of the moulding machine, softened by heat and then moulded to come out of the other end in the shape of tubes, sheets or rods. It is easy to manufacture coloured articles by adding a pigment to the plastic.

The moulding of thermosetting plastics is a **batch process**. The monomer is poured into the mould and heated. As it polymerises, the plastic solidifies and a press forms it into the required shape while it is setting.

Both types of plastic have their advantages. A material used for electrical fittings and counter tops must be able to withstand high temperatures without softening. For these purposes, 'thermosets' are used.

Sometimes gases are mixed with softened plastics to make low density plastic foam for use in car seats, thermal insulation, sound insulation and packaging. Plastics can be strengthened by the addition of other materials; for example the composite material **glass fibre-reinforced plastic** is used for the manufacture of boat hulls and car bodies.

16.4 Materials

Plastics are one of the most widely used type of materials, along with metals and ceramics. The materials chosen for a particular job depend on their chemical and physical properties.

Metals

The properties of metals result from the nature of the metallic bond.

Metals

- are **crystalline** and are generally **hard**, **tough** and **shiny**
- change shape without breaking (are **ductile** and **malleable**)
- are mostly strong in **tension** (stretching) and **compression** (loading)
- are good **thermal** and **electrical conductors**
- are in many cases **corroded** by water and acids.

Ceramics

Ceramics are crystalline compounds of metallic and non-metallic elements, for example soda glass, silica glass, aluminium oxide (Al_2O_3), titanium carbide (TiC) and silicon nitride (SiN). The bonding in ceramics may be ionic or covalent. The bonds are directed in space, and this structure makes ceramics

- **hard** (able to cut steel and glass)
- of **high melting point**
- **poor conductors of heat** and **electricity**, because they lack free electrons
- usually **opaque**, because light is reflected by grain boundaries in the crystal structure
- rather **brittle** because the bonds are rigid, making it difficult to change the shape without breaking.

Some examples of the many uses of ceramics are listed below.

★ **Vehicle components** with a ceramic coating have improved resistance to wear and tear.

★ **Machine tools** made of ceramics can run at higher temperatures than metal tools without deforming or wearing out.

★ **Space shuttles** have a covering of ceramic tiles to protect them from the high temperatures they meet on re-entering Earth's atmosphere.

Glasses

Glasses are similar to ceramics. Glasses

- have **lower melting points** than ceramics
- are generally **transparent**, because they are non-crystalline so light can pass through without meeting any reflecting surfaces
- **shatter** easily, because they contain surface defects or scratches.

Plastics

Plastics consist of a tangled mass of very long polymer molecules. The structure is described as **amorphous** (shapeless) because the polymer chains take up a random arrangement. The bonds between chains are weak in **thermosoftening** plastics and strong in **thermosetting** plastics. In some polymers, such as high density poly(ethene), there are crystalline regions where the chains are packed together in a regular way. As a result of their structure

- plastics are **strong**, **soft** and **flexible**
- plastics are **thermal** and **electrical insulators**
- thermoplastics **soften** easily when heated.

Synthetic fibres

These fibres are made by forcing molten plastic through a fine hole. As the fibre cools and solidifies, it is stretched to align its molecules along the length of the fibre. This is why fibres have great tensile strength along the length of the fibre.

Composite materials

In a **composite material**, two or more materials are combined to give a material which is more useful for a particular purpose than the individual components.

★ **Reinforced concrete** is the building material used in high-rise buildings and bridges. Concrete alone is weak in tension, strong in compression and brittle. When it is reinforced with steel wires or bars, which are strong in tension, the combination is a tough, relatively cheap material.

★ **Glass-fibre-reinforced polyester (GRP):** the polyester is flexible but weak. The glass fibres are extremely strong, but relatively brittle. The combination of the two materials produces a tough, strong material which is used for products such as small boats, skis and motor vehicle bodies.

★ **Carbon-fibre-reinforced epoxy resin** is used in tennis racquets and in aircraft. It is stronger and lower in density than conventional materials such as aluminium alloys.

Draw your own Mind Map of this topic. Here is a starting point:

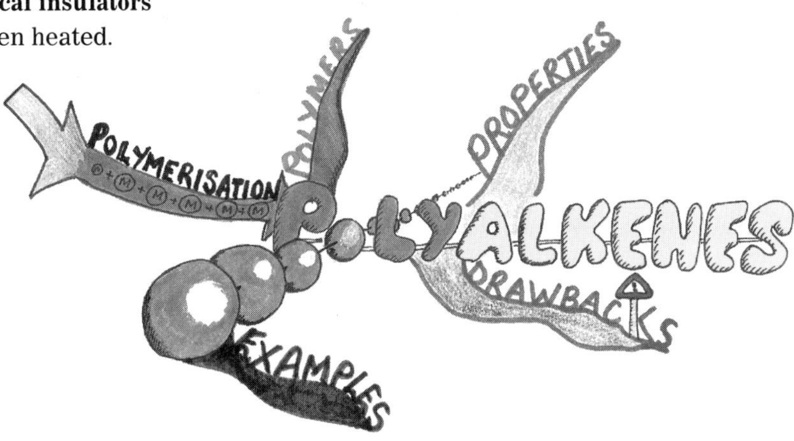

round-up

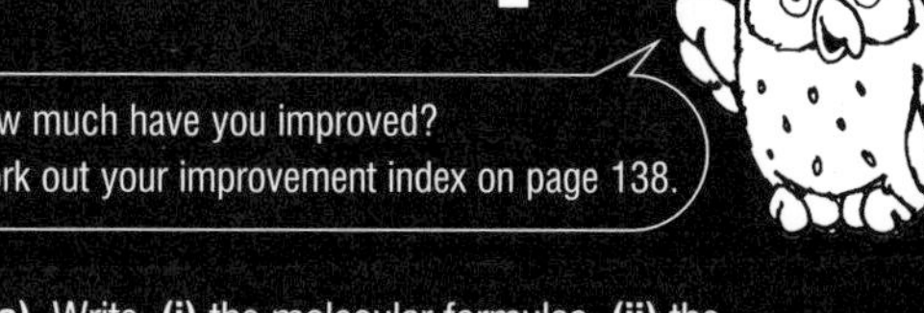

How much have you improved?
Work out your improvement index on page 138.

1 a) Write **(i)** the molecular formulas **(ii)** the structural formulas of ethane and ethene. [4]
b) State the difference between the chemical bonding in the two compounds. [4]

2 a) Give two examples of substances which react with ethene but not with ethane. [2]
b) What name is given to the type of reactions in **a**? [1]
c) How can ethene be converted into ethane? [2]

3 Alkanes and alkenes burn in a similar way. Alkanes are important fuels.
a) What are the main products of combustion of alkanes and alkenes? [2]
b) Why are alkenes not used as fuels? [1]

4 a) Sketch the structural formulas of propane and propene. [2]
b) Which of the two compounds will decolorise bromine water? [1]
c) Sketch the structural formula of the product formed in the reaction between bromine and the compound in **b**. [1]

5 State the advantage that plastic has
a) over china for making cups and saucers and dolls [1]
b) over lead for making toy farmyard animals and soldiers [1]
c) over glass for making motorbike windscreens. [1]

6 The formula of propenamide is: Draw the formula of the polymer poly(propenamide). [1]

$$\begin{array}{l} H-C-CONH_2 \\ \quad\ \ \| \\ H-C-H \end{array}$$

7 a) What does the word 'plastic' mean? [2]
b) There are two big classes of plastics, which behave differently when heated. Name the two classes. Describe the difference in behaviour. Say how this difference is related to the molecular nature of the plastics. [5]

8 Name two addition polymers, and give uses for them. [4]

9 a) What is meant by the statement that plastics are non-biodegradable? [1]
b) Why is this a disadvantage? [1]
c) What is wrong with burning plastic waste? [2]
d) Suggest an alternative to burning plastic waste. [1]

10 Explain the following observations.
a) It is possible to bend a piece of poly(ethene) tubing more easily than a piece of glass tubing. [3]
b) A piece of metal is dented by a hammer blow but a piece of pottery shatters. [4]

11 a) Give one advantage that glass-fibre-reinforced polyester has for building small boats **(i)** over wood **(ii)** over metal. [2]
b) Give **(i)** an advantage **(ii)** a disadvantage of GRP compared with steel for making vehicle bodies. [2]

Well done if you've improved. Don't worry
if you haven't. Take a break and try again.

Agricultural chemicals

17

preview

At the end of this topic you will:

- **understand why NPK fertilisers are important**
- **know about the manufacture and reactions of ammonia**
- **know about the manufacture of nitric acid, sulphuric acid and NPK fertilisers**
- **know some reactions of concentrated sulphuric acid.**

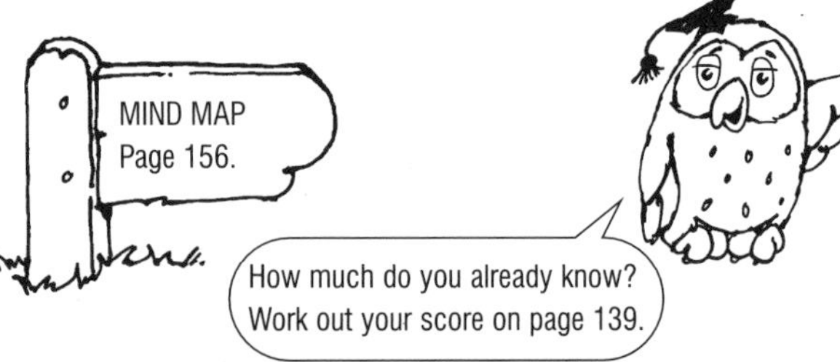
MIND MAP
Page 156.
How much do you already know?
Work out your score on page 139.

Test yourself

1 Unlike most plants, clover can convert nitrogen in the air into nitrogen compounds. How does it do this? [3]

2 What do nitrifying bacteria do? [2]

3 What do denitrifying bacteria do? [3]

4 NPK fertilisers are widely used. What types of compound do they contain? [3]

5 Some of the nitrate content of fertilisers washes into lake water. What problems does this cause? [3]

6 What is the percentage by mass of nitrogen in urea, CON_2H_4? (Relative atomic masses: H = 1, C = 12, N = 14, O = 16) [2]

7 In the Haber process for manufacturing ammonia, what conditions are used? [3]

8 **a)** Name the industrial process used for the manufacture of sulphuric acid. [1]
b) Write the equation for the first stage of the process. [2]

9 Name three raw materials needed for the manufacture of NPK fertilisers. [3]

17.1 Fertilisers

Plants need

- carbon, hydrogen and oxygen compounds, which are in plentiful supply
- small quantities of **trace elements** (iron, manganese, boron, copper, cobalt, molybdenum, zinc), which are present in most soils
- fairly large quantities of compounds containing nitrogen, phosphorus, potassium, calcium, magnesium, sulphur and, for some crops, sodium.

NITROGEN CYCLE
Page 51.

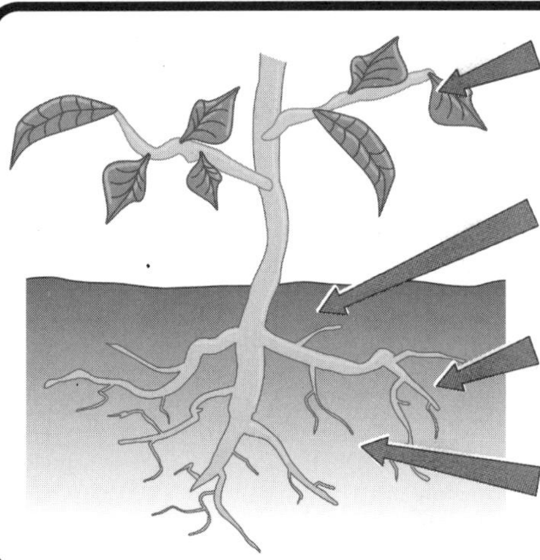

Potassium: potassium compounds assist photosynthesis. NPK fertilisers contain potassium chloride.

Nitrogen: nitrogenous fertilisers increase both the size of the crop and the protein content of the plants. Plants can absorb nitrates from the soil. Ammonium salts can also be used as fertilisers, because ammonium salts are converted into nitrates by microorganisms in the soil.

Phosphorus: phosphates stimulate root development. The soluble fertiliser ammonium phosphate supplies phosphorus to crops.

Sodium: a few crops, e.g. sugar beet, grow better if common salt is added as a fertiliser.

Some of the elements that plants need

Fertilisers that supply nitrogen, phosphorus and potassium are called **NPK fertilisers**. They are used in huge quantities: about 20 million tonnes a year worldwide. Fertilisers cost about £80 per tonne and are a large item in a farmer's budget. The use of excessive fertilisers is wasteful and often causes pollution.

17.2 Ammonia

The first step in the manufacture of nitrogenous fertilisers is the manufacture of ammonia by the Haber process. A test for ammonia, which is also a test for hydrogen chloride, is shown in the diagram opposite, and the reactions of ammonia are summarised in the concept map below.

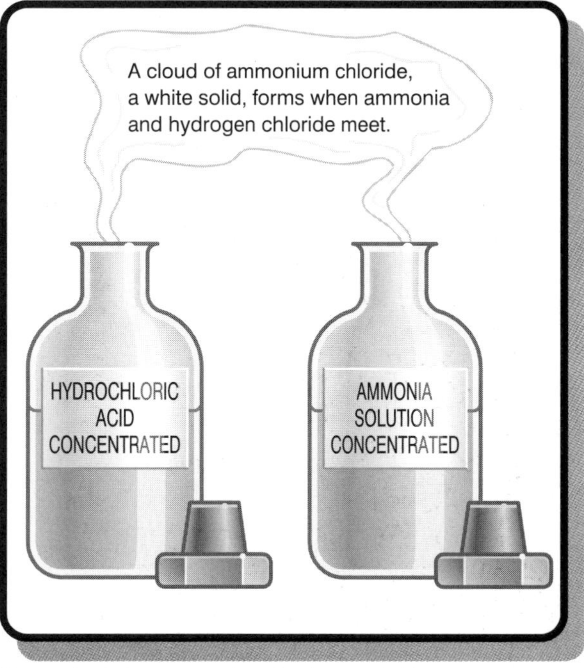

The reaction between ammonia and hydrogen chloride

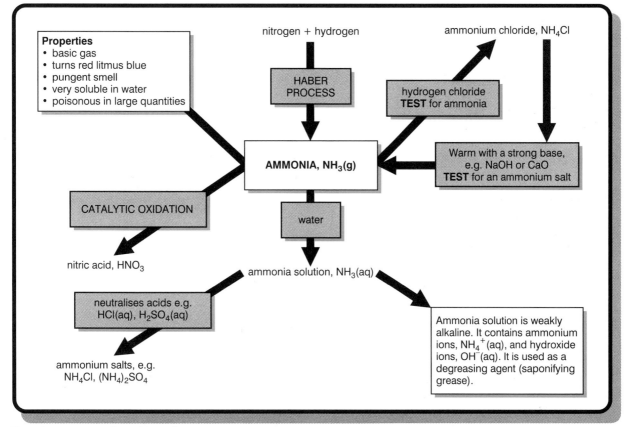

Properties
- basic gas
- turns red litmus blue
- pungent smell
- very soluble in water
- poisonous in large quantities

nitrogen + hydrogen

HABER PROCESS

AMMONIA, NH_3(g)

ammonium chloride, NH_4Cl

hydrogen chloride **TEST** for ammonia

Warm with a strong base, e.g. NaOH or CaO **TEST** for an ammonium salt

CATALYTIC OXIDATION

nitric acid, HNO_3

water

ammonia solution, NH_3(aq)

neutralises acids e.g. HCl(aq), H_2SO_4(aq)

ammonium salts, e.g. NH_4Cl, $(NH_4)_2SO_4$

Ammonia solution is weakly alkaline. It contains ammonium ions, NH_4^+(aq), and hydroxide ions, OH^-(aq). It is used as a degreasing agent (saponifying grease).

Concept map: some reactions of ammonia

17.3 Manufacture of nitric acid

Nitric acid is made from ammonia, air and water. The reactions that take place are listed below.

1 ammonia + oxygen $\xrightarrow{\text{catalyst (Pt) at 900°C}}$ nitrogen monoxide, NO + steam

2 nitrogen monoxide + oxygen → nitrogen dioxide, NO_2

3 nitrogen dioxide + oxygen + water → nitric acid, HNO_3

17.4 Sulphuric acid

The main uses of sulphuric acid (130 million tonnes a year worldwide) are

- the manufacture of soapless detergents
- converting calcium phosphate into ammonium phosphate, a soluble fertiliser (see diagram on page 112)
- making sulphates for use as white pigments in paints
- the manufacture of titanium(IV) oxide, TiO_2, a white pigment which is added to paints and also used in 'liquid paper'
- lead–acid batteries.

The Contact process

The **Contact process** is used to manufacture sulphuric acid. The process is summarised on the flow diagram opposite.

The sulphur dioxide needed for the Contact process is obtained from:

- the combustion of sulphur
- the removal of unpleasant-smelling sulphur compounds from petroleum oil
- the removal of hydrogen sulphide from natural gas
- roasting metal sulphides in order to extract metals from their ores.

Sulphur dioxide and oxygen react to form sulphur trioxide:

$$2SO_2(g) + O_2(g) \rightleftharpoons 2SO_3(g) \qquad \text{heat is given out}$$

The reaction is reversible and exothermic; raising the temperature makes sulphur trioxide decompose. High pressure cannot be used to increase the speed of the reaction because sulphur dioxide liquefies easily under pressure. To increase the speed of the reaction, a catalyst is used.

Note that sulphur trioxide is absorbed into sulphuric acid to form oleum. This is safer than using water because as soon as sulphur trioxide meets water vapour, it forms a mist of sulphuric acid.

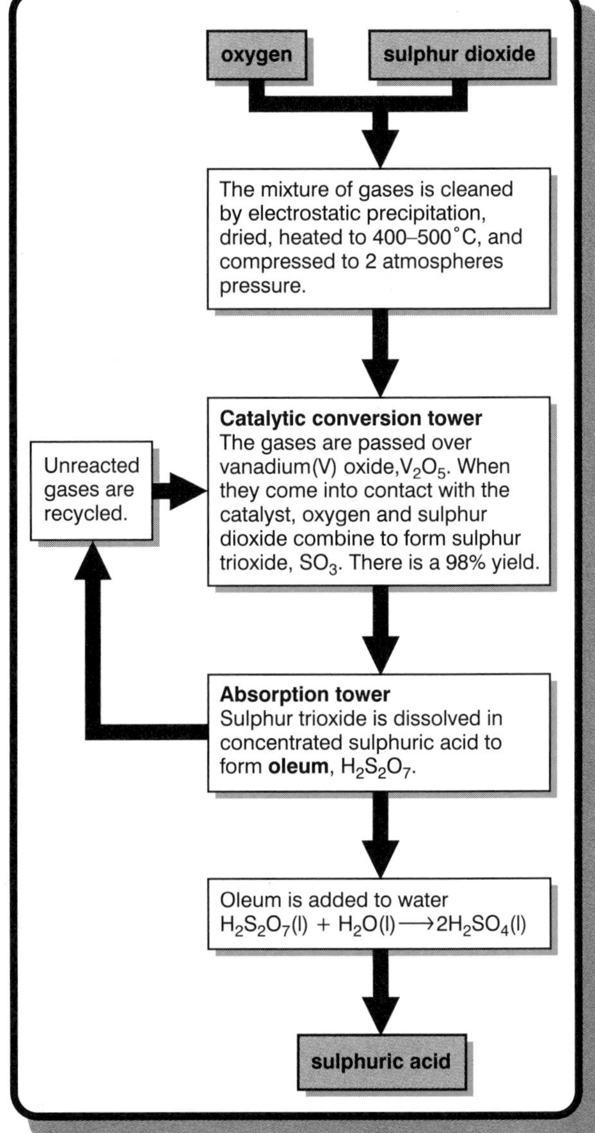

Flow diagram of the Contact process for the manufacture of sulphuric acid

Concentrated sulphuric acid

Concentrated sulphuric acid takes part in the same reactions as dilute sulphuric acid, and has additional properties as well. It is an **oxidising agent** and a **dehydrating agent**.

Oxidising agent

1 Copper and other metals that are low in the reactivity series do not react with dilute sulphuric acid. However, concentrated sulphuric acid reacts with these metals.

copper + conc. sulphuric acid → copper(II) sulphate + sulphur dioxide + water

Concentrated sulphuric acid has acted as an oxidising agent; it has taken electrons from copper atoms to form copper ions.

2 Hot, dilute sulphuric acid reacts with iron to form iron(II) sulphate, $FeSO_4$. With concentrated sulphuric acid, the product is iron(III) sulphate, $Fe_2(SO_4)_3$. Concentrated sulphuric acid has acted as an oxidising agent, taking electrons from Fe^{2+} ions to form Fe^{3+} ions.

Dehydrating agent

A reagent which removes water from a compound is called a **dehydrating agent**.

1 Concentrated sulphuric acid can remove the water of crystallisation from a hydrate, for example:

copper(II) sulphate-5-water (blue crystals) —conc. sulphuric acid→ copper(II) sulphate (white powder) + water

heat is given out

2 Concentrated sulphuric acid dehydrates sucrose (removes the elements of water from it) to leave a form of carbon known as 'sugar charcoal'.

sucrose —conc. sulphuric acid→ carbon + water   heat is given out

$C_{12}H_{22}O_{11}(s) \rightarrow 12C(s) + 11H_2O(l)$

3 The reaction between concentrated sulphuric acid and water itself is highly exothermic. **Never add water to concentrated sulphuric acid.** Heat will be generated in a small volume of acid, which will make the added water boil and splash out of the container, bringing with it a shower of concentrated sulphuric acid. To make a solution, add concentrated sulphuric acid slowly, with stirring, to a large volume of water. Then the heat generated will be spread through a large volume of water.

17.5 Manufacture of NPK fertilisers

Big fertiliser manufacturers carry out the manufacture of ammonia, nitric acid, sulphuric acid and phosphoric acid on the same site. The potassium chloride needed is mined. The flow diagram (overleaf) shows how compounds are mixed to make NPK fertilisers. The proportions are varied to suit different crops and soils.

Location of industrial plants

A sulphuric acid plant may be sited near a port, so that supplies of sulphur can arrive by ship, or close to a supply of sulphur dioxide from a gas refinery or a metal smelter.

There must be good rail or road connections to enable the product to be transported to customers. The question of whether the environment would suffer from the polluting effects of leakage, spillage and the emission of waste materials must be considered. The plant must be near an urban area to have access to a workforce.

phosphate rock
sulphur
air
natural gas
water
potassium chloride
sulphuric acid plant
ammonia plant
nitric acid plant
phosphoric acid plant
ammonium nitrate
ammonium phosphate
NPK fertiliser plant

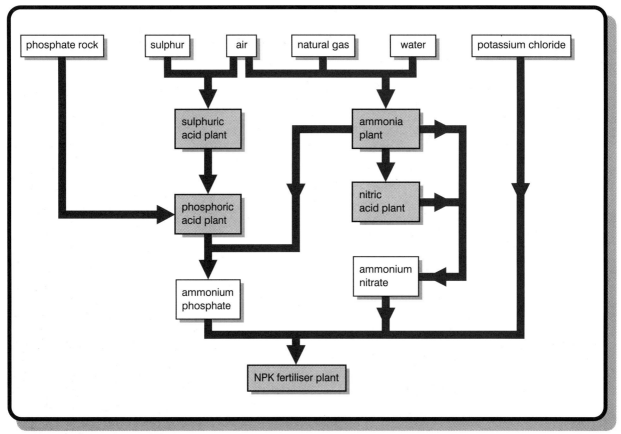

Flow diagram for the manufacture of NPK fertilisers

Copy and complete this Mind Map to help you revise this topic.

round-up

How much have you improved?
Work out your improvement index on page 139.

1 Find the percentage by mass of nitrogen in each of the following fertilisers.
a) ammonia, NH_3 **b)** ammonium nitrate, NH_4NO_3
c) ammonium sulphate, $(NH_4)_2SO_4$ **d)** urea, CON_2H_4 [4]

2 Write the word equation and chemical equation for the reaction between ammonia and hydrogen chloride on page 109. [3]

3 Write a chemical equation for this example of the displacement of ammonia from one of its salts: [3]

ammonium chloride + sodium hydroxide → ammonia + sodium chloride + water

4 Suggest what **A**, **B**, **C**, **D** and **E** might be.

A is a neutral, rather unreactive gas which reacts with hydrogen under pressure.

The indicator **B** is turned blue by ammonia.

The gas **C** reacts with ammonia to form a white solid.

Ammonium sulphate gives ammonia when it is warmed with a solution of **D**.

Gas **E** forms an explosive mixture with air but combines with **A** with difficulty. [5]

5 **a)** What nutritious compounds do plants make from nitrates? [1]
b) How can atmospheric nitrogen be used as a fertiliser by some plants? [2]
c) Name one process that converts atmospheric nitrogen into a compound which can enter the soil and be used by plants. [1]
d) Explain why natural sources of nitrogen will not support the repeated growing of crops on the same land. [2]
e) Why are ammonium salts used as fertilisers when plants cannot absorb them? [3]

6 How good are you at balancing equations? Complete these equations for the steps in the manufacture of nitric acid from ammonia.
a) $4NH_3(g) + \_O_2(g) \rightarrow 4NO(g) + \_H_2O(g)$ [2]
b) $\_NO(g) + \_O_2(g) \rightarrow \_NO_2(g)$ [2]
c) $4NO_2(g) + \_O_2(g) + \_H_2O(l) \rightarrow \_HNO_3(l)$ [3]

7 Copy and complete this paragraph, supplying words or phrases to fill the blanks.

In the ______ process for manufacturing sulphuric acid, the gas sulphur dioxide is obtained by ______. It is mixed with ______ and purified by the method of ______. The mixture of gases is passed over a heated catalyst, ______, and the compound ______ is formed. This compound is absorbed in ______ to form ______. On dilution with water, this gives sulphuric acid. A country which has no sulphur deposits could cut down the quantity of sulphur which it imports by ______ . [9]

8 Balanced fertilisers contain nitrogen, phosphorus and potassium. The table lists four substances which are used in fertilisers.

name	formula
basic slag	$(CaO)_5.P_2O_5.SiO_2$
ammonium sulphate	$(NH_4)_2SO_4$
urea	$CO(NH_2)_2$
sylvite	KCl

a) Which of the substances in the table contains phosphorus? [1]
b) Which three substances would you need to use to obtain a balanced fertiliser? [3]

9 In the Contact process for making sulphuric acid,
a) Why does the process not use high pressure? [1]
b) Why does the process not use a high temperature? [1]
c) What catalyst is used? [1]

10 List two industrial uses of sulphuric acid. [2]

Well done if you've improved. Don't worry if you haven't. Take a break and try again.

Alcohols, acids and esters 18

preview

At the end of this topic you will:

- know the reactions of alcohols
- appreciate the dangers of drinking alcohol
- know how ethanol is made by fermentation and from ethene
- know the reactions of carboxylic acids.

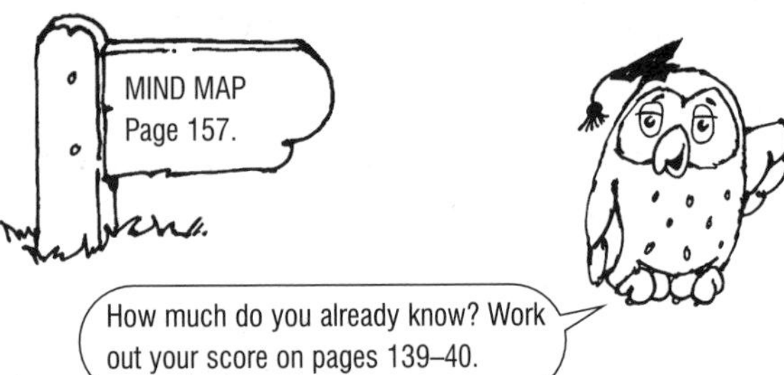

MIND MAP
Page 157.
How much do you already know? Work out your score on pages 139–40.

Test yourself

1 a) To what homologous series does ethanol belong?
b) What is the common name for ethanol?
c) Draw the structural formula for ethanol. [3]

2 Why is it dangerous to drive under the influence of alcohol? [2]

3 Why does wine go sour when it is open to the air? [4]

4 Explain what is meant by fermentation. [4]

5 Give two industrial methods for making ethanol. What is the ethanol produced by each method used for? [6]

6 Name an oxidation product of ethanol, and draw its structural formula. [2]

7 What is the functional group of a carboxylic acid? Draw its structure. [2]

8 What is formed when an alcohol and a carboxylic acid react together? [2]

18.1 The alcohols

The **alcohols** are a homologous series of compounds with the general formula $C_nH_{2n+1}OH$. The members of the alcohol series all possess the **functional group** $\geq$C—O—H, the hydroxyl group. They therefore have similar chemical reactions, as shown in the concept map on page 116. Physical properties change gradually from one member to the next.

The alcohols	
name	**formula**
methanol	CH_3OH
ethanol	C_2H_5OH
propanol	C_3H_7OH
general formula	$C_nH_{2n+1}OH$

18.2 Ethanol

The drug

Ethanol is a drug, with a medical effect that is described as a **depressant** of the central nervous system. In small quantities, ethanol makes people feel relaxed. However, drinking large amounts of ethanol regularly causes damage to the liver, kidneys, arteries and brain. Methanol is so toxic that drinking only small amounts of it can lead to blindness and death.

Manufacture from fermentation

Ethanol is obtained by the fermentation of carbohydrates, such as glucose and starch.

$$\text{glucose} \xrightarrow{\text{enzyme in yeast}} \text{ethanol} + \text{carbon dioxide}$$

$$C_6H_{12}O_6(aq) \rightarrow 2C_2H_5OH(aq) + 2CO_2(g)$$

Yeast is added to fruit juices, which contain sugars, and left to ferment until the content of ethanol in the solution reaches 14%, when it kills the yeast. More concentrated solutions of ethanol can be obtained by distillation.

Ethanol can be made from a number of starchy foods, such as potatoes, rice and hops. The starch is first treated with germinated barley (malt). This contains an enzyme that hydrolyses starch to a mixture of sugars. The sugars are then fermented by yeast.

Ethanol is sold as

- absolute alcohol (96% ethanol)
- industrial alcohol (methylated spirit), which has 5% methanol added to make the liquid unfit for drinking
- spirits (35% ethanol)
- beers and ciders (3–7% ethanol)
- wines (12–14% ethanol).

Preparation from ethene

Ethanol that is to be used as an industrial solvent is made by the catalytic hydration of ethene.

18.3 Reactions of alcohols

The reactions of ethanol are summarised in the concept map overleaf.

Dehydration

When ethanol is dehydrated, it gives ethene. The apparatus for this reaction is shown below.

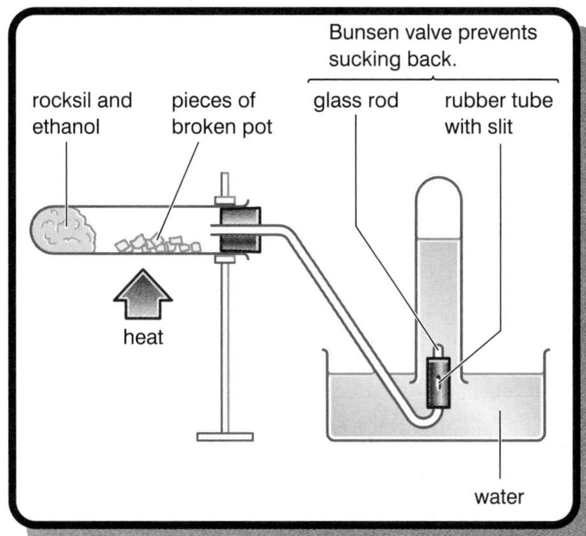

Making ethene by the dehydration of ethanol

Catalysts for the reaction include aluminium oxide, unglazed porcelain and pumice stone.

Oxidation

Ethanol is oxidised by air if certain micro-organisms are present. The reaction is used commercially to make ethanoic acid.

$$\text{ethanol} + \text{oxygen} \xrightarrow{\text{certain microorganisms}} \text{ethanoic acid} + \text{water}$$

$$C_2H_5OH(aq) + O_2(g) \rightarrow CH_3CO_2H(aq) + H_2O(l)$$

Acidified potassium dichromate(VI), $K_2Cr_2O_7$, is a powerful oxidising agent. It is orange. It oxidises ethanol to ethanoic acid, and is reduced to chromium(III) ions, which are blue. As the reaction proceeds, the colour changes from orange through green to blue. This reaction was used as a breathalyser test for motorists.

Esterification

Alcohols react with organic acids to form sweet-smelling liquids called **esters** (see overleaf).

$$\text{ethanol} + \text{ethanoic acid} \xrightarrow{\text{catalysed by conc. sulphuric acid}} \text{ethyl ethanoate} + \text{water}$$

$$C_2H_5OH(l) + CH_3CO_2H(l) \rightarrow CH_3CO_2C_2H_5(l) + H_2O(l)$$

The structural formula of ethyl ethanoate is:

```
    H
    |    O
    |   //      H   H
H — C — C       |   |
    |    \      |   |
    H     O — C — C — H
              |   |
              H   H
```

18.4 Gasohol

Gasohol is a mixture of petrol and ethanol. Ethanol can be used in a petrol engine because

- it dissolves in petrol
- it vaporises at the engine temperature
- ethanol produces 70% as much heat per litre as petrol on combustion
- the engine need not be modified if less than 10% ethanol is used in the vehicle
- ethanol forms harmless combustion products ($CO_2 + H_2O$).

Most of the petrol in Brazil now contains 10% ethanol. Brazil has land available for growing suitable crops for fermentation, e.g. sugar cane, and also enough sunlight to ripen the crops.

ethene, $CH_2{=}CH_2$

sugar or starch

dehydration by e.g. Al_2O_3

catalytic hydration INDUSTRIAL METHOD

fermentation by yeast – the method used to make alcoholic drinks

ethanol C_2H_5OH

burn in air → carbon dioxide + water

oxygen and microorganisms, oxidising agents, e.g. acid + potassium dichromate(VI)

ethanoic acid CH_3CO_2H

Properties and uses
industral solvent:
- dissolves many covalent substances
- miscible with water

reacts with organic acids to form sweet-smelling liquids called esters, e.g. ethyl ethanoate

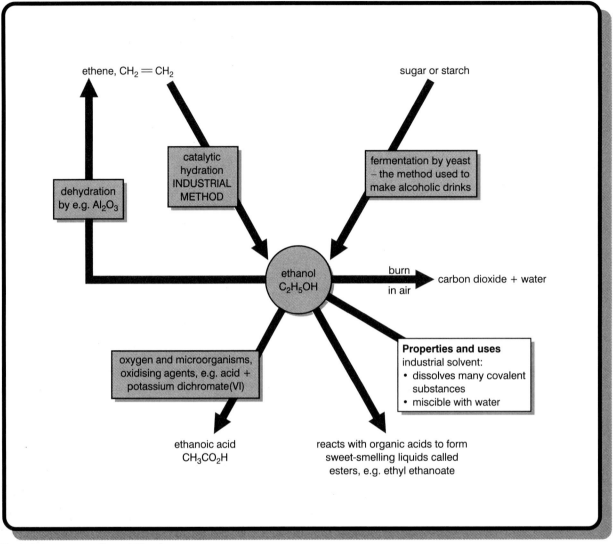

Concept map: some reactions of ethanol

18.5 Ethanoic acid

Ethanoic acid, CH_3CO_2H, is a member of the homologous series of **carboxylic acids**. The general formula is $C_nH_{2n+1}CO_2H$, and the functional group is the carboxyl group, —CO_2H. Ethanoic acid ionises in solution to give hydrogen ions:

carboxylic acid + water ⇌ hydrogen ions + carboxylate ions

$$RCO_2H(aq) \rightleftharpoons H^+(aq) + RCO_2^-(aq)$$

Since ionisation is only partial, carboxylic acids are weak acids.

Some of the reactions of ethanoic acid are shown in the concept map opposite.

18.6 Esters

Esters occur naturally in fruits and are used as food additives to give flavour and aroma to processed foods. Esters are also used as solvents, for example in glues. The people we call 'glue-sniffers' enjoy the effects of inhaling esters. This dangerous habit is called **solvent abuse** and causes disorientated behaviour such as walking through traffic and jumping out of windows. It also causes brain damage and heart failure.

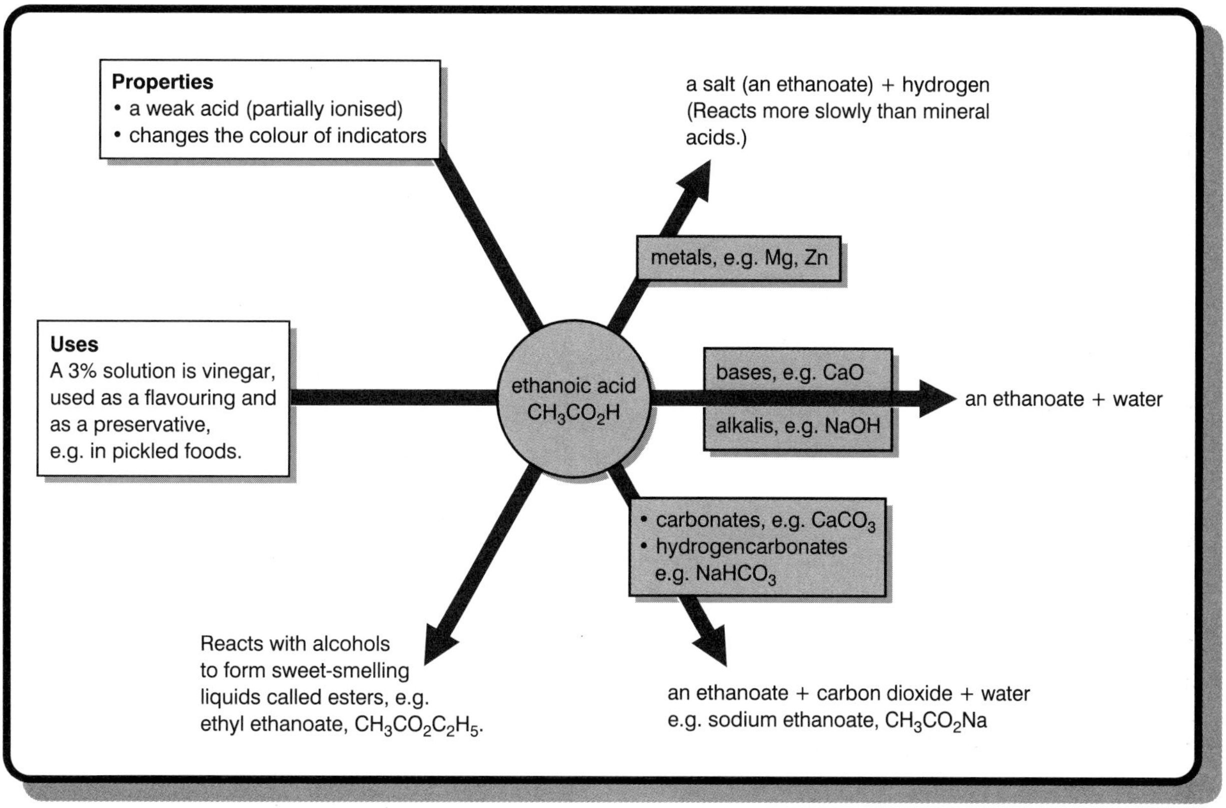

Properties
- a weak acid (partially ionised)
- changes the colour of indicators

Uses
A 3% solution is vinegar, used as a flavouring and as a preservative, e.g. in pickled foods.

ethanoic acid
CH_3CO_2H

metals, e.g. Mg, Zn → a salt (an ethanoate) + hydrogen (Reacts more slowly than mineral acids.)

bases, e.g. CaO / alkalis, e.g. NaOH → an ethanoate + water

- carbonates, e.g. $CaCO_3$
- hydrogencarbonates e.g. $NaHCO_3$

→ an ethanoate + carbon dioxide + water e.g. sodium ethanoate, CH_3CO_2Na

Reacts with alcohols to form sweet-smelling liquids called esters, e.g. ethyl ethanoate, $CH_3CO_2C_2H_5$.

Concept map: reactions of ethanoic acid

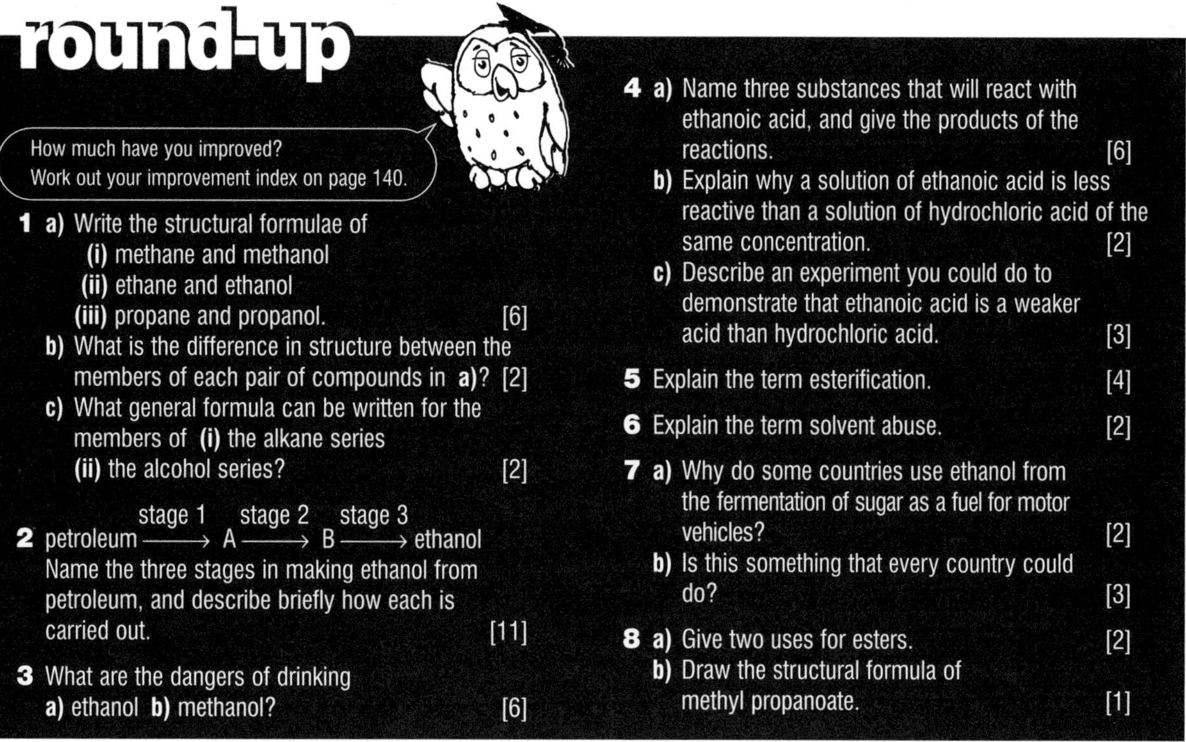

round-up

How much have you improved?
Work out your improvement index on page 140.

1 a) Write the structural formulae of
  (i) methane and methanol
  (ii) ethane and ethanol
  (iii) propane and propanol. [6]

b) What is the difference in structure between the members of each pair of compounds in **a)**? [2]

c) What general formula can be written for the members of **(i)** the alkane series **(ii)** the alcohol series? [2]

2 petroleum —stage 1→ A —stage 2→ B —stage 3→ ethanol
Name the three stages in making ethanol from petroleum, and describe briefly how each is carried out. [11]

3 What are the dangers of drinking **a)** ethanol **b)** methanol? [6]

4 a) Name three substances that will react with ethanoic acid, and give the products of the reactions. [6]

b) Explain why a solution of ethanoic acid is less reactive than a solution of hydrochloric acid of the same concentration. [2]

c) Describe an experiment you could do to demonstrate that ethanoic acid is a weaker acid than hydrochloric acid. [3]

5 Explain the term esterification. [4]

6 Explain the term solvent abuse. [2]

7 a) Why do some countries use ethanol from the fermentation of sugar as a fuel for motor vehicles? [2]

b) Is this something that every country could do? [3]

8 a) Give two uses for esters. [2]

b) Draw the structural formula of methyl propanoate. [1]

Analytical chemistry

19

preview

At the end of this topic you will know:

- **the flame colours of some metals**
- **how to test for ions in solution**
- **how to identify some gases.**

How much do you already know? Work out your score on page 141.

Test yourself

1 A firework display releases a stream of brick-red stars. Which metal **A–E** do the fireworks contain?

A barium **B** sodium **C** aluminium
D calcium **E** lithium [1]

2 To a solution of the salt MA are added dilute nitric acid and silver nitrate solution. A white precipitate is formed. Suggest what the anion A may be. [1]

3 A salt XY is warmed with dilute sodium hydroxide solution. A gas is given off which turns damp litmus paper blue. What is **a)** the gas **b)** the cation X? [2]

4 The labels have come off two bottles of green crystals. One label reads 'copper(II) chloride', and the other reads 'iron(II) chloride'. You are given the job of sticking the correct label on each bottle. Say what tests you would do and how you would interpret your results. [6]

Fact file

★ **Qualitative analysis** lets us find out which substances are present in a sample.

★ **Quantitative analysis** lets us find the quantity of one or more components of a sample, for example by **titration**.

Are you drawing your Mind Maps?

As you study each topic, draw your own Mind Map. Start with a central picture and draw branches radiating out from the centre.

There are Mind Maps for many of the topics in this book on pages 144–57. You may use them for revision if you like, but your own will be better. They will mean more to you because you have drawn them, and you will remember them much better than someone else's Mind Maps.

Revise your Mind Maps from time to time. If you have forgotten what you had in mind when you drew some of the branches, a little more revision is called for. Keeping the topics fresh in your mind is more efficient than letting them slide and then having to do a panic revision.

The night before the exam, do not sit up late at night trying to cram. A last glance through the Mind Maps you have made yourself is as much as your brain can take in at the last minute.

When you go into the exam you will know that you have done your revision. You can be confident that it will stand you in good stead.

19.1 Flame colour

Some metals and their compounds give characteristic colours, as shown in the table below.

Some flame colours

metal	colour of flame
barium	apple-green
calcium	brick-red
copper	green with blue streaks
lithium	crimson
magnesium	white
potassium	lilac
sodium	yellow

19.2 Tests for ions in solution

A soluble solid can be analysed by dissolving it in distilled water and then applying the tests in the following table.

Tests for ions in solution (ppt = precipitate)

anion	test and observation
chloride, $Cl^-(aq)$	Add a few drops of dilute nitric acid followed by a few drops of silver nitrate solution. A white ppt of silver chloride is formed. The ppt is soluble in ammonia solution.
bromide, $Br^-(aq)$	Add a few drops of dilute nitric acid followed by a few drops of silver nitrate solution. A pale yellow ppt of silver bromide is formed. The ppt is slightly soluble in ammonia solution.
iodide, $I^-(aq)$	Add a few drops of dilute nitric acid followed by a few drops of silver nitrate solution. A yellow ppt of silver iodide is formed. It is insoluble in ammonia solution.
sulphate, $SO_4^{2-}(aq)$	Add a few drops of barium chloride solution followed by a few drops of dilute hydrochloric acid. A white ppt of barium sulphate is formed.
sulphite, $SO_3^{2-}(aq)$	Test as for sulphate. A white ppt of barium sulphite appears and then reacts with acid to give sulphur dioxide.
carbonate, $CO_3^{2-}(aq)$	Add dilute hydrochloric acid to the solution (or add it to the solid). Bubbles of carbon dioxide are given off.
nitrate, $NO_3^-(aq)$	Make the solution strongly alkaline. Add Devarda's alloy and warm. Ammonia is given off. (If the solution contains ammonium ions, warm with alkali to drive off ammonia before testing for nitrate.)

cation	add sodium hydroxide solution	add ammonia solution
ammonium, $NH_4^+(aq)$	warm; ammonia is given off	—
copper, $Cu^{2+}(aq)$	blue jelly-like ppt, $Cu(OH)_2(s)$	blue jelly-like ppt which dissolves in excess $NH_3(aq)$ to form a deep blue solution
iron(II), $Fe^{2+}(aq)$	green gelatinous ppt, $Fe(OH)_2(s)$	green gelatinous ppt, $Fe(OH)_2(s)$
iron(III), $Fe^{3+}(aq)$	rust-brown gelatinous ppt, $Fe(OH)_3(s)$	rust-brown gelatinous ppt, $Fe(OH)_3(s)$
lead(II), $Pb^{2+}(aq)$	white ppt, $Pb(OH)_2(s)$, dissolves in excess NaOH(aq)	white ppt, $Pb(OH)_2$ (s)
zinc, $Zn^{2+}(aq)$	white ppt, $Zn(OH)_2(s)$, dissolves in excess NaOH(aq)	white ppt, $Zn(OH)_2(s)$, dissolves in excess $NH_3(aq)$
aluminium, $Al^{3+}(aq)$	colourless ppt, $Al(OH)_3(s)$, dissolves in excess NaOH(aq)	colourless ppt, $Al(OH)_3(s)$

19.3 Tests for gases

gas	colour and smell	test and observation
ammonia*	colourless pungent smell	Hold damp red litmus paper or universal indicator paper in the gas. The indicator turns blue.
carbon dioxide	colourless odourless	Bubble the gas through limewater (calcium hydroxide solution). A white solid precipitate appears, making the solution cloudy.
chlorine*	green gas choking smell	Hold damp blue litmus litmus paper in the gas. Litmus turns red and is quickly bleached. Chlorine turns damp starch–iodide paper blue-black.
hydrogen	colourless odourless	Introduce a lighted splint. Hydrogen burns with a squeaky 'pop'.
hydrogen chloride	colourless pungent smell	Hold damp blue litmus paper in the gas. Litmus turns red. With ammonia, a white smoke of NH_4Cl forms.
oxygen	colourless odourless	Hold a glowing wooden splint in the gas. The splint bursts into flame.
sulphur dioxide*	colourless choking smell	Dip a filter paper in potassium dichromate(VI) solution, and hold it in the gas. The solution turns from orange through green to blue. Potassium manganate(VII) solution turns very pale pink.

These gases are poisonous. Test with care.

round-up

How much have you improved?
Work out your improvement index on page 141.

1 Doctor Sparkler is asked to design a firework display. Suggest what compounds he should include to give **a)** yellow light **b)** blue-green light **c)** apple-green light. [3]

2 A geologist is investigating a newly discovered ore which she believes may contain both calcium carbonate and magnesium carbonate. How can she test to see whether the ore **a)** is a carbonate **b)** contains magnesium **c)** contains calcium? [9]

3 A solution contains the ions of metals X and Y. When a solution of sodium hydroxide is added, a precipitate is obtained. Addition of excess of sodium hydroxide to this precipitate gives a rust-coloured precipitate containing X and a colourless solution containing Y. When dilute hydrochloric acid is added to this solution, a white precipitate is obtained. Deduce what X and Y may be, explaining your reasoning. [5]

4 A factory orders sodium sulphite and potassium sulphate. A delivery van deposits two unlabelled cartons at the factory and drives off. The works chemist has to sort out which carton is which. Suggest two tests she could use. [8]

5 Two gas jars contain colourless gases. One is ammonia, and the other is hydrogen. Describe two tests you could do to tell which is which. [6]

6 You are given two gas jars. One contains hydrogen chloride and the other contains chlorine. Describe two tests you could do to find out which is which. [6]

Food chemistry

20

preview

At the end of this topic you will know about:

- **carbohydrates – sugars, starch, glycogen and cellulose**
- **fats and oils**
- **amino acids and proteins**
- **food additives.**

How much do you already know? Work out your score on page 141.

Test yourself

1 Glucose, maltose and starch are carbohydrates.
  a) Which one of them tastes sweet? [1]
  b) Which one is sparingly soluble in water? [1]
  c) Which elements are present in these compounds? [1]
  d) Explain how starch is formed from glucose. [1]

2 **a)** Write the general formula of an amino acid. [1]
  b) Name **(i)** the kind of reaction by which amino acids join to form proteins **(ii)** the type of linkage formed. [2]

3 The following equation represents the formation of a fat.

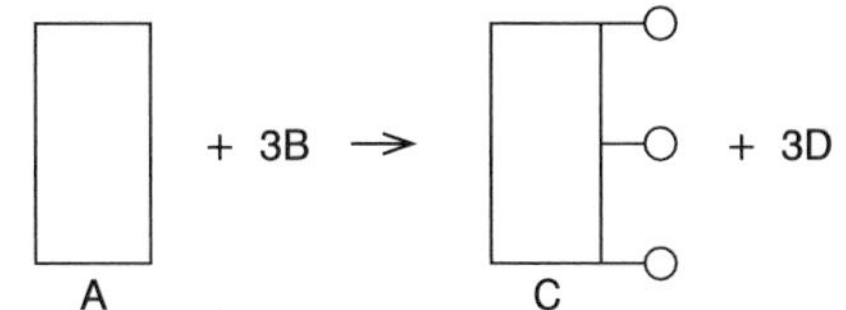

  a) Name the substances A and D. [2]
  b) What type of chemical compounds are **(i)** B **(ii)** C? [2]

4 Which organisation allocates an E-number to a food additive? [1]

20.1 Carbohydrates

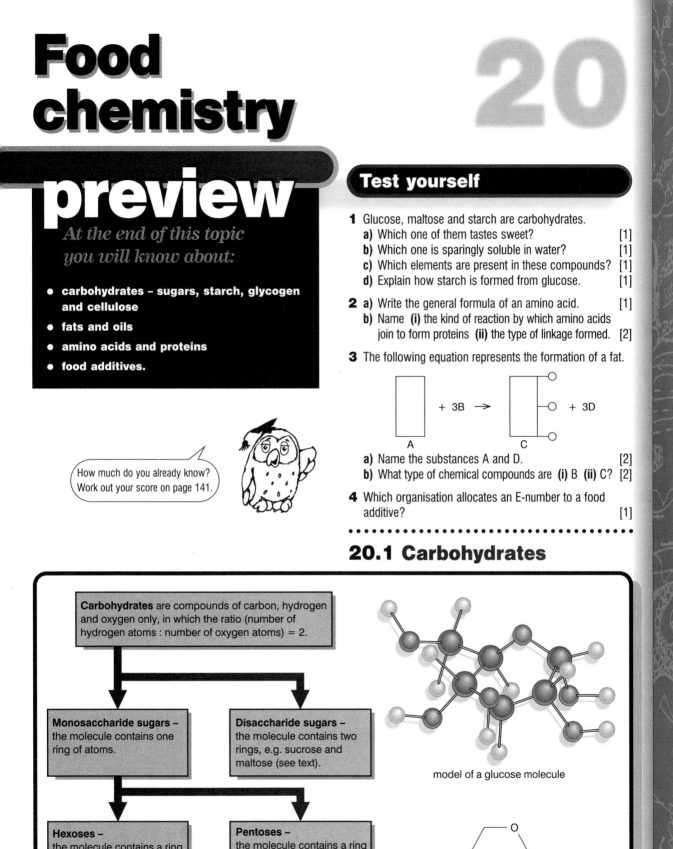

Carbohydrates are compounds of carbon, hydrogen and oxygen only, in which the ratio (number of hydrogen atoms : number of oxygen atoms) = 2.

Monosaccharide sugars – the molecule contains one ring of atoms.

Disaccharide sugars – the molecule contains two rings, e.g. sucrose and maltose (see text).

Hexoses – the molecule contains a ring of six atoms, e.g. glucose and fructose, both of formula $C_6H_{12}O_6$.

Pentoses – the molecule contains a ring of five atoms, e.g. ribose, formula $C_5H_{10}O_5$.

model of a glucose molecule

O

formula of glucose in shorthand form

Carbohydrates

Sucrose is formed from glucose and fructose:

glucose + fructose → sucrose + water

$C_6H_{12}O_6(aq) + C_6H_{12}O_6(aq) \rightarrow C_{12}H_{22}O_{11}(aq) + H_2O(l)$

Maltose is formed from glucose:

glucose → maltose + water

$2C_6H_{12}O_6(aq) \rightarrow C_{12}H_{22}O_{11}(aq) + H_2O(l)$

Shorthand formula for maltose

These reactions are examples of **condensation polymerisation**. Further condensation polymerisation of glucose results in the formation of starch.

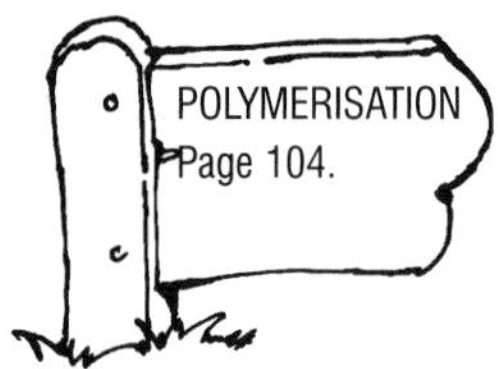

Carbohydrates have a vital function in all living organisms: they provide energy. In respiration, carbohydrates are oxidised to carbon dioxide and water with the release of energy. Living organisms also respire fats, oils and proteins.

Starch, glycogen and cellulose

Starch and **glycogen** are food substances. Starch is stored in plant cells and glycogen is stored in animal cells. The structure of starch is shown at the top of the next column. **Cellulose** is the substance of which plant cell walls are composed. All these substances are carbohydrates. They are **polysaccharides**, that is, their molecules contain a large number of glucose rings (several hundred).

Starch and glycogen make good food stores because they are only slightly soluble in water. They can remain in the cells of an organism without dissolving until energy is needed. Then cells convert starch and glycogen into glucose, which is soluble, and respire the glucose.

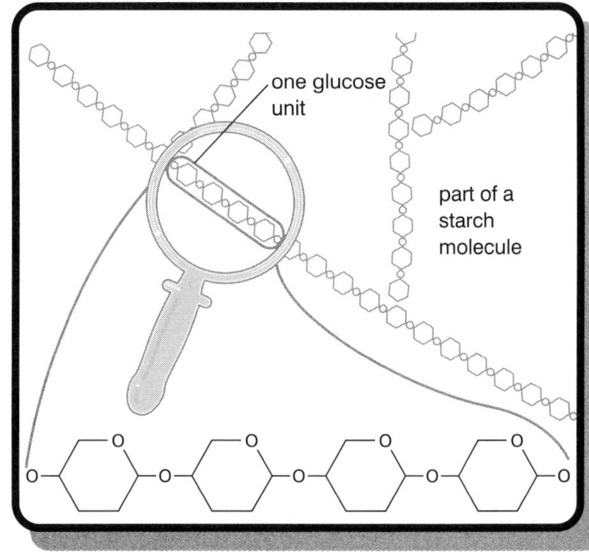

Structure of starch

20.2 Fats and oils

Fats and oils are together called **lipids**. They contain carbon, hydrogen and oxygen only. Most fats are solid and most oils are liquid at room temperature. Fats and oils are insoluble in water. Their functions are as follows.

- ★ **Source of energy:** the oxidation of lipids provides about twice as much energy per gram as the oxidation of carbohydrates.
- ★ **Thermal insulation:** mammals have a layer of fat under the skin which acts as insulation.
- ★ **Protection:** delicate organs, such as the kidneys, are protected by a layer of fat.
- ★ **Vitamins:** foods containing lipids provide vitamins which are insoluble in water but soluble in lipids.
- ★ **Cell membranes:** lipids are incorporated in cell membranes.

Saturated and unsaturated fats and oils

Fats and oils are mixtures of esters. The esters are formed between **glycerol** and **fatty acids** (carboxylic acids with long alkyl groups, such as hexadecanoic acid, $C_{15}H_{31}CO_2H$).

CH_2OH	$CH_2OCOC_{15}H_{31}$
$\vert$	$\vert$
$CHOH$	$CHOCOC_{15}H_{31}$
$\vert$	$\vert$
CH_2OH	$CH_2OCOC_{15}H_{31}$
glycerol	glycerol trihexadecanoate (a fat)

The fatty acid may be

- **saturated** (with no carbon–carbon double bonds)
- **unsaturated** (with one carbon–carbon double bond in the molecule)
- **polyunsaturated** (with more than one carbon–carbon double bond).

Fats are called saturated, unsaturated or polyunsaturated fats, depending on the number of double bonds in a molecule of the fatty acid. Animal fats contain a large proportion of saturated esters; plant oils contain a large proportion of unsaturated esters. Many scientists believe that eating a lot of saturated fats increases the risk of heart disease.

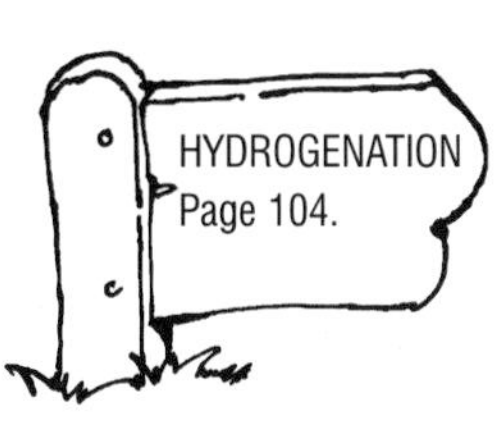

Unsaturated oils can be converted into saturated fats by **catalytic hydrogenation.** The vapour of the oil is passed with hydrogen over a nickel catalyst.

Oils are immiscible with water. When an **emulsifier** is added, oil and water mix to form an emulsion (see page 61).

20.3 Proteins

Proteins are compounds of carbon, hydrogen, oxygen, nitrogen and sometimes sulphur.

Proteins:

- are the compounds from which new tissues are made
- include enzymes and hormones
- can be used as a source of energy in respiration.

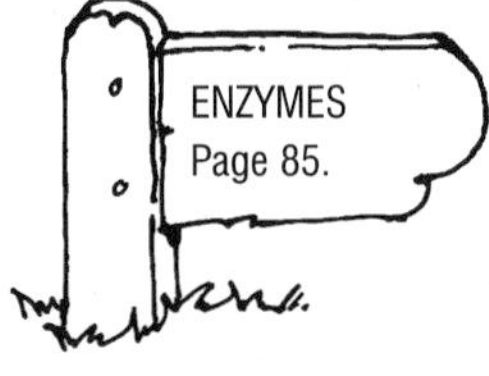

Proteins have large molecules. A protein molecule consists of a large number of **amino acid** groups. There are about 20 amino acids. The simplest is glycine, $H_2NCH_2CO_2H$. The general formula of an amino acid is shown below.

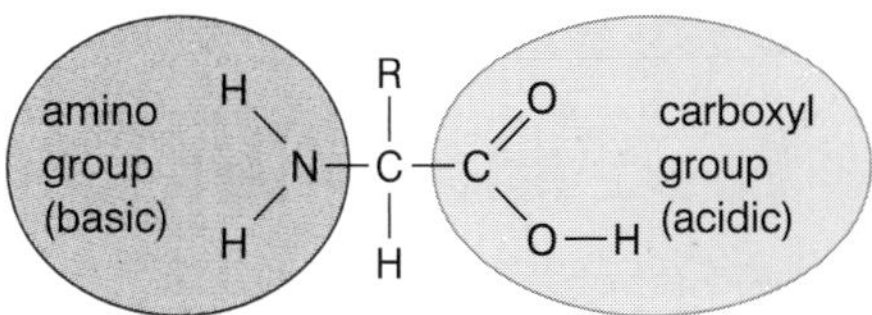

R is a different group in each amino acid; it can be —H, $—CH_3$, $—CH_2OH$, —SH and many other groups.

The basic amino group of one amino acid can react with the acidic carboxyl group of another amino acid to form a peptide and water.

$$H_2NCH_2CO_2H + H_2NCH_2CO_2H \rightarrow H_2NCH_2CONHCH_2CO_2H + H_2O$$

The bond that has formed between the two amino acids, —CONH—, is called the **peptide link**. Its structure is:

```
  O   H
  ‖   |
—C—N—
```

The peptide formed can use its amino group and its carboxyl group to make more peptide links and form a long chain. The reaction is an example of **condensation polymerisation;** a molecule of water is formed with each link. We can show this by an equation, using a different shape for each different amino acid.

□ + △ → □–△ + H_2O

□–△ + ⬡ + ○ → ⬡–□–△–○ + $2H_2O$

⬡–□–△–○ + △ + ▽ → △–⬡–□–△–○–▽ + $2H_2O$

Building up a protein molecule by condensation polymerisation

A protein molecule contains over 100 amino acid groups.

Diet

Animals are able to make some amino acids in their bodies. The other amino acids which they need to build proteins must be supplied in the diet. These are called **essential amino acids**.

A protein which contains all the essential amino acids is called a **first class protein**. Meat, fish, cheese and soya beans supply first class protein. A protein which lacks some essential amino acids is called a **second class protein**. Such proteins are in flour, rice and oatmeal.

20.4 Food additives

In food processing, many substances are added. They are called **food additives**.

Changing the taste of food

★ **Flavourings** are the largest group of food additives.

★ **Sweeteners** include saccharin, sorbitol and aspartame. (Sucrose is a food, not an additive.)

★ **Flavour enhancers** are substances which stimulate the taste buds, such as monosodium glutamate, MSG.

Changing the colour of food

★ When food is processed, it may lose some of its colour, and the manufacturer will want to add a food dye. Colourings are not added to baby foods.

Changing the texture of food

★ **Emulsifiers and stabilisers** are used to keep oil and water in emulsion.

★ **Anti-caking agents** absorb water without becoming wet.

★ **Humectants** keep foods moist.

★ **Gelling agents** make jams and desserts set.

Preserving food

★ **Anti-oxidants** are added to some foods to prevent oxidation of fats and oils to unpleasant-smelling acids. Anti-oxidants include sulphur dioxide, sulphites, BHA and BHT.

Controls on additives

Before an additive may be used, it must be approved by the Government. Additives which have been approved by the European Community (EC) are given **E-numbers**.

round-up

How much have you improved?
Work out your improvement index on page 141.

1 What compounds are formed when molecules of the following compounds combine?
a) monosaccharides **b)** amino acids
c) glycerol and fatty acids [5]

2 a) What type of compound is this? [1]

$$H_2N-\underset{\underset{CH_2-SH}{|}}{\overset{\overset{H}{|}}{C}}-CO_2H$$

b) Draw the structural formula of the compound (other than water) that is formed when two molecules of the above substance react. [2]
c) What type of linkage is formed in the reaction? [1]
d) What type of compound is the substance in **b)**? [1]
e) What further reaction or reactions can this substance undergo? [2]

3 What type of food additive might be used by the following?
a) a ham manufacturer who wants to increase the weight of his hams by injecting water into them [1]
b) a chef who wants to enhance the taste of her dishes [1]
c) a manufacturer who wants to produce a low-calorie sweet drink [1]
d) a manufacturer of sausages [1]

4 a) Identify the fats and the oils in this list: hard margarine, soft margarine, butter, lard, cooking oil. [5]
b) What is the main difference between fats and oils? [2]

5 'Heltho' margarine is advertised as being 'low in saturated fats'.
a) What is a saturated fat? [1]
b) Name a food that contains a high proportion of saturated fat. [1]
c) Why is 'Heltho' margarine supposed to be good for health? [1]

Dyes

21

preview

At the end of this topic you will know:

- **some of the different types of dyes**
- **the methods used to apply them.**

How much do you already know? Work out your score on page 142.

Test yourself

1 a) What job is performed by a mordant? [1]
b) How does a mordant act? [3]

2 The use of indigo as a dye involves four stages:
A immersion of the fabric in the dye solution
B reduction
C oxidation
D absorption of the dye by the fibres.
Arrange these stages in the correct order. [4]

3 Name two types of dye. [2]

Have you been drawing your Mind Maps as you complete each topic? On pages 144–57 you will find Mind Maps of many topics. You may want to use some of the ideas in your own Mind Maps.

21.1 Synthetic dyes

There are two kinds of colouring materials.

★ **Pigments** are completely insoluble and are in the form of very small solid particles containing millions of molecules, for example inks and paints.

★ **Dyestuffs** are usually present as single molecules.

Natural dyes have been extracted from plant and animal sources since ancient times. Synthetic dyes are now made by the chemical industry. A group of commercial dyes must have the following properties:

- a wide range of colours
- no hazard to health in manufacture or in use
- reliable and reproducible results
- fastness to light, water, perspiration and heat
- a competitive price.

21.2 Mordants

In order to be 'fast', a dye must bond to the fibres of the fabric. The bonds may be strong covalent bonds, or weaker intermolecular forces of attraction. The fastness of natural dyes is improved by treating the fabric with a **mordant**, such as alum (aluminium ammonium sulphate or aluminium potassium sulphate). The fabric is soaked in a dilute solution of ammonia and then in a solution of alum. A gelatinous white precipitate of aluminium hydroxide forms in the pores of the cloth.

$Al^{3+}(aq)$	+	$3OH^{-}(aq)$	$\rightarrow$	$Al(OH)_3(s)$
(from alum solution)		(from ammonia solution)		(precipitated in the fibres of the cloth)

When the mordanted fabric is immersed in a solution of a dye , the dye can bond to particles of aluminium hydroxide dispersed between the fibres of the cloth. Different mordants can give different colours with the same dye. Modern synthetic dyes do not need mordants.

21.3 Vat dyes

Blue denim is dyed with indigo. Indigo is a **vat dye**; it is insoluble and must be converted into a soluble substance before it can be used to dye cloth. The process, which was traditionally carried out in vats, is as follows.

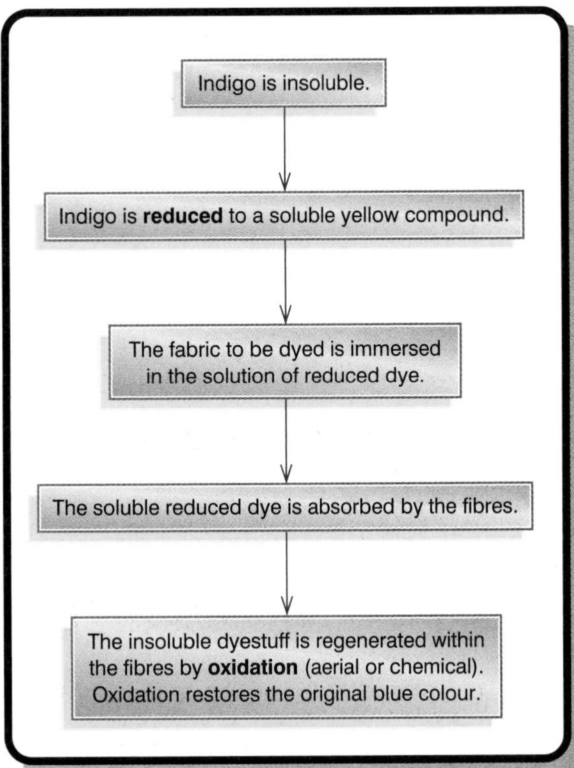

Using a vat dye

21.4 Some other types of dyes

Sulphur dyes

Sulphur dyes are blue and black organic compounds containing sulphur. They are applied in the same way as vat dyes and are colour-fast.

Azo dyes

Azo dyes are formed by allowing two chemicals to react within the fabric. Azo dyes are insoluble and very water-fast. Some are used as food colourings.

Direct dyes

Direct dyes are water soluble and can dye cellulose fibres without the aid of a mordant. They do not have great water-fastness.

Fibre-reactive dyes

Fibre-reactive dyes or Procion dyes form covalent bonds to synthetic fibres and are therefore fast dyes. They are water soluble, easy to use and offer a wide colour range.

Disperse dyes

These insoluble dyes are used as a suspension or **dispersion**. In the dyeing process, the particles are absorbed into the fibres. These dyes are used on fabrics that are impermeable to water and cannot be dyed with water soluble dyes, such as polyesters.

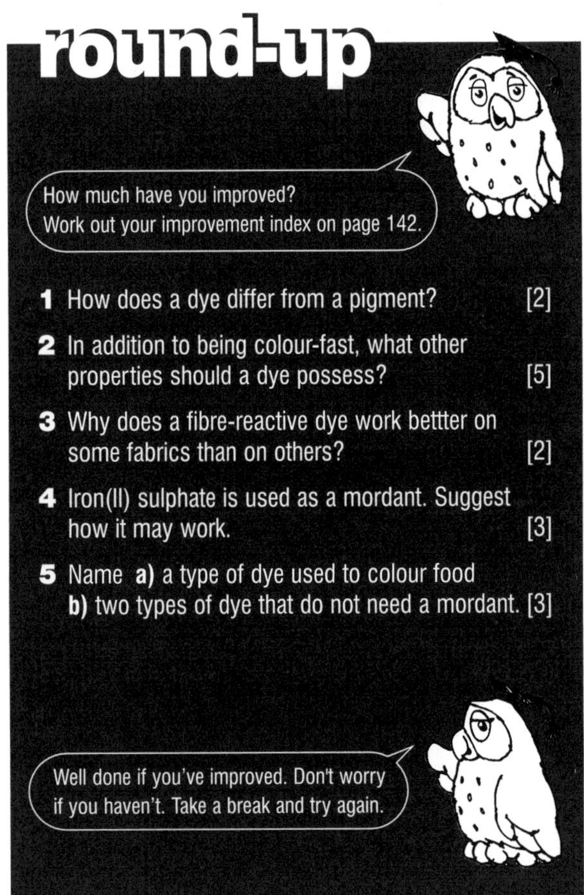

round-up

How much have you improved?
Work out your improvement index on page 142.

1. How does a dye differ from a pigment? [2]
2. In addition to being colour-fast, what other properties should a dye possess? [5]
3. Why does a fibre-reactive dye work bettter on some fabrics than on others? [2]
4. Iron(II) sulphate is used as a mordant. Suggest how it may work. [3]
5. Name **a)** a type of dye used to colour food **b)** two types of dye that do not need a mordant. [3]

Well done if you've improved. Don't worry if you haven't. Take a break and try again.

Answers

1 Test yourself (page 10)

Matter and the kinetic theory

1. solid (✓), liquid (✓), gas (✓).
2. A pure solid melts at a fixed temperature (✓); an impure solid melts over a range of temperature (✓).
3. Evaporation takes place over a range of temperature (✓). Boiling takes place at a certain temperature (✓).
4. Bubbles of vapour appear in the body of the liquid (✓).
5. In a pressure cooker, water boils at a temperature above 100°C (✓) and foods cook faster at higher temperature (✓).
6. On a high mountain, air pressure is lower than at sea level (✓), and water boils below 100°C (✓).
7. **a)** Both change shape when a force is applied (✓).
   b) When the force ceases, a plastic material retains its new shape (✓), but an elastic material returns to its previous shape (✓).
8. Crystals consist of a regular arrangement of particles (✓). As a result the surfaces are smooth (✓) and reflect light (✓).
9. The particles that make up the solid gain enough energy to break free from the attractive forces (✓) between particles which maintain the solid structure, and the particles move independently (✓).
10. In a gas, e.g. steam, the molecules are very much further apart (✓) than in a liquid (✓).
11. Particles (✓) of salt dissolve (✓) and spread out (✓) through the soup.

Your score: ☐ out of 25

1 Round-up (page 12)

Matter and the kinetic theory

1. At A, the temperature of the liquid is rising (✓). At B, the temperature stays constant because the liquid is boiling (✓) and all the heat is being used to convert liquid into gas (✓).
2. At C, the temperature of the solid is rising as it is heated (✓). At D the solid starts to melt (✓), and the temperature stays constant at the melting point (✓) while heat is used in the conversion of solid into liquid (✓). At E all the solid has melted (✓), and the temperature of the liquid rises as it is heated (✓). The sharp melting point shows that the solid is a pure substance (✓).
3. Under pressure, water boils at a temperature above 100°C (✓) and the hotter steam kills more bacteria than steam at 100°C (✓).
4. Most of a gas is space; the molecules are far apart (✓).
5. There is so much space between the molecules of a gas (✓) that it is easy for them to move closer together (✓) when the pressure is increased.
6. One example, e.g. heating a lump of bread dough, e.g. air in a hot air balloon expands and is less dense than the air outside the balloon (✓).
7. One example, e.g. increase in the pressure of air in car tyres, e.g. removing a dent from a table tennis ball by warming, e.g. a balloon filled with gas bursts if it is heated (✓).
8. The liquid vaporises (✓). A gas diffuses (✓) to occupy the whole of its container, i.e. the whole of the room (✓).
9. Liquids need energy to vaporise (see page 10) (✓). Aftershave lotion takes this energy from the skin (✓).

Your score: ☐ out of 22

Your improvement index: $\frac{\square/22}{\square/25} \times 100\% = \square\%$

2 Test yourself (page 13)

Elements, compounds and equations

1. An element is a pure substance (✓) that cannot be split up (✓) into simpler substances (✓).
2. Zinc reacts with dilute acids (✓) to form hydrogen (✓) and a salt (✓). It forms the cation Zn^{2+} (✓). The oxide and hydroxide are basic (✓) (and amphoteric). The chloride is a solid salt (✓). It forms no hydride (✓).
3. In diamond every carbon atom is covalently bonded to four other carbon atoms (✓). In graphite carbon atoms are covalently bonded together in layers (✓). The layers are joined by weak forces (✓), so one layer can slide over another (✓).
4. Thermal decomposition (✓), electrolysis (✓).
5. 14 (✓)
6. $2Na(s) + 2H_2O(l) \rightarrow 2NaOH(aq) + H_2(g)$
   (✓✓✓✓ for state symbols, ✓✓✓✓ for balancing)

Your score: ☐ out of 25

2 Round-up (page 16)

Elements, compounds and equations

1. Metallic (✓)
2. Non-metallic (✓)
3. Metallic (✓)
4. Non-metallic (✓)

5 For example:
a) Appearance: sulphur is dull, whereas copper is shiny (✓).
b) Sulphur is shattered by hammering, whereas copper can be hammered into shape (✓).
c) Sulphur does not conduct heat or electricity, whereas copper is a good thermal and electrical conductor (✓).
d) Sulphur is not sonorous; copper is sonorous (✓).

6 The appearance of the mixture (speckled yellow and grey) is different from that of the compound (dark grey throughout) (✓). The iron in the mixture reacts with dilute acids to give hydrogen (✓). The compound, iron(II) sulphide, reacts with acids to give hydrogen sulphide (✓), with a characteristic smell. The iron in the mixture is attracted to a magnet (✓).

7 45 (✓)

8 $CaCO_3(s) + 2HCl(aq) \rightarrow CaCl_2(aq) + CO_2(g) + H_2O(l)$
(✓✓✓ for state symbols, ✓ for factor 2)

9 $Fe^{2+}(aq) + 2OH^-(aq) \rightarrow Fe(OH)_2(s)$ (✓✓✓)

Your score: ☐ out of 20

Your improvement index: $\frac{\square/20}{\square/25} \times 100\% = \square\%$

3 Test yourself (page 17)

Separating substances

1 a) Use a coarse seive to hold back the gravel and let sand through (✓).
b) Centrifuge (✓)
c) Dissolve the mixture of A and B in hot water (✓). Cool (✓). Filter to obtain A (✓). Evaporate the solution to obtain B (✓).
d) Use a separating funnel (✓). Olive oil forms a layer on top of vinegar.
e) Stir with warm water to dissolve the salt (✓). Filter to obtain the diamonds (✓).
f) Fractional distillation (✓)

Your score: ☐ out of 10

3 Round-up (page 19)

Separating substances

1 Use a magnet or a magnetic field (✓) to attract the steel cans but not the aluminium cans (✓).

2 Stir the mixture of C and D with ethanol (✓). Filter to obtain D (✓). Evaporate the solution to obtain C (✓). Ethanol is flammable (✓): evaporate over a water bath (✓).

3 By fractional distillation (✓) (see page 19). Fractions with low boiling points are collected from the top of the distillation column (✓), while fractions with high boiling points are collected from the bottom of the column (✓).

4 The chromatogram shows that P1 contains A and C (✓), while P2 contains A and B (✓).

5 Allow to settle in a tank so that the oil forms a layer on top of the water (✓). Then carefully withdraw the oil from the top of the tank (✓) by suction (✓).

Your score: ☐ out of 15

Your improvement index: $\frac{\square/15}{\square/10} \times 100\% = \square\%$

4 Test yourself (page 20)

The structure of the atom

1 The number of protons = number of electrons (✓) and the positive charge on a proton has the same value as the negative charge on an electron (✓).

2 a) 19 (✓) **b)** 20 (✓)

3 Their chemical reactions are identical because it is the electrons that determine the chemical behaviour (✓), and isotopes have the same electron arrangement (✓).

4 a) The number of protons (= number of electrons) in an atom of the element (✓).
b) The number of protons + neutrons in an atom of the element (✓✓).

5 a) ${}^{31}_{15}P$ (✓✓) **b)** ${}^{39}_{19}K$ (✓✓)

6 Two in the first shell (✓), four in the second shell (✓).

Your score: ☐ out of 15

4 Round-up (page 22)

The structure of the atom

1 a) 27 (✓) **b)** 5 (✓) **c)** 0.7 (✓) **d)** 4 (✓)

2 a) ${}^{75}_{33}As$ (✓) **b)** ${}^{235}_{92}U$ (✓), ${}^{238}_{92}U$ (✓), ${}^{239}_{92}U$ (✓)

3 a) 63.6 (✓) **b)** 69.8 (✓)

4

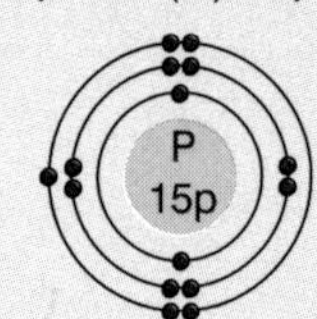

(✓)

5 a)

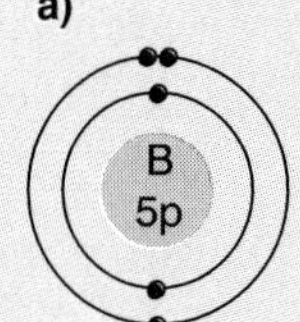

b)

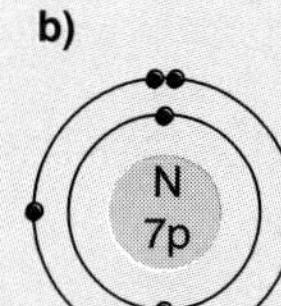

c)

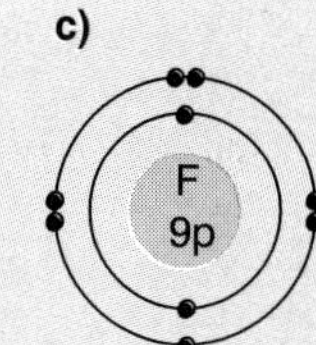

d)

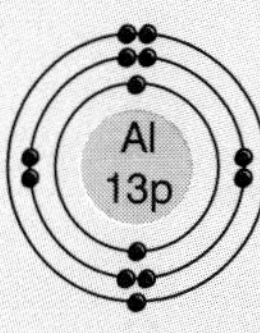

(✓✓✓✓)

Your score: ☐ out of 15

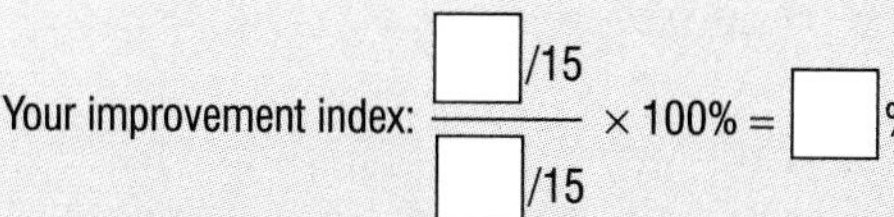

5 Test yourself (page 24)

Electrolysis

1 **A** (✓) **C** (✓)

2 **A** (✓) **B** (✓) **D** (✓)

3 **a)** A compound which conducts electricity (✓) when molten (✓) or in solution (✓) and is split up in the process (✓).
b) An object which conducts electricity into or out of a cell (✓).

4 **a)** Cation – a positively charged atom or group of atoms (✓).
Anion – a negatively charged atom or group of atoms (✓).
For examples see table on page 25 (✓✓✓✓).
b) Ions are charged (✓) and move towards the electrode of opposite charge (✓).
c) In the solid the ions are held in place in a crystal structure (✓). In solution, they are free to move (✓).

5 If water is present, hydrogen ions are discharged in preference to sodium (see page 26) (✓).

6 Chromium plate is not easily chipped off, as paint would be on door handles, etc. (✓).

7 **a)** Gold plate is cheaper than gold (✓).
b) Gold does not tarnish as brass does (✓).

8 **a)** The melting point of the mixture is much lower than that of aluminium oxide (✓).
b) Cathode: $Al^{3+}(l) + 3e^- \rightarrow Al(l)$ (✓✓)
Anode: $O^{2-}(l) \rightarrow O(g) + 2e^-$ (✓✓)
followed by: $2O(g) \rightarrow O_2(g)$ (✓)
c) It requires a lot of energy (✓).

Your score: ☐ out of 31

5 Round-up (page 28)

Electrolysis

1 **a)** Copper(II) ions are discharged in preference to the ions of more reactive metals (see page 26) (✓).
b) Metals which are less reactive than copper, e.g. silver and gold, do not go into solution (✓); they are part of the anode sludge (✓).

2 **a)** The coating is even (✓) and it can be as thin as required (✓).
b) Your diagram should similar to be the one on page 25, using an iron nail as cathode and a solution of e.g. nickel(II) sulphate as electrolyte (✓✓).

3 **a)** Bromine (✓) **b)** Positive electrode/anode (✓)
c) Hydrogen (✓) **d)** Hydroxide ion (✓)
e) Cathode: $H^+(aq) + e^- \rightarrow H(g)$ (✓✓)
followed by: $2H(g) \rightarrow H_2(g)$ (✓)
Anode: $Br^-(aq) \rightarrow Br(aq) + e^-$ (✓✓)
followed by: $2Br(aq) \rightarrow Br_2(aq)$ (✓)

4 **a)** Cathode: copper (✓), anode: oxygen (✓).
b) Cathode: $Cu^{2+}(aq) + 2e^- \rightarrow Cu(s)$ (✓✓)
Anode: $OH^-(aq) \rightarrow OH(aq) + e^-$ (✓✓)
followed by: $4OH(aq) \rightarrow O_2(g) + 2H_2O(l)$ (✓✓✓)
c) Oxygen is not evolved at the anode (✓). Copper dissolves from the anode (✓).
d) Cathode: $Cu^{2+}(aq) + 2e^- \rightarrow Cu(s)$ (✓✓)
Anode: $Cu(s) \rightarrow Cu^{2+}(aq) + 2e^-$ (✓✓)

Your score: ☐ out of 32

Your improvement index: $\frac{\square/32}{\square/31}$ × 100% = ☐ %

6 Test yourself (page 29)

The chemical bond

1 Positive (✓), negative (✓), electrostatic (✓), crystal (✓).

2 Each atom of E loses two electrons to become E^{2+} (2.8) (✓).
Each atom of Q gains one electron to become Q^-(2.8.8) (✓).
The compound EQ_2 is formed (✓).

3

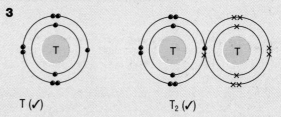

T (✓)

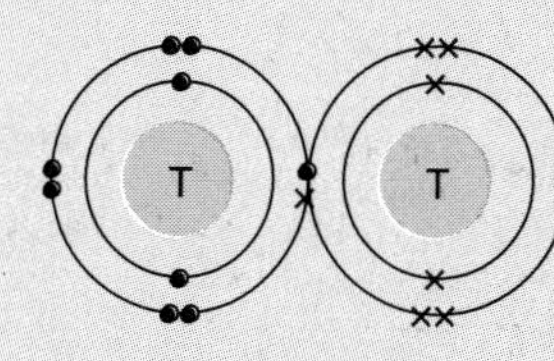

T_2 (✓)

4 **a)** Magnesium bromide (✓) **b)** Iron(II) chloride (✓)
c) Iron(III) chloride (✓) **d)** Sodium oxide (✓)
e) Barium sulphate (✓)

5 **a)** KBr (✓) **b)** $CaCO_3$ (✓) **c)** PbO (✓) **d)** $PbSO_4$ (✓)
e) AgCl (✓)

Your score: ☐ out of 19

6 Round-up (page 33)

The chemical bond

1 **a)** Sodium ions, Na^+ (✓) and chloride ions, Cl^- (✓).
b) Electrostatic attraction (✓).
c) A three-dimensional arrangement (✓) of alternate Na^+ ions and Cl^- ions (✓).

2

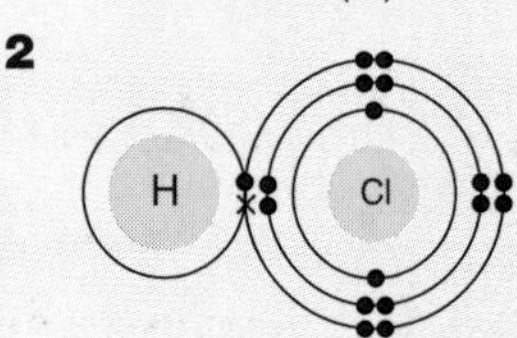

(✓✓)

3 For example, one of: **a)** O_2, CH_4 (✓) **b)** $I_2(s)$, $CO_2(s)$ (✓)
c) Diamond, graphite, silicon(IV) oxide (✓).

4 **a)** Calcium hydroxide (✓) **b)** Sodium sulphite (✓)
c) Copper(II) carbonate (✓) **d)** Magnesium hydrogencarbonate (✓)
e) Potassium nitrate (✓)

5 **a)** NH_4NO_3 (✓) **b)** Na_2SO_4 (✓) **c)** $(NH_4)_2SO_4$ (✓)
d) Al_2O_3 (✓) **e)** $Zn(OH)_2$ (✓)

Your score: ☐ out of 20

Your improvement index: $\frac{\square /20}{\square /19} \times 100\% = \square \%$

7 Test yourself (page 34)

The periodic table

1 **a)** He, Ne, Ar, Kr, Xe (✓), a set of very unreactive gases present in air (✓).
b) Group 0 (✓)
c) **(i)** They have a full outer shell of electrons (✓).
(ii) They are very unreactive (✓). (Some take part in no chemical reactions. Krypton and xenon react with fluorine.)

2 Group 2 (✓)

3 Group 7 (✓)

4 Group 1 (✓)

5 **a)** Fluorine (✓), chlorine (✓), bromine (✓), iodine (✓).
b) Group 7 (✓) **c)** Decreases (✓)
d) **(i)** NaF (✓), NaCl (✓), NaBr (✓), NaI (✓)
(ii) FeF_3 (✓), $FeCl_3$ (✓), $FeBr_3$ (✓), FeI_2 (✓)

6 An element in the block of the periodic table between Groups 2 and 3 (✓).
See page 35 (✓).

7 Gain (✓), loss (✓), loss (✓).

Your score: ☐ out of 27

7 Round-up (page 39)

The periodic table

1 Magnesium chloride is a three-dimensional structure of ions (✓) with strong forces of attraction between them (✓). Tetrachloromethane consists of individual covalent molecules (✓) with only weak forces of attraction between them (✓).

2 **a)** Na (✓), Mg (✓) **b)** Na (✓), Mg (✓), Al (✓)
c) **(i)** Argon (✓) **(ii)** Chlorine (✓) **d)** Silicon (✓)

3 **a)** Na (✓) **b)** S (✓) **c)** Al (✓) **d)** S (✓)

4 Na_2O (✓), MgO (✓), Al_2O_3 (✓), SiO_2 (✓)

5 They do not exist (✓).

6 They both have one electron in the outermost shell (✓). It is the electrons in the outermost shell that decide chemical reactions (✓).

7 **a)** Basic (✓), ionic solid (✓), formula RaO (✓).
b) Reacts readily to form hydrogen (✓) and the alkali radium hydroxide (✓), $Ra(OH)_2$ (✓).
c) Reacts readily to form hydrogen (✓) and a solution of the ionic compound (✓) radium chloride (✓), $RaCl_2$ (✓).

8 **a)** Hydrogen astatide is a gas (✓), a covalent compound (✓) which forms an acidic solution in water (✓).
b) Astatine reacts slowly with sodium (✓) to form the ionic solid (✓) sodium astatide (✓), NaAt (✓) .

9 **a)** Chlorine + sodium iodide → iodine + sodium chloride (✓✓)
$Cl_2(aq) + NaI(aq) \rightarrow I_2(aq) + NaCl(aq)$ (✓✓)
b) Bromine + potassium iodide → iodine + potassium bromide (✓✓)
$Br_2(aq) + KI(aq) \rightarrow I_2(aq) + KBr(aq)$ (✓✓)

10 Dissolve a little of each solid in distilled (✓) water (✓). To each solution (✓) add chlorine water (✓) followed by a little of the organic solvent (✓).
Potassium chloride – no change (✓). Potassium bromide – brown colour appears in the solution (✓), forms an orange solution in the solvent (✓). Potassium iodide – black colour appears (✓), turns violet in the solvent (✓).

11 B (✓) C (✓)

12 a) (i) Iron oxide (✓) (ii) Aluminium (✓)
b) (i) Oxygen (✓) (ii) Tin sulphide (✓)
c) (i) Tin oxide (✓) (ii) Carbon (✓)

Your score: ☐ out of 66

Your improvement index: $\frac{\square/66}{\square/27} \times 100\% = \square\%$

8 Test yourself (page 40)

Acids, bases and salts

1 a) SA (✓) b) WA (✓) c) WB (✓) d) WB (✓)
e) WA (✓) f) N (✓) g) SB (✓)

2 You could compare the rates (✓) at which hydrogen is given off (✓) in the reactions of the two acids with magnesium or another metal (✓),
or the rates (✓) at which carbon dioxide is given off (✓) in the reactions of the acids with a carbonate or hydrogencarbonate (✓).

3 a) Hydrochloric acid (✓) b) For example, magnesium hydroxide (✓) c) Citric acid (✓) d) Ammonia (✓)

4 a) Sodium hydroxide converts grease into soap (✓).
b) Sodium hydroxide is a stronger base than ammonia (✓).
c) Wear glasses (✓) and rubber gloves (✓).
d) Sodium hydroxide would be too dangerous or corrosive (✓).
e) The saponification of fats by a weak base, e.g. ammonia, is very slow (✓).

Your score: ☐ out of 20

8 Round-up (page 47)

Acids, bases and salts

1 a) A solid base can be separated by filtration (✓).
b) If any acid remains it will be concentrated in the evaporation step (✓).
c) (i) Note when the evolution of hydrogen stops (✓).
(ii) Test with indicator paper to find out when the solution is no longer acidic (✓).
(iii) Note when the evolution of carbon dioxide stops (✓).

2 a) Zinc + sulphuric acid → zinc sulphate + hydrogen (✓✓)
b) Cobalt oxide + sulphuric acid → cobalt sulphate + water (✓✓)
c) Nickel carbonate + hydrochloric acid → nickel chloride + carbon dioxide + water (✓✓✓)
d) Potassium hydroxide + nitric acid → potassium nitrate + water (✓✓)
e) Ammonia + nitric acid → ammonium nitrate (✓✓)

3 a) Mix e.g. lead(II) nitrate solution and sodium sulphate solution (✓✓).
b) Lead(II) nitrate + sodium sulphate → lead(II) sulphate + sodium nitrate (✓✓✓✓)
$Pb(NO_3)_2(aq) + Na_2SO_4(aq) \rightarrow PbSO_4(s) + 2NaNO_3(aq)$ (✓✓✓✓)
$Pb^{2+}(aq) + SO_4^{2-}(aq) \rightarrow PbSO_4(s)$ (✓✓✓)
c) Do not touch the lead salts with your hands. Wash your hands after the experiment (✓).

4 a) Sodium sulphate + water (✓✓).
b) Ammonium chloride, no other product (✓).
c) Zinc chloride + hydrogen (✓✓).
d) Copper(II) sulphate + water (✓✓).
e) Calcium chloride + carbon dioxide + water (✓✓✓).

Your score: ☐ out of 40

Your improvement index: $\frac{\square/40}{\square/20} \times 100\% = \square\%$

9 Test yourself (page 48)

Air

1 More water vapour (✓), more carbon dioxide (✓), no oxygen (✓), same amount of nitrogen (✓).

2 21% O_2 (✓), 78% N_2 (✓)

3 Two from, for example, oxyacetylene flame, steel-making, sewage treatment, combatting pollution (✓✓).

4 Combustion (✓)

5 It makes a glowing splint burn more brightly (✓).

6 **A** = S (✓), **B** = Na (✓), **C** = Mg (✓), **D** = C (✓)

7 Two from, for example, lightning, vehicle engines, Haber process, fixation by bacteria (✓✓).

8 For example, dissolving in oceans, photosynthesis (✓✓).

9 Pass through limewater, $Ca(OH)_2(aq)$ (✓). A white precipitate shows that the gas is carbon dioxide (✓).

10 Four from, for example, carbon monoxide – vehicle engines; sulphur dioxide – combustion of fuels; hydrocarbons – combustion of fuels; NO_x – vehicle engines; dust – combustion of fuels, mining, factories; lead compounds – vehicle engines (✓✓✓✓✓✓✓✓).

Your score: ☐ out of 28

9 Round-up (page 56)

Air

1 a) **(i)** Zinc oxide (✓) **(ii)** Carbon (✓)
b) **(i)** Carbon (✓) **(ii)** Zinc oxide (✓)

2 a) Airships need to be lighter than air (✓).
b) Helium is a noble gas (✓); hydrogen forms an explosive mixture with air (✓).

3 a) Poisonous (✓); removed by soil bacteria (✓).
b) Causes respiratory difficulties (✓); acid rain (✓).
c) Causes respiratory difficulties (✓); washed out in rain (✓).

4 a) From vehicle exhausts, power stations, factories (✓).
b) One of the causes of acid rain (✓).
c) Catalytic converters (✓).

5 a) See page 53 (✓✓).
b) See page 53 (✓✓).
c) **(i)** Icecaps will melt (✓) **(ii)** Flooding (✓)
(iii) Decrease in wheat crop (✓).

6 Tall chimneys carry pollutants away from the area of the power station (✓). Taller chimneys do not prevent acid rain (✓).

7 a) Acidic water is released suddenly in the spring thaw (✓).
b) Calcium hydroxide + sulphuric acid → calcium sulphate + water (✓✓)
$Ca(OH)_2(s) + H_2SO_4(aq) \rightarrow CaSO_4(aq) + 2H_2O(l)$ (✓✓)
c) Neutralisation (✓)

8 a) Iron + sulphuric acid → iron(II) sulphate + water (✓✓)
b) Calcium carbonate + sulphuric acid → calcium sulphate + carbon dioxide + water (✓✓✓)
c) Calcium hydroxide + sulphuric acid → calcium sulphate + water (✓✓)
(Nitric acid can be stated instead of sulphuric acid.)

9 a) Carbon dioxide (✓), carbon monoxide (✓), carbon (✓), water (✓).
b) Oxides of nitrogen (✓), hydrocarbons (✓), sulphur dioxide (✓).

Your score: ☐ out of 45

Your improvement index: $\frac{\square/45}{\square/28} \times 100\% = \square\%$

10 Test yourself (page 57)

Water

1 Evaporation (✓), respiration (✓), transpiration (✓).

2 Carbon dioxide dissolves in rainwater (✓).

3 Limestone reacts with acidic rainwater to form the soluble salt calcium hydrogencarbonate (✓).

Calcium carbonate + carbon dioxide + water → calcium hydrogencarbonate (✓✓)
$CaCO_3(s) + CO_2(aq) + H_2O(l) \rightarrow Ca(HCO_3)_2(aq)$ (✓✓).

4 a) Water turns anhydrous copper(II) sulphate (✓) from white to blue (✓) (*or* anhydrous cobalt(II) chloride from blue to pink).
b) Pure water boils at 100°C (or freezes at 0°C) (✓).

5 For example, aquatic plants (✓), fish (✓), aerobic bacteria (✓).

6 Three from, for example, filtration, sedimentation, coagulation, bacterial oxidation, chlorination (✓✓✓).

7 A soap ion has a polar head (✓) which dissolves in water (✓) and a non-polar tail (✓) which dissolves in oil (✓). The soap ion forms a bridge (✓) between oil and water (✓). Repulsion between soap ions (✓) keeps oil droplets in emulsion (✓).

8 a) It is easy to get a lather with soap in soft water (✓); it is difficult in hard water (✓), which forms a scum (✓).
b) Hard water contains calcium ions and magnesium ions (✓).

9 Two from: add washing soda (✓); add sodium carbonate-10-water (accept sodium carbonate) (✓); pass through an ion-exchange resin (✓).

Your score: ☐ out of 32

10 Round-up (page 66)

Water

1 a) Small animals are eaten by predators (✓); larger predators eat the smaller predators (✓), and so on.
b) A pollutant in the water becomes incorporated into the bodies of small animals (✓). A predator which eats many small animals has a higher concentration of the pollutant in its body (✓). A larger predator eats many smaller predators and builds up a still higher concentration of the pollutant in its body, and so on up the food chain (✓).

2 A rise in temperature decreases the solubility of oxygen in water (✓). It makes fish (✓) and aerobic bacteria more active (✓) thus increasing the biochemical oxygen demand (✓).

3 Oil is discharged from sewers into waterways (✓). The oxidation of hydrocarbons in the oil uses up dissolved oxygen in the water (✓).

4 Modern tankers are very large (✓). Any accident that happens involves a large loss of oil (✓).

5 Disperse oil with detergents (✓), sink it with e.g. chalk (✓), absorb the oil in straw etc. (✓), contain the oil in booms and suck it up (✓).

6 a) Eutrophication leads to an increase in the growth of algae (✓).
b) Fertilisers do not accumulate as much in running water (✓).
c) (i) You cannot drink water full of algae (✓).
(ii) Propellers get entangled in algae (✓).
(iii) Fish die because decaying algae use up all the dissolved oxygen (✓).

7 a) Excess fertiliser washes off fields in the rain and passes into groundwater (✓).
b) Nitrates can be converted into nitrites which can cause 'blue baby syndrome' and stomach cancer (✓✓).

8 a) Calcium and magnesium salts (✓✓).
b) For example, add sodium carbonate crystals (✓) to precipitate calcium and magnesium ions as the insoluble carbonates (✓).
c) Soaps give a scum in hard water (✓); detergents work as well in hard water as in soft water (✓).

9 a) Sodium hydroxide saponifies grease (✓) – it converts it into glycerol and the sodium salts of fatty acids (✓).
b) Sodium hydroxide will saponify oil in your skin (✓).
c) The reaction takes place faster at a higher temperature (✓).
d) Hard water deposits calcium carbonate in the iron (✓).

10 a) A soapless detergent (✓) because soap and hard water form scum which will stick to hair (✓).
b) Calcium builds bones and teeth (✓) and also has a preventive effect against heart disease (✓).
c) The negative charges on the emulsifier ions (✓) that are attached to the oil droplets (✓) repel one another (✓).
d) The emulsified oil droplets (✓) must be removed or they will stick to the cloth again (✓).

11 a) A soap is the sodium or potassium salt of a fatty acid (✓). A soapless detergent is the sodium or potassium salt of a sulphonic acid (✓).
b) Soaps are made from fats and oils (✓), which are valuable foods (✓). Soapless detergents are made from petroleum oil (✓), of which Earth has a limited supply (✓).

12 Sedimentation (✓), filtration (✓), chlorination (✓).

13 a) A solution is transparent; a suspension is not (✓).
b) Solid material settles out of a suspension but not out of a colloid (✓).
c) A colloidal solution scatters light; a solution does not (✓).

14 a) Add a salt containing ions of opposite charge to the colloidal particles (✓).
b) Electrostatic precipitation (✓).

15 The head is polar and water-loving (✓); the tail is hydrocarbon and oil-loving (✓). The water-loving head and the oil-loving tail make a bridge between the oil and water (✓).

16 a) A membrane that allows ions and small molecules to pass through (✓) but not colloidal particles and large molecules (✓).
b) Blood is passed through a dialysis tube (✓). Particles of waste products pass through the dialysis membrane out of the blood into an aqueous solution (✓).

Your score: ☐ out of 66

Your improvement index: $\frac{\square/66}{\square/32} \times 100\% = \square\%$

11 Test yourself (page 67)

Planet Earth

1 D (✓)

2 C (✓)

3 B (✓)

4 B (✓)

5 a) Outer core (✓) **b)** Oceanic crust (✓)
c) Continental crust (✓) **d)** Atmosphere (✓)
e) Outer core (✓) **f)** Crust (✓)

6 a) Igneous (✓) **b)** Sedimentary (✓)
c) Metamorphic (✓)

7 Igneous (✓)

8 Carbon dioxide is removed from the atmosphere by photosynthesis (✓) and by dissolution in oceans (✓).

9 Three from, for example, rain, rivers, glaciers, wind (✓✓✓).

10 Plate tectonics (✓)

11 Three from, for example, to neutralise acidity in lakes and soils; used as a building material; in the manufacture of cement, quicklime, glass and iron (✓✓✓).

12 For example, silicon, glass (✓✓).

Your score: ☐ out of 25

11 Round-up (page 73)

Planet Earth

1 a) Eurasian Plate (✓). **b)** Pacific and Nazca Plates (✓✓). **c)** San Andreas Fault (✓). **d)** Eurasian and Indo-Australian Plates (✓✓). **e)** Andes (✓). **f)** Pacific Plate (✓). **g)** American Plate and African Plate (✓✓). **h)** Constructive (✓) **i)** See page 69 (✓✓✓✓✓).

2 a) Look for fossils and date the fossils (✓✓).
b) High pressure and temperature (✓✓).

3 a) Limestone (✓), sandstone (✓).
b) Basalt (✓), granite (✓), pumice (✓).
c) Marble (✓), slate (✓).

4 a) A volcanic eruption (✓).
b) An earthquake (✓).

5 a) Powdered limestone is mixed with clay or shale (✓) in a rotary kiln (✓).
b) Three from water, sand, crushed rock, calcium sulphate (✓✓✓).

6 a) The reaction can take place in the reverse direction as well as the forward direction (✓).
b) Carbon dioxide is removed by air blowing through the kiln (✓).

7 Silicon(IV) oxide (silica), calcium carbonate, sodium carbonate (✓✓✓).

Your score: ☐ out of 39

Your improvement index: $\dfrac{\square/39}{\square/25} \times 100\% = \square\%$

12 Test yourself (page 74)

Metals and alloys

1 Metals can change shape without breaking (✓), conduct heat (✓), conduct electricity (✓).

2 Three from, for example, potassium, sodium, lithium, calcium, magnesium, aluminium, zinc, iron (✓✓✓).

3 Two from, for example, silver, gold, platinum (✓✓).

4 Three from, for example, lithium, sodium, potassium, calcium, magnesium (slowly) (✓✓✓). Products are hydrogen (✓) and the metal hydroxide (✓).

5 Hydrogen (✓) and the metal chloride (✓).

6 a) Group 1 (✓) **b)** Group 2 (✓)
c) Between Group 2 and Group 3 (✓).

7 Electrolysis (✓) of the molten anhydrous chloride or oxide (✓).

8 The ore is heated with limestone and coke in a blast furnace (✓✓✓).

9 Two from, for example, aluminium, chromium, nickel (✓✓).

Your score: ☐ out of 25

12 Round-up (page 82)

Metals and alloys

1 a) $4Na(s) + O_2(g) \rightarrow 2Na_2O(s)$ (✓✓✓, one for each symbol or formula)
b) $2Mg(s) + O_2(g) \rightarrow 2MgO(s)$ (✓✓✓)
c) $2Zn(s) + O_2(g) \rightarrow 2ZnO(s)$ (✓✓✓)
d) $3Fe(s) + 2O_2(g) \rightarrow Fe_3O_4(s)$ (✓✓✓)
e) Similar to **b** (✓✓✓)
f) Similar to **b** (✓✓✓)
g) Similar to **b** (✓✓✓)

2 a) (i) $Mg(s) + 2HCl(aq) \rightarrow MgCl_2(aq) + H_2(g)$ (✓✓✓✓, one for each)
(ii) $Fe(s) + 2HCl(aq) \rightarrow FeCl_2(aq) + H_2(g)$ (✓✓✓✓)
(iii) $Sn(s) + 2HCl(aq) \rightarrow SnCl_2(s) + H_2(g)$ (✓✓✓✓)

b) (i) $Mg(s) + H_2SO_4(aq) \rightarrow MgSO_4(aq) + H_2(g)$ (✓✓✓✓)
(ii) $Fe(s) + H_2SO_4(aq) \rightarrow FeSO_4(aq) + H_2(g)$ (✓✓✓✓)

3 a) Magnesium sulphate and hydrogen (✓✓).
e) Zinc sulphate and hydrogen (✓✓).
b), c), d) and **f)** No reaction (✓✓✓✓).

4 Copper alloys do not rust (✓). They are softer than iron (✓) and easier to mint (✓).

5 a) With water, calcium reacts steadily (✓), magnesium over several days (✓), iron rusts over a period of weeks (✓), and copper does not react (✓).
b) With dilute hydrochloric acid, calcium reacts extremely vigorously (✓), magnesium reacts in minutes (✓), iron reacts at moderate speed with warm acid (✓), and copper does not react (✓).

6 a) The blue colour of the solution fades (✓) and a reddish brown solid is precipitated (✓).
Zinc + copper(II) sulphate → copper + zinc sulphate (✓✓)
$Zn(s) + CuSO_4(aq) \rightarrow Cu(s) + ZnSO_4(aq)$ (✓✓)
b) Grey crystals appear (✓).
Zinc + lead(II) nitrate → lead + zinc nitrate (✓✓)
$Zn(s) + Pb(NO_3)_2(aq) \rightarrow Pb(s) + Zn(NO_3)_2(aq)$ (✓✓)

7 $Z > X > Y$ (✓✓)

8 a) Au (✓) **b)** Na (✓), Mg (✓) **c)** Zn(✓), Fe (✓)
d) Na (✓), Mg (✓), Zn (✓), Fe (✓) **e)** Na (✓)
f) Mg (✓), Al (✓), Zn (✓), Fe (✓) (Na reacts with water instead of with Pb^{2+}).

9 A: electrolysis (✓) of the molten anhydrous (✓) chloride or oxide (✓).
B: reduction of the oxide (✓) with carbon or carbon monoxide (✓).
C: electrolysis of a solution of the chloride (✓) or reduction of the oxide (✓).
D: electrolysis (✓) of the molten anhydrous (✓) chloride or oxide (✓).

10 a) Rubidium (Group 1) reacts vigorously with cold water (✓), bursting into flame because of the hydrogen formed (✓) and forming a solution of the alkali rubidium hydroxide (✓).
b) Palladium (transition metal, resembling iron) reacts with warm dilute hydrochloric acid to form hydrogen and palladium chloride (✓✓).

11 **a)** Copper(II) oxide (✓) **b)** Aluminium oxide + iron (✓) **d)** Carbon dioxide + iron (✓) **f)** Copper + zinc sulphate solution (✓) **c)** and **e)** No reaction (✓✓).

12 For uses of aluminium related to properties, see table on page 80. (✓✓✓✓ for four uses, ✓✓✓✓ for four properties).

13 **a)** Oiling (✓) **b)** Chromium-plating (✓)
c) Galvanising (coating with zinc) (✓)
d) Stainless steel (✓) **e)** Painting (✓)
f) Sacrificial protection by e.g. zinc (✓)
g) Tin-plating (✓)

14 Saving of Earth's resources (✓), saving of energy used in extracting the metal, (✓) limiting damage to the environment through mining (✓).

Your score: ☐ out of 126

Your improvement index: $\dfrac{\square/126}{\square/25} \times 100\% = \square\%$

13 Test yourself (page 83)

Reaction speeds

1 Indigestion powders (✓) because the ratio surface area : mass is greater (✓).

2 **a)** Use smaller pieces of zinc (✓), use a more concentrated solution of acid (✓), raise the temperature (✓).
b) In smaller particles, the ratio surface area : mass is larger (✓). At a higher concentration, collisions take place more frequently between hydrogen ions and zinc (✓). At a higher temperature, the hydrogen ions have higher energy (✓), and collide more frequently with the particles of zinc (✓).

3 An apparatus with a gas syringe, see page 84, and a clock (✓✓✓✓✓).

4 A catalyst is a substance which increases the rate of a chemical reaction without being used up in the reaction (✓✓).

5 Industrial manufacturers can make their product more rapidly or at a lower temperature with the use of a catalyst (✓✓).

6 Photosynthesis, photography (✓✓).

Your score: ☐ out of 20

13 Round-up (page 86)

Reaction speeds

1 **a)** Carbon dioxide is given off (✓).
b) **(i) C (ii) A (iii) B** (✓✓).
c) The ratio of surface area : volume differs (✓).

2 Cut them into smaller pieces (✓). Use a higher temperature by using a pressure cooker (✓).

3 Use an apparatus such as that shown on page 84 (bottom) (✓). Using potato, measure the volume of oxygen formed at certain times after the start of the reaction (✓). Plot volume against time(✓). Repeat the measurement using manganese(IV) oxide. Compare the two graphs (✓).

4 You could take pieces of magnesium ribbon of the same length and therefore approximately the same mass (✓). You could find out how long it took (✓) for a piece of magnesium ribbon to react completely with a certain volume of acid (✓) of a certain concentration (✓) at different temperatures (✓). You could plot time against temperature or 1/time (rate) against temperature (✓).

5 **a)** Axes labelled correctly and units shown (✓), points plotted correctly (✓), points covering at least half of each scale (✓), smooth lines drawn through the points (✓).
b) B (✓)
c) Your line should should show very slow evolution of oxygen (✓).

6 **a)** The substance that an enzyme enables to react (✓).
b) The region of the enzyme molecule that is involved in catalysis (✓).
c) The enzyme catalyses the reaction of that substrate only (✓).
d) A substrate molecule must fit into the active site of the enzyme molecule (✓).
e) Bonds form from the substrate to the active site (✓) and weaken other bonds in the substrate (✓) which therefore reacts more readily (✓).

Your score: ☐ out of 29

Your improvement index: $\dfrac{\square/29}{\square/20} \times 100\% = \square\%$

14 Test yourself (page 87)

Tackling chemical calculations

1 **a)** 64 (✓) **b)** 80(✓) **c)** 98 (✓) **d)** 60 (✓) **e)** 249.5 (✓)

2 **a)** 2.0 mol (✓) **b)** 2 mol (✓) **c)** 0.25 mol (✓)

3 **a)** 20.1 g (✓) **b)** 24.5 g (✓) **c)** 120 g (✓)

4 **a)** $HgBr_2$ (✓) **b)** $CuCl_2$ (✓) **c)** Na_2O (✓)

5 **a)** 50% (✓) **b)** 40% (✓) **c)** 33% (✓)

6 1 g (✓)

7 **a)** 6.6 g (✓) **b)** 3.6 dm^3 at rtp (✓)

8 **a)** 1250 tonnes (✓) **b)** 9.4×10^8 dm^3 (✓)

9 Loss (✓) of £8.30 (✓)

Your score: ☐ out of 24

14 Round-up

The mole (page 89)

1 **a)** Gram, kilogram (✓) **b)** Mole (✓)

2 Weigh out **a)** the relative atomic mass in grams (✓) **b)** the relative molecular mass in grams (✓).

3 **a)** 24 g (✓) **b)** 69 g (✓) **c)** 8 g (✓) **d)** 16 g (✓) **e)** 8 g (✓) **f)** 16 g (✓)

4 **a)** 0.33 mol (✓) **b)** 0.25 mol (✓) **c)** 2.0 mol (✓) **d)** 0.010 mol (✓) **e)** 0.33 mol (✓) **f)** 20 mol (✓)

5 **a)** 88 g (✓) **b)** 980 g (✓) **c)** 117 g (✓) **d)** 37 g (✓)

6 **a)** 16 (✓) **b)** 28 (✓) **c)** 44 (✓) **d)** 64 (✓) **e)** 40 (✓) **f)** 74.5 (✓) **g)** 40 (✓) **h)** 74 (✓) **i)** 63 (✓) **j)** 123.5 (✓) **k)** 80 (✓) **l)** 159.5 (✓) **m)** 249.5 (✓)

Your score: ☐ out of 33

Formulas (page 90)

1 D (✓)

2 **A** = Mg_3N_2 (✓), **B** = Fe_3O_4 (✓), **C** = SiO_2 (✓), **D** = $MgSO_4$ (✓), **E** = C_3H_8 (✓)

3 **a)** C = 80%, H = 20% (✓✓)
b) S = 40%, O = 60% (✓✓)
c) N = 35%, H = 5%, O = 60% (✓✓✓)
d) Ca = 20%, Br = 80% (✓✓)

4 **a)** $CuSO_4.5H_2O$ (✓✓) **b)** $MgSO_4.7H_2O$ (✓✓)

Your score: ☐ out of 19

Reacting masses (page 91)

1 8.0 g (✓)

2 71 g (✓)

3 0.05 g (✓)

4 3.06 kg (✓)

5 0.26 g (✓)

Your score: ☐ out of 5

Reacting volumes of gases (page 92)

1 2.4 dm^3 (✓)

2 600 cm^3 (✓)

3 **a)** 120 dm^3 (✓) **b)** 72.0 dm^3 (✓)

4 25 g (✓)

Your score: ☐ out of 5

Electrolysis (page 95)

1 **a)** 25.9 g (✓) **b)** 20.0 g (✓) **c)** 27.0 g (✓) **d)** 2.25 g (✓)

2 0.518 g (✓)

3 B (✓)

4 120 cm^3 (✓)

5 +2 (✓)

6 **a)** 965 C (✓) **b)** 1.0×10^{-2} mol (✓) **c)** 5.0×10^{-3} mol(✓) **d)** 2 (✓) **e)** $Ni^{2+}(aq) + 2e^- \rightarrow Ni(s)$ (✓✓)

7 **a)** **B** (✓) **b)** **C** (✓) **c)** **B** (✓)

8 +3 (✓) (charge = 180 C = 1.86×10^{-3} mol of electrons (✓); amount of M = 6.23×10^{-4} mol (✓); ratio = 3)

Your score: ☐ out of 20

Solutions (page 96)

1 $\text{Concentration of solution} = \dfrac{\text{amount of solute}}{\text{volume of solution}}$ (✓✓)

2 **a)** 0.2 mol/dm^3 (✓) **b)** 0.02 mol/dm^3 (✓) **c)** 0.2 mol/dm^3 (✓) **d)** 8 mol/dm^3 (✓)

3 **a)** 0.25 mol (✓) **b)** 0.01 mol (✓) **c)** 0.05 mol (✓) **d)** 0.0025 mol (✓)

Your score: ☐ out of 10

Titration (page 97)

1 0.15 mol/dm^3 (✓)

2 a) 0.25 mol/dm^3 (✓) b) 10.0 cm^3 (✓)

3 a) Stoppo (✓) b) Speed of action (✓); taste (✓).

4 Concentration of H^+ = 1.0×10^{-5} mol/dm^3 (✓✓)

Your score: ☐ out of 8

Total round-up score = ☐ + ☐ + ☐ + ☐ + ☐ + ☐ + ☐ out of 95

Your improvement index: $\frac{\square/95}{\square/24} \times 100\% = \square\%$

15 Test yourself (page 98)

Fuels

1 Coal and oil were formed from the remains of plants and trees (coal) (✓) and sea animals and plants (oil) (✓) which lived millions of years ago (✓) .

2 It is burnt in power stations (✓).

3 a) Fractional distillation (✓).
b) Four from: petroleum gas, gasoline, kerosene, diesel oil, fuel oil (✓✓✓✓).
c) Two from: lubricating oil, bitumen, naphtha (✓✓).

4 a) Methane (✓) b) Ethane (✓) c) Propane (✓)
d) The alkane series (✓).

5 Converting hydrocarbons with large molecules (✓) and high boiling points (✓) into hydrocarbons with smaller molecules (✓) and lower boiling points (✓).

6 a) Combustion (✓), respiration (✓).
b) Photosynthesis (✓), cracking of hydrocarbons (✓).

Your score: ☐ out of 23

15 Round-up (page 102)

Fuels

1 a) Fossil fuels are formed by the decay (✓) of the remains of plants (✓) and animals (✓) over long periods of time (✓).
b) Fossil fuels took millions of years to form (✓) and we are using them up much more quickly (✓).

2 Three of the five methods mentioned on page 59 (✓✓✓).

3 a) Fractional distillation (✓) separates the fractions on the basis of their different boiling point ranges (✓).
b) For uses see the diagram on page 99 (✓✓✓✓✓✓).
c) Gasoline has a lower boiling point (✓), lower ignition temperature (✓) and lower viscosity than fuel oil (✓).
d) It does not vaporise (✓) and does not ignite (✓).
e) Fuels from petroleum oil are important in transport (✓), industry (✓) and power generation (✓). Oil is a source of valuable petrochemicals (✓).

4 As for exothermic energy diagram on page 101 (✓✓), exothermic (✓).

5 As for endothermic energy diagram on page 101 (✓✓), endothermic (✓).

6 a) –124 kJ/mol (✓)
b) –484 kJ/mol (✓)
c) –56 kJ/mol (✓)

Your score: ☐ out of 35

Your improvement index: $\frac{\square/35}{\square/23} \times 100\% = \square\%$

16 Test yourself (page 103)

Alkenes and plastics

1 $>C=C<$ (✓), addition reactions (✓).

2 Alkenes are reactive (✓) and are therefore the starting materials for the manufacture of many other compounds (✓).

3 Bromine adds across the double bond to form $BrCH_2CH_2Br$ (✓).

4 a) Addition of water across the double bond (✓).
b) Ethanol, C_2H_5OH (✓).

5 a) Addition of hydrogen across a double bond (✓).
b) Catalytic hydrogenation is used to convert unsaturated oils (vegetable oils) into saturated fats, which are solid, in the manufacture of margarine (✓).

6 The addition of many identical small molecules to form a large molecule (✓). The substance with small molecules is the monomer; the substance with large molecules is the polymer (✓).

7 Thermosetting plastics can be softened by heat and hardened by cooling (✓) many times (✓). Thermosetting plastics are softened by heat (✓) only during manufacture (✓).

8 For thermosoftening plastics a continuous process is used (✓). For thermosetting plastics, a batch process is used (✓).

Your score: ☐ out of 17

16 Round-up (page 107)

Alkenes and plastics

1 a) **(i)** Ethane C_2H_6 (✓), ethene C_2H_4 (✓)

(ii)

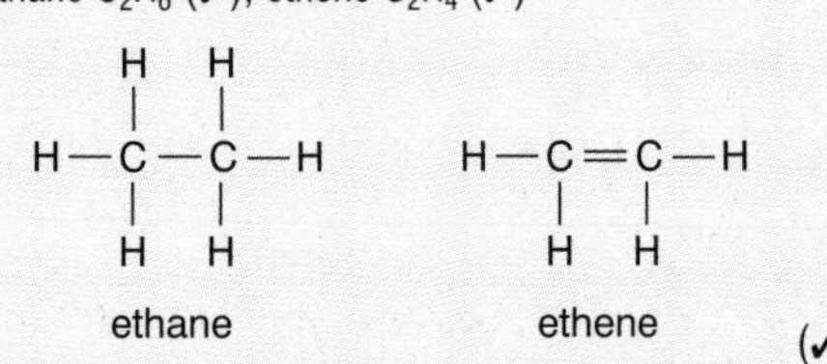

(✓✓)

b) Ethane has only single bonds (✓); it is a saturated compound (✓). Ethene has a carbon–carbon double bond (✓); it is an unsaturated compound (✓).

2 a) Two from: hydrogen, bromine, water, sulphuric acid (✓✓).
b) Addition reactions (✓).
c) Hydrogen with a nickel catalyst (✓✓).

3 a) Carbon dioxide (✓) and water (✓).
b) Alkenes are a source of valuable chemicals (✓).

4 a)

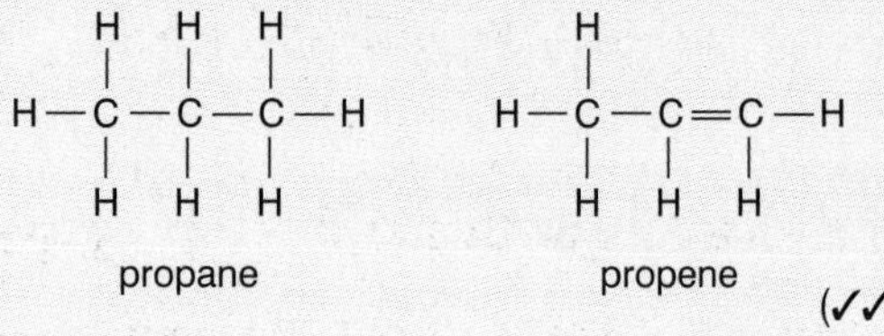

(✓✓)

b) Propene (✓)
c)

```
     H   Br  Br
     |   |   |
 H — C — C — C — H
     |   |   |
     H   H   H
```
(✓✓)

5 a) Less breakable (✓).
b) Cheaper, less breakable, non-toxic (✓).
c) Much less breakable (✓).

6

```
   H    CONH2
 ( |    |   )
—( C —  C  —)—
 ( |    |   )n
   H    H
```
(✓)

7 a) When deformed, a plastic changes shape (✓) and retains the new shape when the deforming force is removed (✓).
b) Thermoplastic – can be softened by heat (✓) many times (✓).
Thermosetting – can be moulded only once (✓).
Thermoplastic – Individual chains can move with respect to one another (✓).
Thermosetting – chains are cross-linked (✓).

8 Two from, for example, poly(ethene), poly(chloroethene), poly(propene) (✓✓). Uses: poly(ethene) for plastic bags, kitchenware, laboratory tubing, toys; poly(chloroethene) for plastic bottles, wellington boots, raincoats, electrical insulation, gutters; poly(propene) for hospital equipment that must be sterilised, as fibres for ropes and fishing nets (✓✓).

9 a) Most plastics cannot be decomposed by natural biological processes (✓).
b) Plastic rubbish accumulates in landfill sites and never decomposes (✓).
c) Some plastics form toxic combustion products (✓). Also, burning them is a waste of Earth's resources (✓).
d) Recycling (✓).

10 a) The molecules of poly(ethene) are long, flexible chains (✓). Glass is a three-dimensional structure of covalently bonded atoms which cannot change their positions in the structure (✓) until energy is supplied by heating (✓).
b) A piece of metal consists of cations and a cloud of free electrons (✓). The cations can change their positions while still remaining bonded by the cloud of electrons (✓). In a piece of pottery every atom is covalently bonded to other atoms (✓) in a rigid structure (✓).

11 a) **(i)** For example, one of: lower density; does not warp; easier to mould into shape (✓).
(ii) For example, one of: lower density; easier to mould into shape; does not corrode (✓).
b) **(i)** For example, one of: lower density therefore the vehicle uses less fuel; does not corrode (✓).
(ii) Less strong (✓).

Your score: ☐ out of 51

Your improvement index: $\dfrac{\square/51}{\square/17} \times 100\% = \square\%$

17 Test yourself (page 108)

Agricultural chemicals

1 The roots of clover bear nodules (✓) containing nitrogen-fixing bacteria (✓) that convert nitrogen into compounds (✓).

2 They convert ammonium salts (which plants cannot use) (✓) into nitrates (which plants can use to make proteins) (✓).

3 They convert nitrates (✓) and ammonium salts (✓) into gaseous nitrogen (✓).

4 Nitrogen compounds (ammonium salts and nitrates) (✓), phosphates (✓) and potassium salts (✓).

5 Nitrates encourage the growth of algae (✓). When algae die and decay, they use up the dissolved oxygen (✓) and fish cannot live in the water (✓).

6 $(28/60) \times 100 = 47\,\%$ (✓✓)

7 High pressure (about 350 atm) (✓), a moderate temperature (about 450°C) (✓) and a catalyst (iron) (✓).

8 **a)** The Contact process (✓).
b) $2SO_2(g) + O_2(g) \rightarrow 2SO_3(g)$ (✓✓)

9 Phosphate rock (✓), sulphur (✓), potassium chloride (✓).

Your score: ☐ out of 25

17 Round-up (page 113)

Agricultural chemicals

1 **a)** 82% (✓) **b)** 35% (✓) **c)** 21% (✓) **d)** 47% (✓).

2 Ammonia + hydrogen chloride → ammonium chloride (✓)
$NH_3(g) + HCl(g) \rightarrow NH_4Cl(s)$ (✓✓)

3 $NH_4Cl(s) + NaOH(aq) \rightarrow NH_3(g) + NaCl(s) + H_2O(l)$ (✓✓✓)

4 **A** nitrogen (✓), **B** litmus (✓), **C** hydrogen chloride (✓), **D** alkali, e.g. sodium hydroxide (✓), **E** hydrogen (✓).

5 **a)** Proteins (✓)
b) Legumes have nitrogen-fixing bacteria (✓) in nodules on their roots (✓).
c) One of: by lightning; fixation by bacteria; Haber process; in vehicle engines (✓).
d) Crops are harvested (✓), not left to decay and return nitrogen compounds to the soil (✓).
e) Ammonium salts are converted by nitrifying bacteria (✓) into nitrates (✓), which plants can absorb (✓).

6 **a)** $4NH_3(g) + 5O_2(g) \rightarrow 4NO(g) + 6H_2O(g)$ (✓✓)
b) $2NO(g) + O_2(g) \rightarrow 2NO_2(g)$ (✓✓)
c) $4NO_2(g) + O_2(g) + 2H_2O(l) \rightarrow 4HNO_3(l)$ (✓✓✓)

7 Contact (✓), combustion of sulphur *or* smelting metal sulphides *or* natural gas (✓), air (✓), electrostatic precipitation (✓), vanadium(V) oxide (✓), sulphur trioxide (✓), concentrated sulphuric acid (✓), oleum (✓), recovering sulphur from the sulphur dioxide emitted from factory chimneys and power stations (✓).

8 **a)** Slag (✓) **b)** Slag (✓), sylvite (✓) and *either* urea *or* ammonium sulphate (✓).

9 **a)** At high pressure, sulphur dioxide liquefies (✓).
b) At high temperature, SO_3 dissociates into SO_2 and O_2 (✓).
c) Vanadium(V) oxide, V_2O_5 (✓).

10 The manufacture of, for example, fertilisers, plastics, paints, detergents, fibres, vehicle batteries (any two) (✓✓).

Your score: ☐ out of 49

Your improvement index: $\dfrac{\square/49}{\square/25} \times 100\% = \square\%$

18 Test yourself (page 114)

Alcohols, acids and esters

1 **a)** The alcohols (✓) **b)** 'Alcohol' (✓)
c)

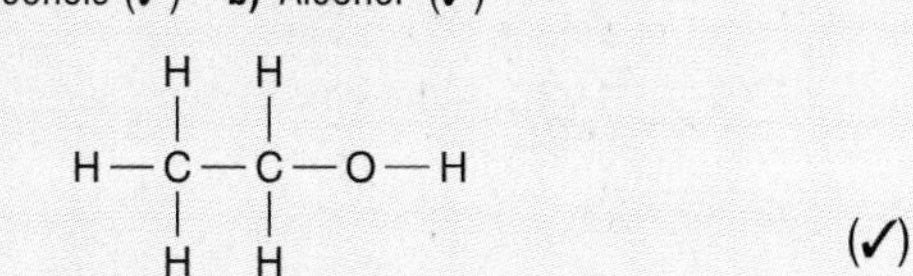

2 Alcohol blurs the vision (✓) and increases reaction times (✓).

3 Ethanol (✓) in the wine is oxidised (✓) to sour-tasting (✓) ethanoic acid (✓).

4 The action of enzymes (✓) on carbohydrates (✓) to form ethanol (✓) and carbon dioxide (✓).

5 The fermentation (✓) of sugars and starches (✓) is used to make ethanol for alcoholic drinks (✓). The hydration (✓) of ethene (✓) is used to make ethanol for use as a solvent (✓).

6 Ethanoic acid (✓)

```
     H   O
     |   ||
  H—C—C
     |    \
     H     O—H
```
(✓)

7 The carboxyl group (✓)

```
       O
      //
   —C
      \
       O—H
```
(✓)

8 An ester (✓) and water (✓).

Your score: ☐ out of 25

18 Round-up (page 117)

Alcohols, acids and esters

1 a) (i)

```
     H              H
     |              |
  H—C—H         H—C—O—H
     |              |
     H              H
```
(✓✓)

(ii)

```
     H   H           H   H
     |   |           |   |
  H—C—C—H       H—C—C—O—H
     |   |           |   |
     H   H           H   H
```
(✓✓)

(iii)

```
     H   H   H           H   H   H
     |   |   |           |   |   |
  H—C—C—C—H       H—C—C—C—O—H
     |   |   |           |   |   |
     H   H   H           H   H   H
```
(✓✓)

b) A hydroxyl group (✓✓).
c) (i) C_nH_{2n+2} (✓) **(ii)** $C_nH_{2n+1}OH$ (✓)

2 Stage 1: fractional distillation (✓). Crude oil is heated in a fractional distillation column (✓). Fractions with different boiling point ranges (✓) are run off from different heights in the column (✓).
Stage 2: cracking of alkanes (✓). The vapour of an alkane is passed over a heated catalyst, e.g. aluminium oxide (✓). Alkenes and hydrogen are formed (✓) and separated by fractional distillation (✓).
Stage 3: hydration (✓). Ethene and steam are passed over a heated catalyst (✓) under pressure (✓).

3 a) In the short term, slurred speech, blurred vision, long reaction times (✓✓); in the long term, damage to liver, kidneys, arteries and brain (✓✓).
b) Small amounts can cause blindness (✓) and death (✓).

4 a) Refer to the concept map on page 117 if you need help. Choose three of:

a metal, e.g. Zn → an ethanoate + hydrogen

a base, e.g. CaO → an ethanoate + water

an alkali, e.g. NaOH → an ethanoate + water

a carbonate or hydrogencarbonate → an ethanoate + water + carbon dioxide

an alcohol, e.g. ethanol → an ester, e.g. ethyl ethanoate
(✓✓✓ for three substances; ✓✓✓ for three sets of products)

b) Ethanoic acid is incompletely ionised (✓); hydrochloric acid is completely ionised (✓).
c) Compare the rates of the reactions of the two acids in solutions of the same concentration (✓). With a metal, e.g. Mg (✓), compare the rates of evolution of hydrogen (✓) *or* with a carbonate or hydrogencarbonate (✓), compare the rates of evolution of carbon dioxide (✓).

5 Esterification is the reaction of an alcohol (✓) and a carboxylic acid (✓) to form an ester and water (✓). A catalyst, e.g. concentrated sulphuric acid, is needed (✓).

6 Inhaling a solvent to get a 'high' (✓). This results in disorientation which may lead to dangerous, reckless behaviour and death (✓).

7 a) They want to reduce the cost of importing oil (✓). Other benefits are reduced pollution from vehicle exhausts (✓) and saving oil for use in the petrochemical industry (✓).
b) A country must have large areas of land to spare for growing sugar cane (✓) and plenty of sunshine to ripen the crop (✓).

8 a) Esters are used as food additives (✓) and as solvents (✓).
b)

```
     H   H    O
     |   |   //      H
  H—C—C—C          |
     |   |    \      |
     H   H     O—C—H
                     |
                     H
```
(✓)

Your score: ☐ out of 52

Your improvement index: $\frac{\square/52}{\square/25} \times 100\% = \square\%$

19 Test yourself (page 118)

Analytical chemistry

1 D (✓)

2 Cl^- (✓)

3 a) Ammonia (✓) **b)** NH_4^+ (✓)

4 Dissolve a little of each solid in distilled water (✓), and add sodium hydroxide solution (✓). Copper(II) chloride gives a blue gelatinous ppt (✓), which dissolves in ammonia solution (✓). Iron(II)chloride gives a green gelatinous ppt (✓) which does not dissolve in ammonia solution (✓).

Your score: ☐ out of 10

19 Round-up (page 120)

Analytical chemistry

1 a) Sodium compounds (✓) **b)** Copper compounds (✓)
c) Barium compounds (✓)

2 a) Add dilute acid (✓). Test the gas evolved with limewater (✓). If it turns limewater milky (✓), the gas is carbon dioxide (✓), and a carbonate is present (✓).
b) A flame test (✓) gives white light (✓).
c) A flame test (✓) gives brick-red light (✓).

3 X ions are Fe^{3+} (✓), rust-coloured ppt is $Fe(OH)_3(s)$ (✓); Y ions are Zn^{2+}(✓), $Zn(OH)_2(s)$ is white (✓) and dissolves in sodium hydroxide (✓).

4 Flame test (✓): sodium gives yellow (✓); potassium gives lilac (✓).
Barium chloride solution (✓) and dilute hydrochloric acid (✓). Sulphate gives a white ppt (✓). Sulphite gives a gas (✓) which is sulphur dioxide (✓).

5 Damp red litmus paper (✓) turns blue with ammonia (✓); with hydrogen it does not change (✓).
A lighted splint (✓) is extinguished in ammonia (✓); in hydrogen it burns with a 'pop' (✓).

6 Damp blue litmus paper (✓) turns red in hydrogen chloride (✓); it is bleached in chlorine (✓).
Ammonia (✓) reacts with hydrogen chloride to give a white cloud of precipitate (✓); with cold chlorine there is no reaction (✓).

Your score: ☐ out of 37

Your improvement index: $\dfrac{\square/37}{\square/10} \times 100\% = \square\%$

20 Test yourself (page 121)

Food chemistry

1 a) Glucose (✓) **b)** Starch (✓)
c) Carbon, hydrogen, oxygen (✓)
d) Many molecules of glucose join by condensation polymerisation to form a molecule of starch (✓).

2 a) $H_2NCHRCO_2H$ (✓)
b) **(i)** Condensation polymerisation (✓)
(ii) Peptide link (✓)

3 a) A = glycerol (✓); D = water (✓).
b) **(i)** Fatty acid (✓) **(ii)** Ester (✓)

4 The European Community (✓).

Your score: ☐ out of 12

20 Round-up (page 124)

Food chemistry

1 a) Disaccharides (✓) **b)** Peptides (✓) and proteins (✓)
c) Fats (✓) and oils (✓) (accept lipids)

2 a) Amino acid (✓)
b)

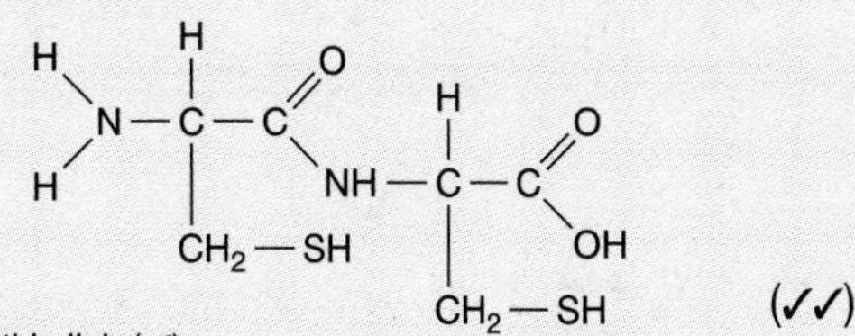

(✓✓)

c) Peptide link (✓)
d) Peptide (✓)
e) Further polymerisation can occur through the formation of more peptide links (✓) to form a protein (✓).

3 a) Emulsifier (✓) **b)** Monosodium glutamate, MSG (✓)
c) Saccharine *or* aspartame (✓) **d)** Flavourings *or* anti-oxidants (✓)

4 a) Fats: butter (✓), lard (✓), hard margarine (✓); oils: cooking oil (✓); mixture: soft margarine (✓).
b) At room temperature fats are solid (✓) and oils are liquid (✓).

5 a) A fat with no carbon–carbon double bonds (✓).
b) For example, butter, lard (✓).
c) It is claimed that eating saturated fat increases the risk of heart disease (✓).

Your score: ☐ out of 26

Your improvement index: $\dfrac{\square/26}{\square/12} \times 100\% = \square\%$

21 Test yourself (page 125)

Dyes

1 **a)** A mordant assists a dye to bond to a fabric (✓).
b) It forms a precipitate (✓) of e.g. $Al(OH)_3$ in the pores of the fabric (✓). A dye bonds to the precipitate (✓).

2 **B A D C** (✓✓✓✓)

3 See page 126. (✓✓).

Your score: ☐ out of 10

21 Round-up (page 126)

Dyes

1 A dye consists of single molecules (✓); a pigment of larger particles (✓).

2 Safe to manufacture (✓) and use (✓), giving reliable (✓) and reproducible results (✓) and competitively priced (✓).

3 A basic dye bonds to fabrics with acidic groups (✓).
An acidic dye bonds to fabrics with basic groups (✓).

4 A ppt of $Fe(OH)_2$ (✓) forms between the fibres (✓), and the dye bonds to it (✓).

5 **a)** Azo dye (✓) **b)** Two of, for example, azo, direct, fibre-reactive, disperse (✓✓).

Your score: ☐ out of 15

Your improvement index: $\frac{\square/15}{\square/10} \times 100\% = \square\%$

THE PERIODIC TABLE OF THE ELEMENTS

1	2	Group										3	4	5	6	7	0
						H hydrogen 1											**He** helium 2
Li lithium 3	**Be** beryllium 4											**B** boron 5	**C** carbon 6	**N** nitrogen 7	[illegible]	**F** fluorine 9	**Ne** neon 10
Na sodium 11	**Mg** magnesium 12											**Al** aluminium 13	**Si** silicon 14	**P** phosphorus 15	[illegible]	**Cl** chlorine 17	**Ar** argon 18
K potassium 19	**Ca** calcium 20	**Sc** scandium 21	**Ti** titanium 22	**V** vanadium 23	**Cr** chromium 24	**Mn** manganese 25	**Fe** iron 26	**Co** cobalt 27	**Ni** nickel 28	**Cu** copper 29	**Zn** zinc 30	**Ga** gallium 31	**Ge** germanium 32	**As** arsenic 33	[illegible]	**Br** bromine 35	**Kr** krypton 36
Rb rubidium 37	**Sr** strontium 38	**Y** yttrium 39	**Zr** zirconium 40	**Nb** niobium 41	**Mo** molybdenum 42	**Tc** technetium 43	**Ru** ruthenium 44	**Rh** rhodium 45	**Pd** palladium 46	**Ag** silver 47	**Cd** cadmium 48	**In** indium 49	**Sn** tin 50	**Sb** antimony 51	[illegible]	**I** iodine 53	**Xe** xenon 54
Cs caesium 55	**Ba** barium 56	**La** lanthanum 57	**Hf** hafnium 72	**Ta** tantalum 73	**W** tungsten 74	**Re** rhenium 75	**Os** osmium 76	**Ir** iridium 77	**Pt** platinum 78	**Au** gold 79	**Hg** mercury 80	**Tl** thallium 81	**Pb** lead 82	**Bi** bismuth 83	**Po** [illegible]	**At** astatine 85	**Rn** radon 86
Fr francium 87	**Ra** radium 88	**Ac** actinium 89															

lanthanum series: elements 58–71
actinium series: elements 90–103

Mind Maps

Elements, compounds and equations (Topic 2)

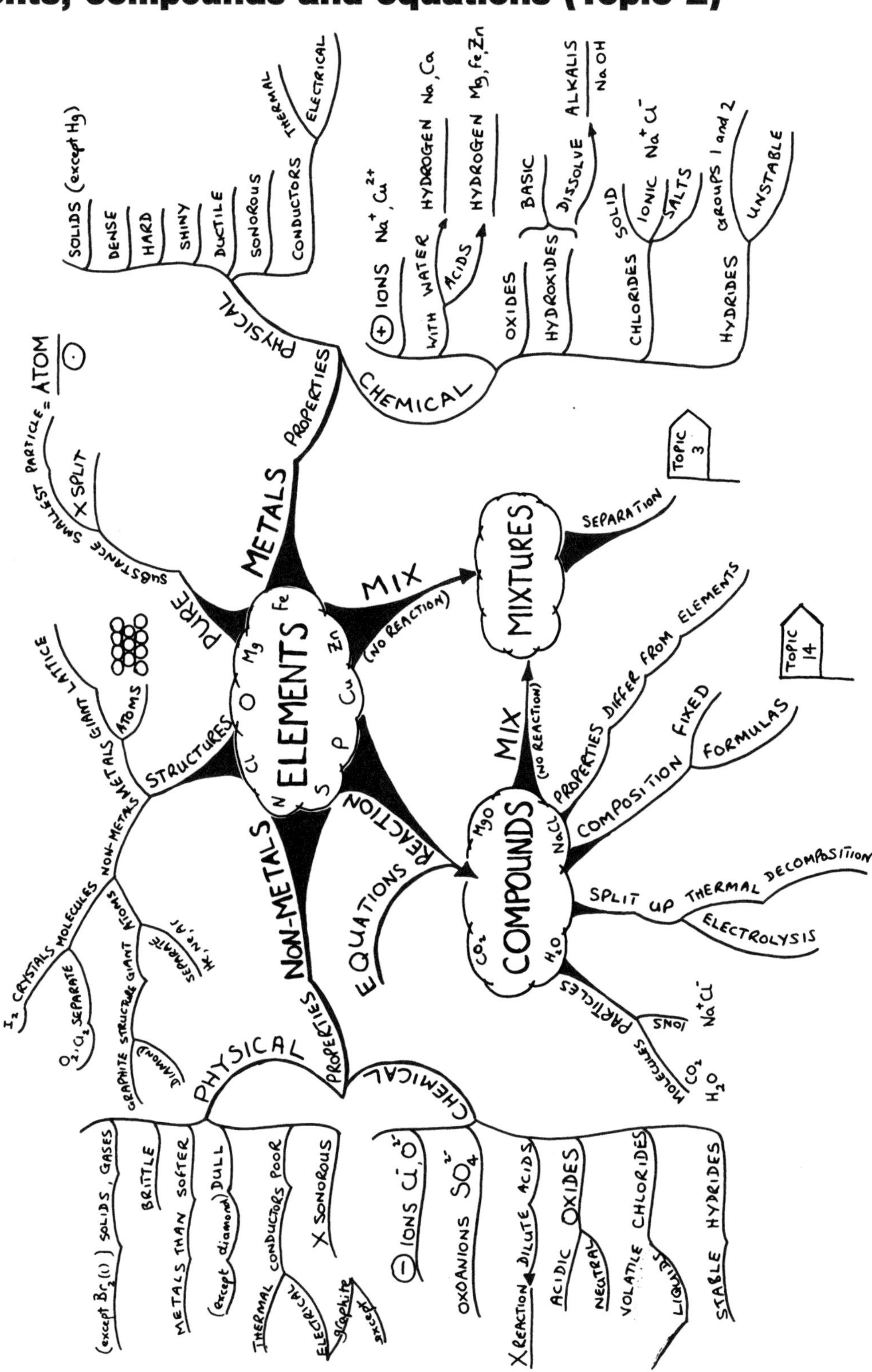

The structure of the atom (Topic 4)

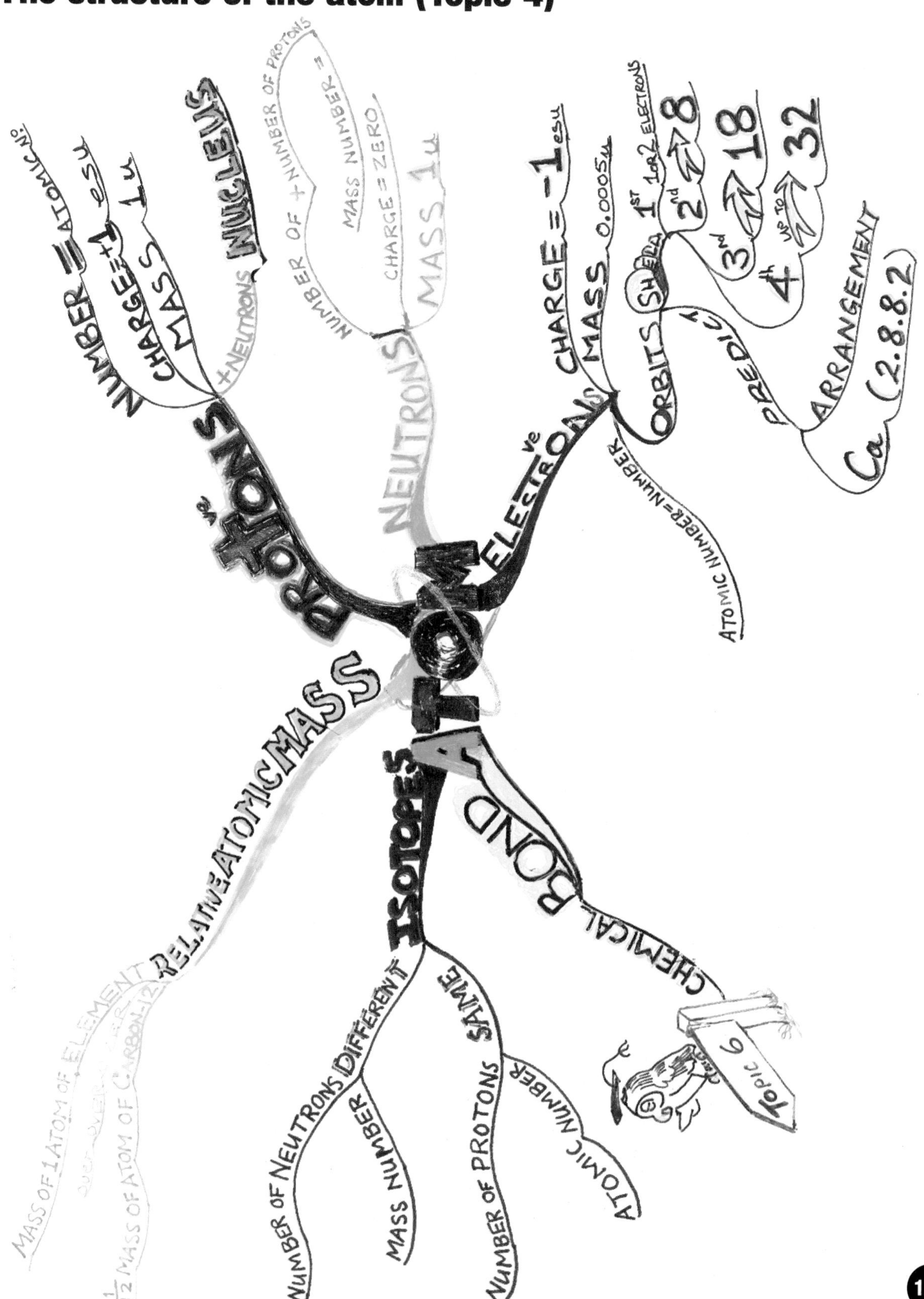

Electrolysis (Topic 5)

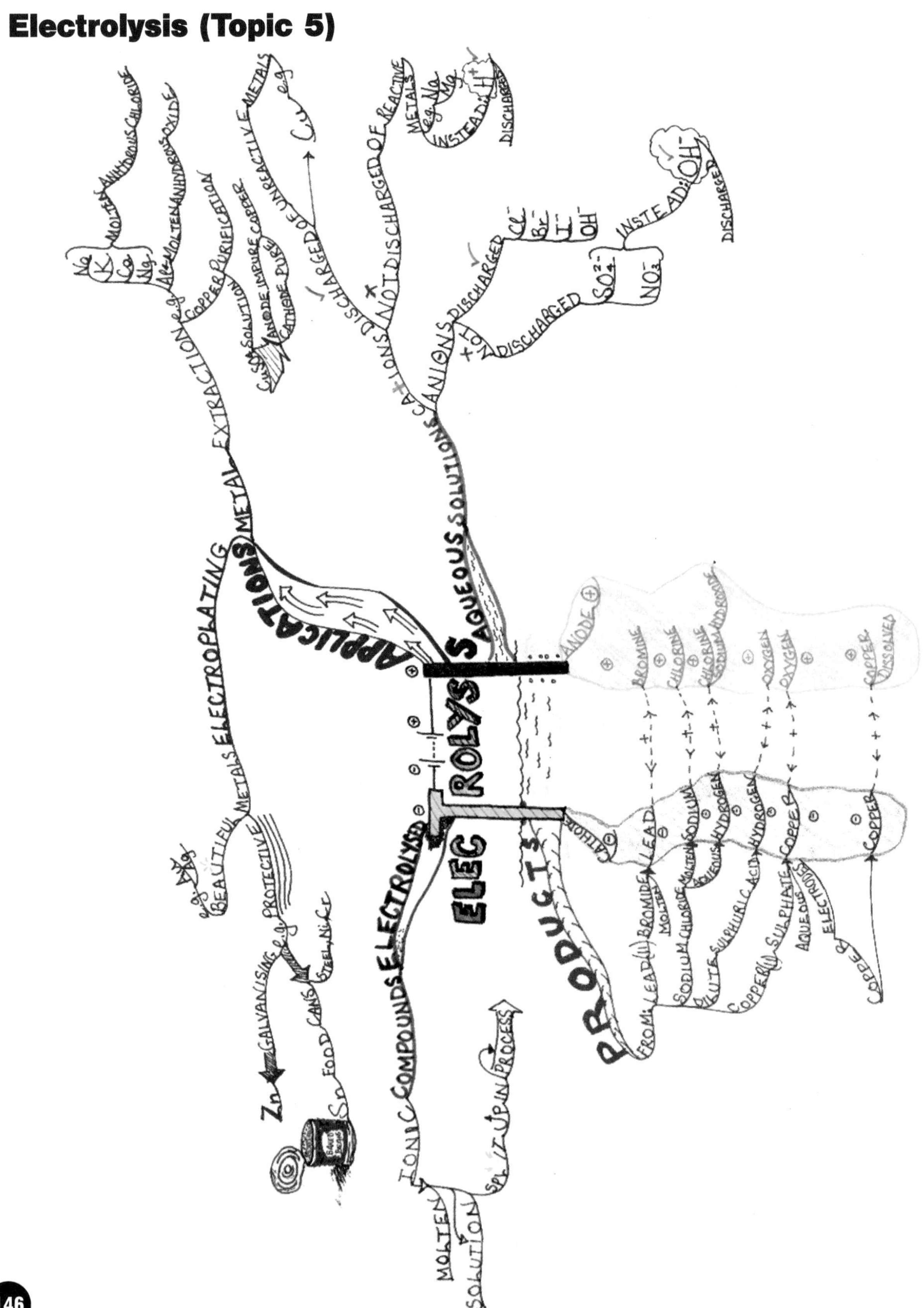

The chemical bond (Topic 6)

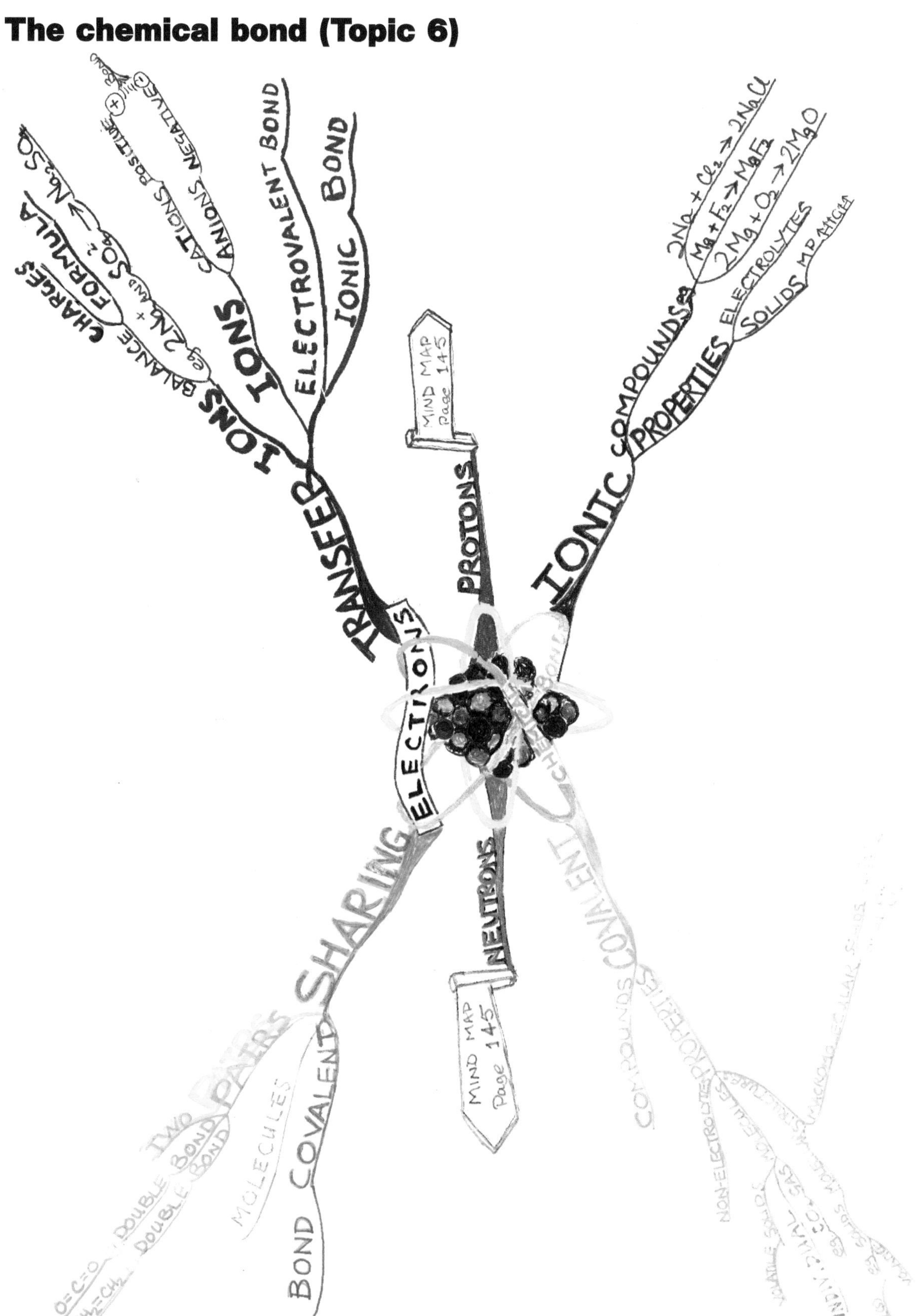

Acids, bases and salts (Topic 8)

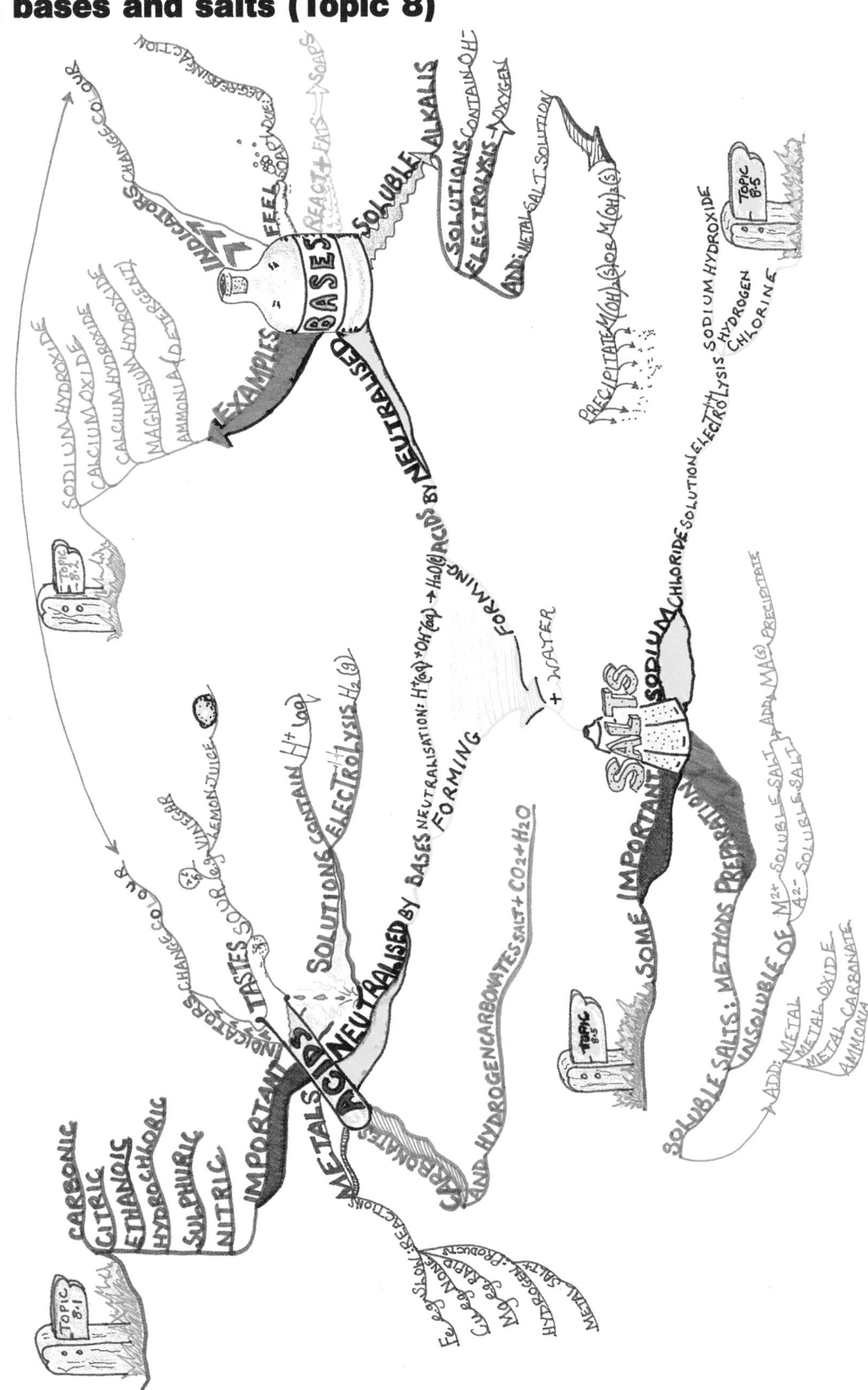

Air (Topic 9)

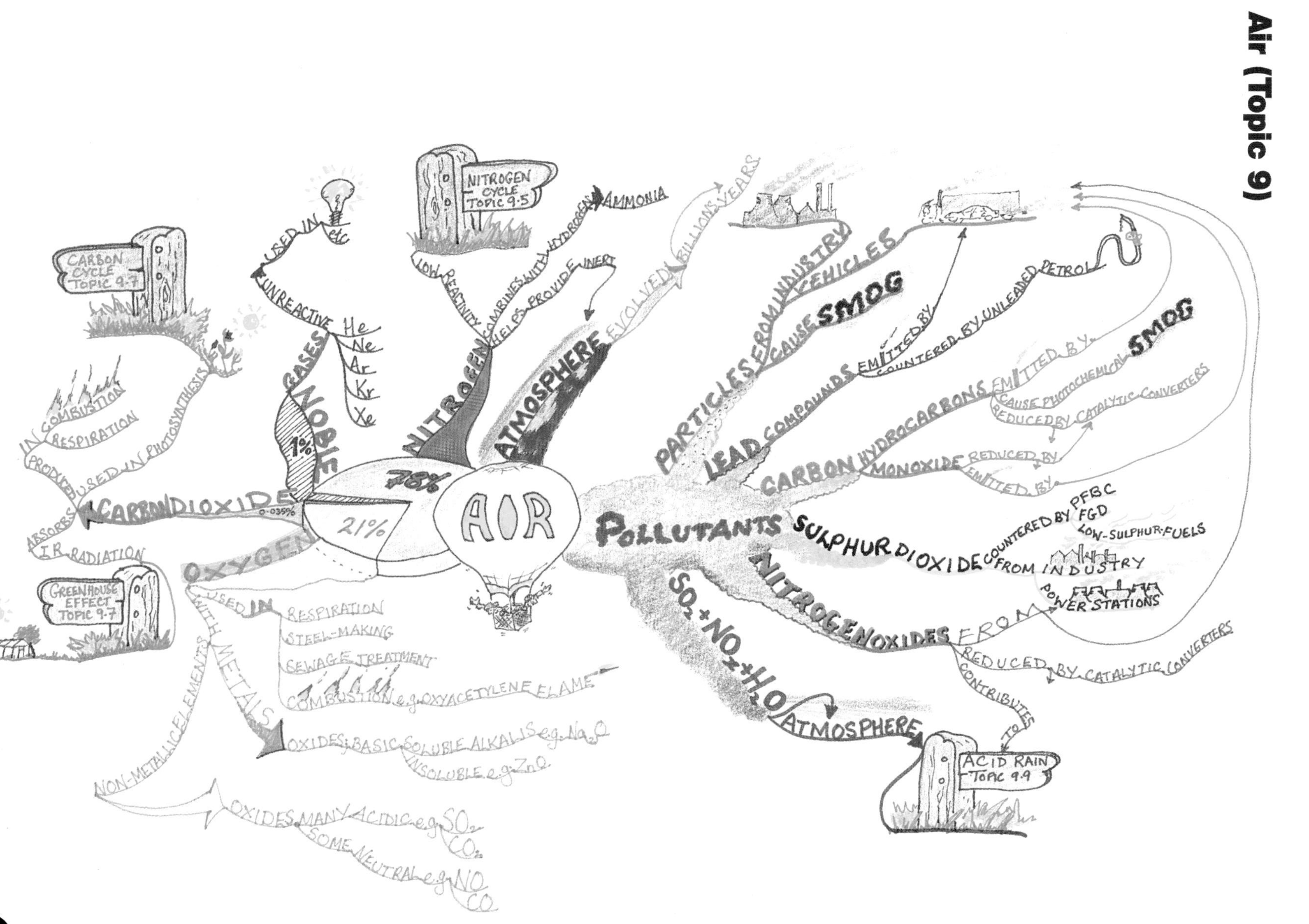
AIR
78%
21%
1%
0-035%
NITROGEN
LOW REACTIVITY
COMBINES WITH HYDROGEN
AMMONIA
HELPS PROVIDE INERT
NITROGEN CYCLE TOPIC 9.5
NOBLE GASES
UNREACTIVE
He
Ne
Ar
Kr
Xe
USED IN
etc
CARBON DIOXIDE
PRODUCED IN
COMBUSTION
RESPIRATION
USED IN PHOTOSYNTHESIS
ABSORBS
I.R. RADIATION
CARBON CYCLE TOPIC 9.7
GREENHOUSE EFFECT TOPIC 9.7
OXYGEN
USED IN
RESPIRATION
STEEL-MAKING
SEWAGE TREATMENT
COMBUSTION e.g. OXYACETYLENE FLAME
WITH METALS
OXIDES: BASIC
SOLUBLE ALKALIS e.g. Na_2O
INSOLUBLE e.g. ZnO
NON-METALLIC ELEMENTS
OXIDES: MANY ACIDIC e.g. SO_2, CO_2
SOME NEUTRAL e.g. NO, CO
ATMOSPHERE
EVOLVED
BILLIONS YEARS
POLLUTANTS
PARTICLES
FROM INDUSTRY
VEHICLES
CAUSE SMOG
LEAD COMPOUNDS
EMITTED BY
COUNTERED BY UNLEADED PETROL
CARBON
HYDROCARBONS
EMITTED BY
CAUSE PHOTOCHEMICAL SMOG
REDUCED BY CATALYTIC CONVERTERS
MONOXIDE
REDUCED BY
EMITTED BY
SULPHUR DIOXIDE
COUNTERED BY
PFBC
FGD
LOW-SULPHUR FUELS
FROM INDUSTRY
POWER STATIONS
NITROGEN OXIDES
FROM
REDUCED BY CATALYTIC CONVERTERS
CONTRIBUTES TO
ACID RAIN TOPIC 9.9
$SO_2 + NO_x + H_2O$
ATMOSPHERE

Water (Topic 10)

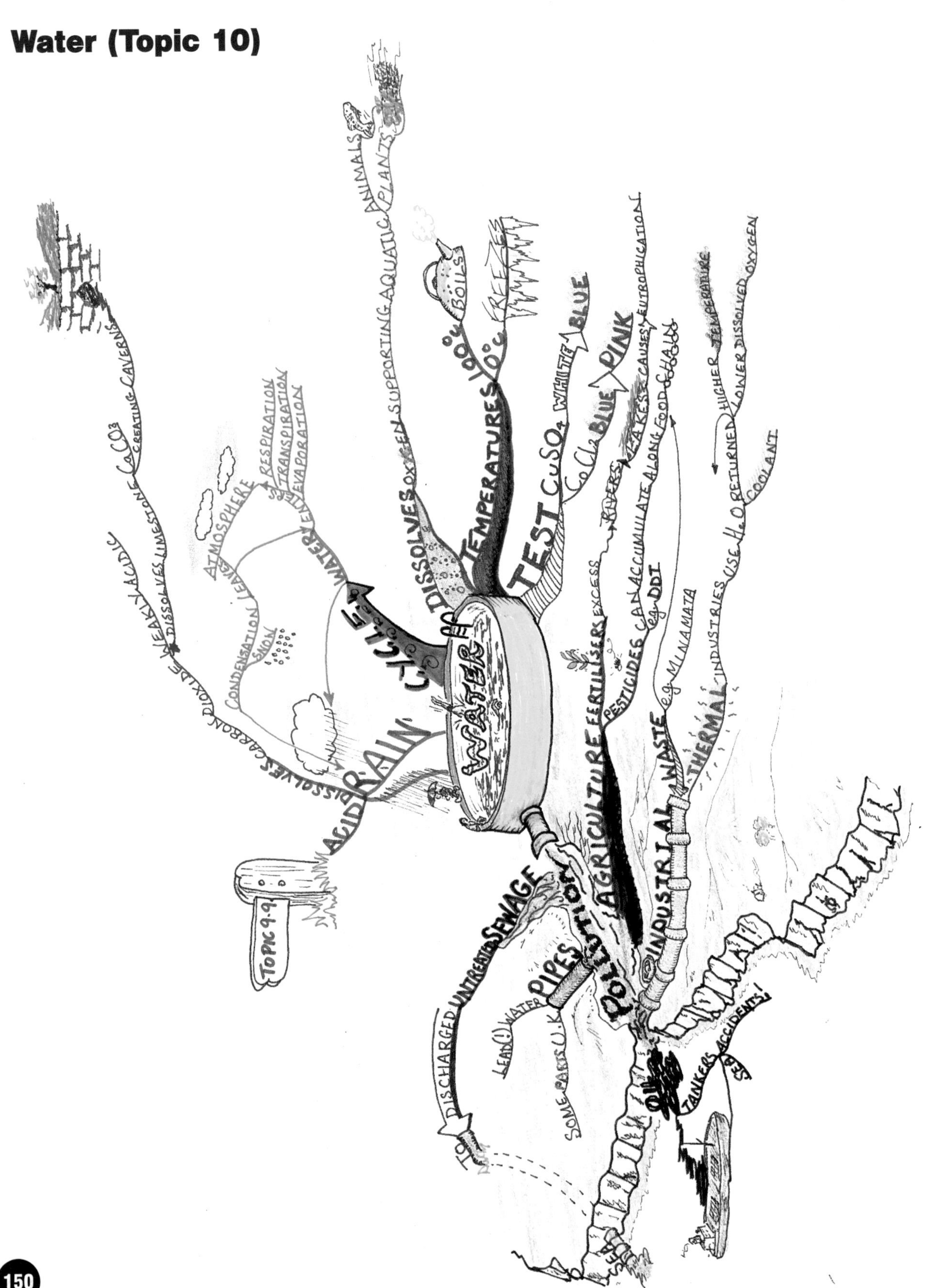

Planet Earth (Topic 11)

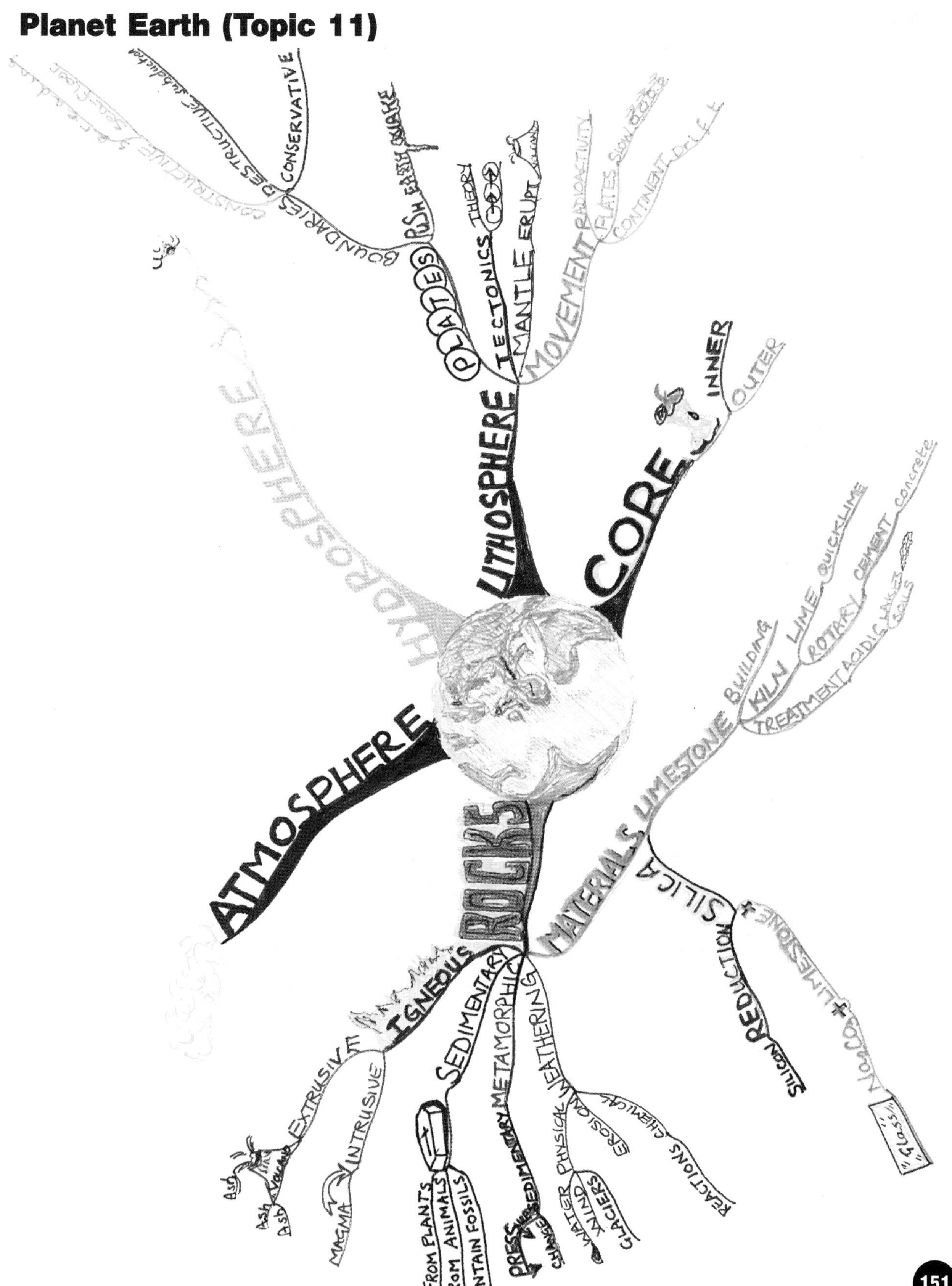

Metals and alloys (Topic 12)

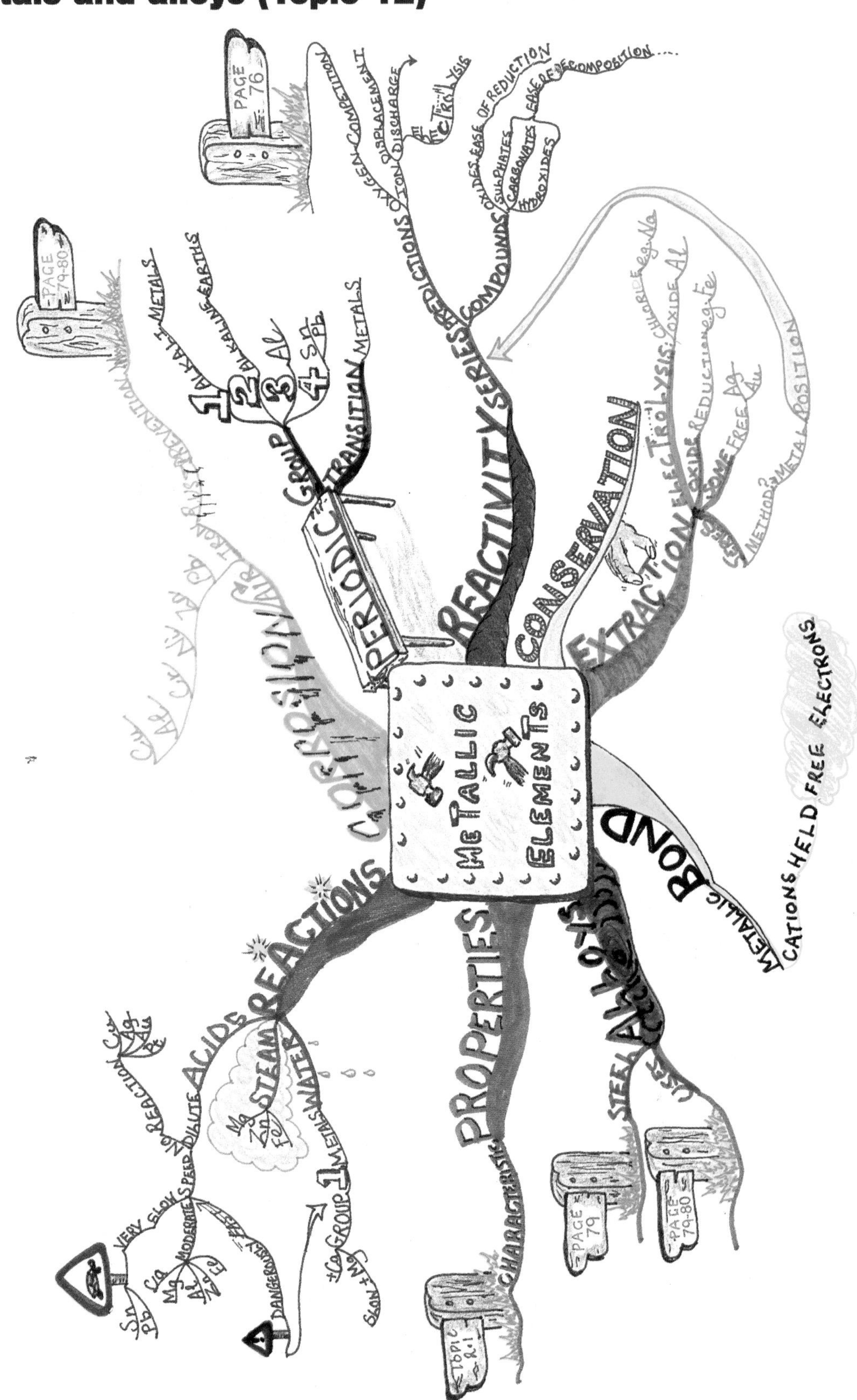

Reaction speeds (Topic 13)

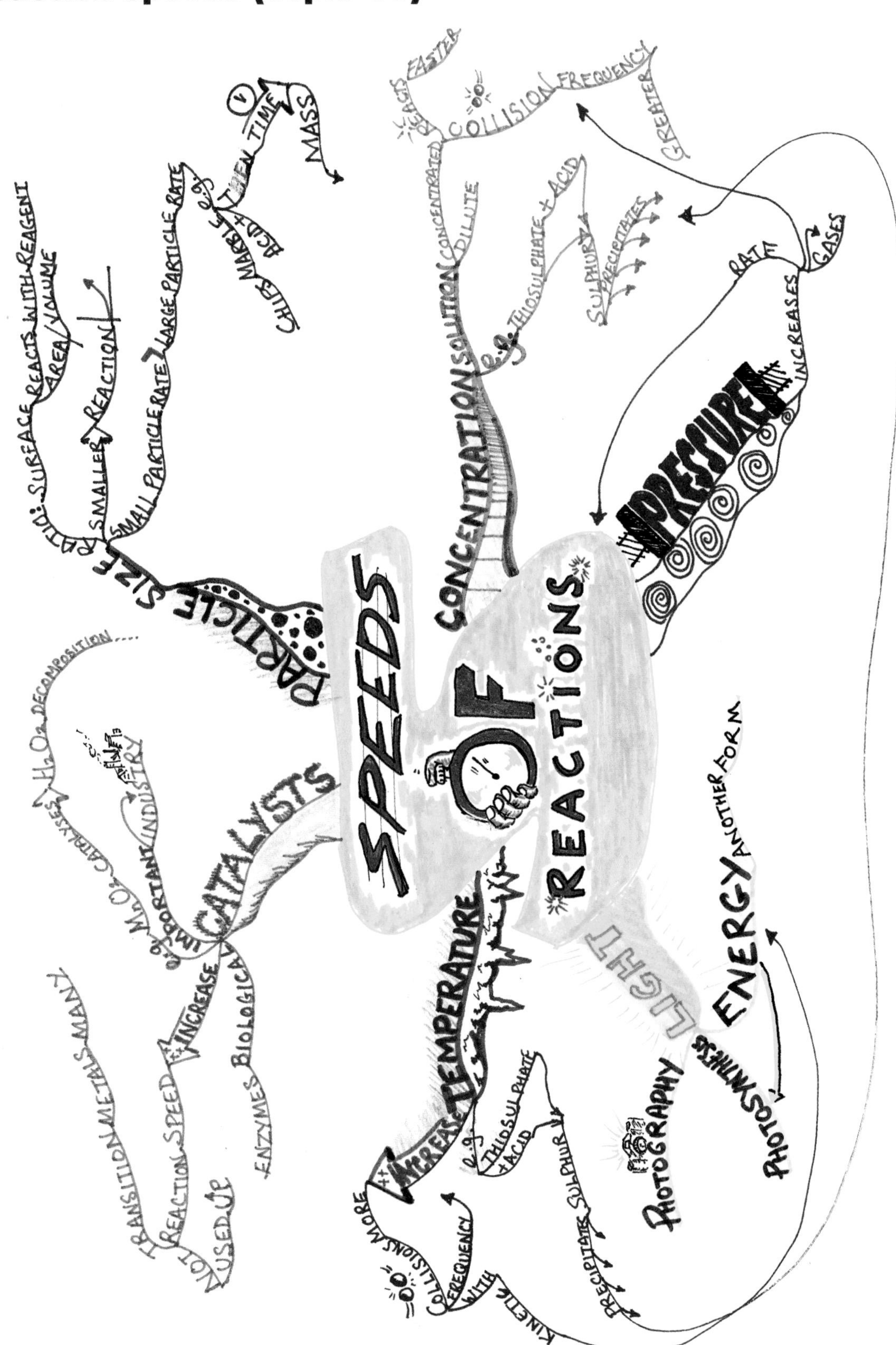
SPEEDS OF REACTIONS
PARTICLE SIZE
RATIO: SURFACE AREA/VOLUME REACTS WITH REAGENT
SMALLER REACTION
SMALL PARTICLE RATE
LARGE PARTICLE RATE
e.g. CHIPS MARBLE + ACID
THEN TIME
MASS
CONCENTRATION
SOLUTION
CONCENTRATED
DILUTE
COLLISION FREQUENCY
GREATER
REACTS FASTER
e.g. THIOSULPHATE + ACID
SULPHUR PRECIPITATES
PRESSURE
INCREASES RATE
GASES
CATALYSTS
MnO_2 CATALYSES H_2O_2 DECOMPOSITION
IMPORTANT INDUSTRY
INCREASE REACTION SPEED
TRANSITION METALS MANY
NOT USED UP
BIOLOGICAL ENZYMES
TEMPERATURE
INCREASE
MORE COLLISIONS
FREQUENCY WITH KINETIC
e.g. THIOSULPHATE + ACID
SULPHUR PRECIPITATE
LIGHT
ENERGY ANOTHER FORM
PHOTOSYNTHESIS
PHOTOGRAPHY

Fuels (Topic 15)

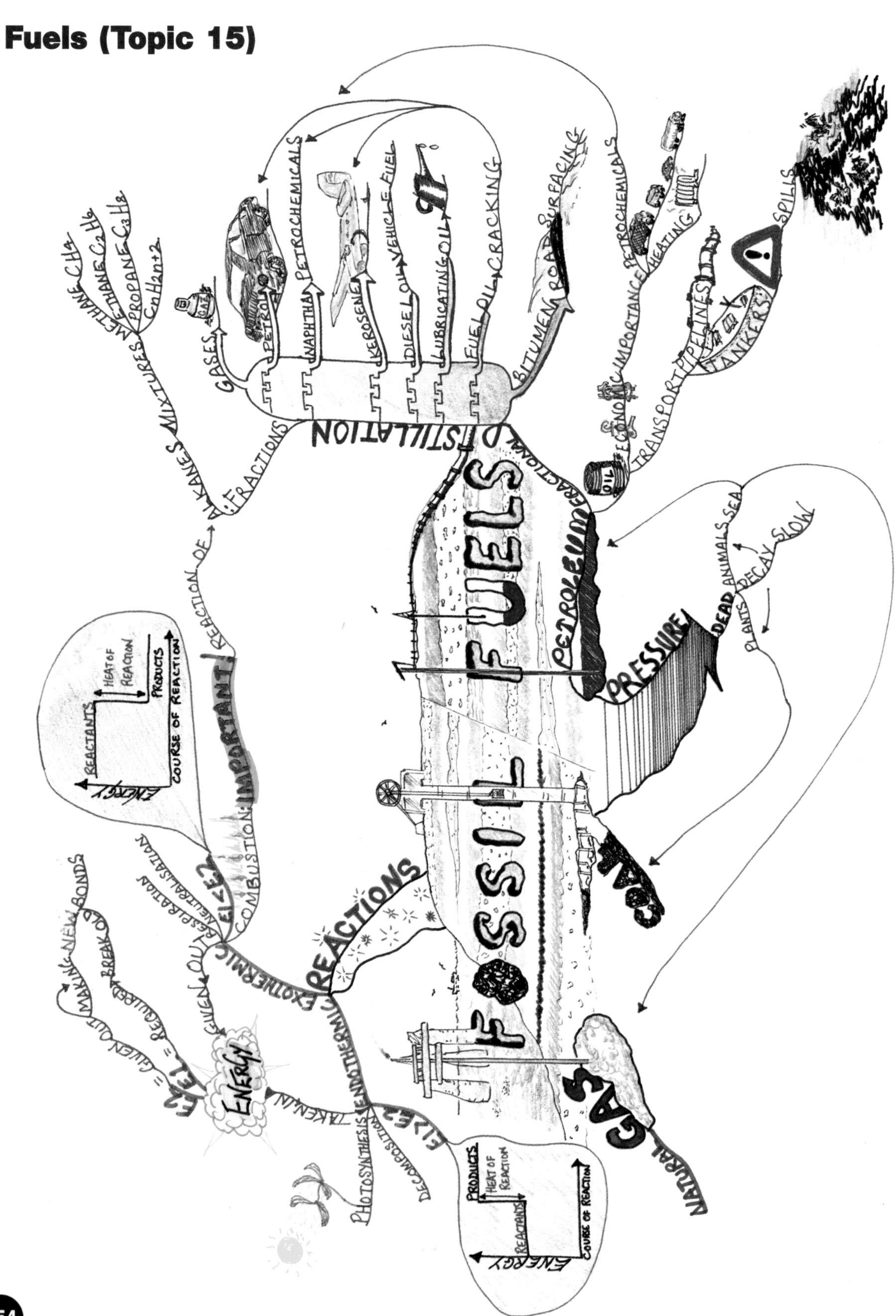

Alkenes and plastics (Topic 16)

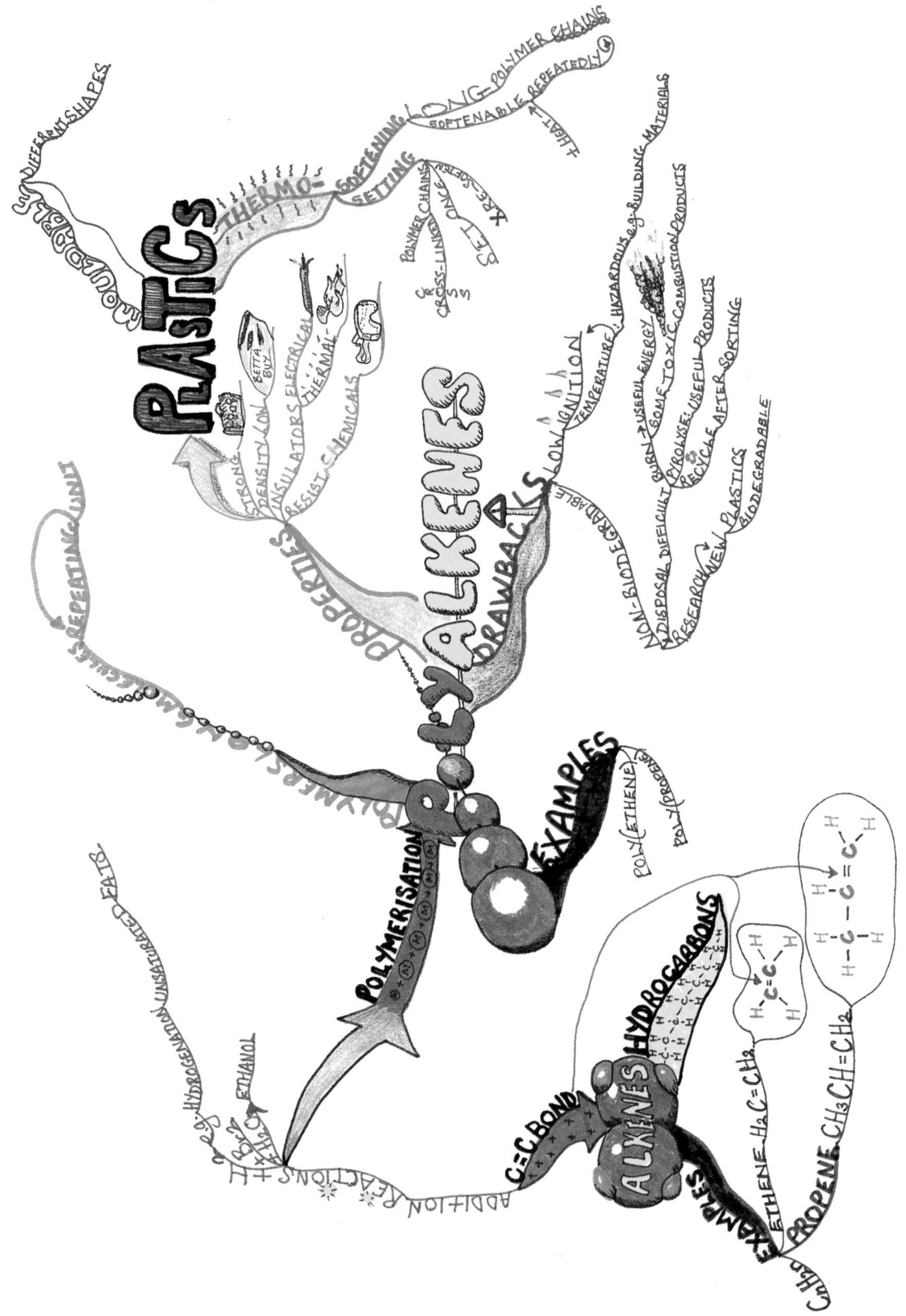

Agricultural chemicals (Topic 17)

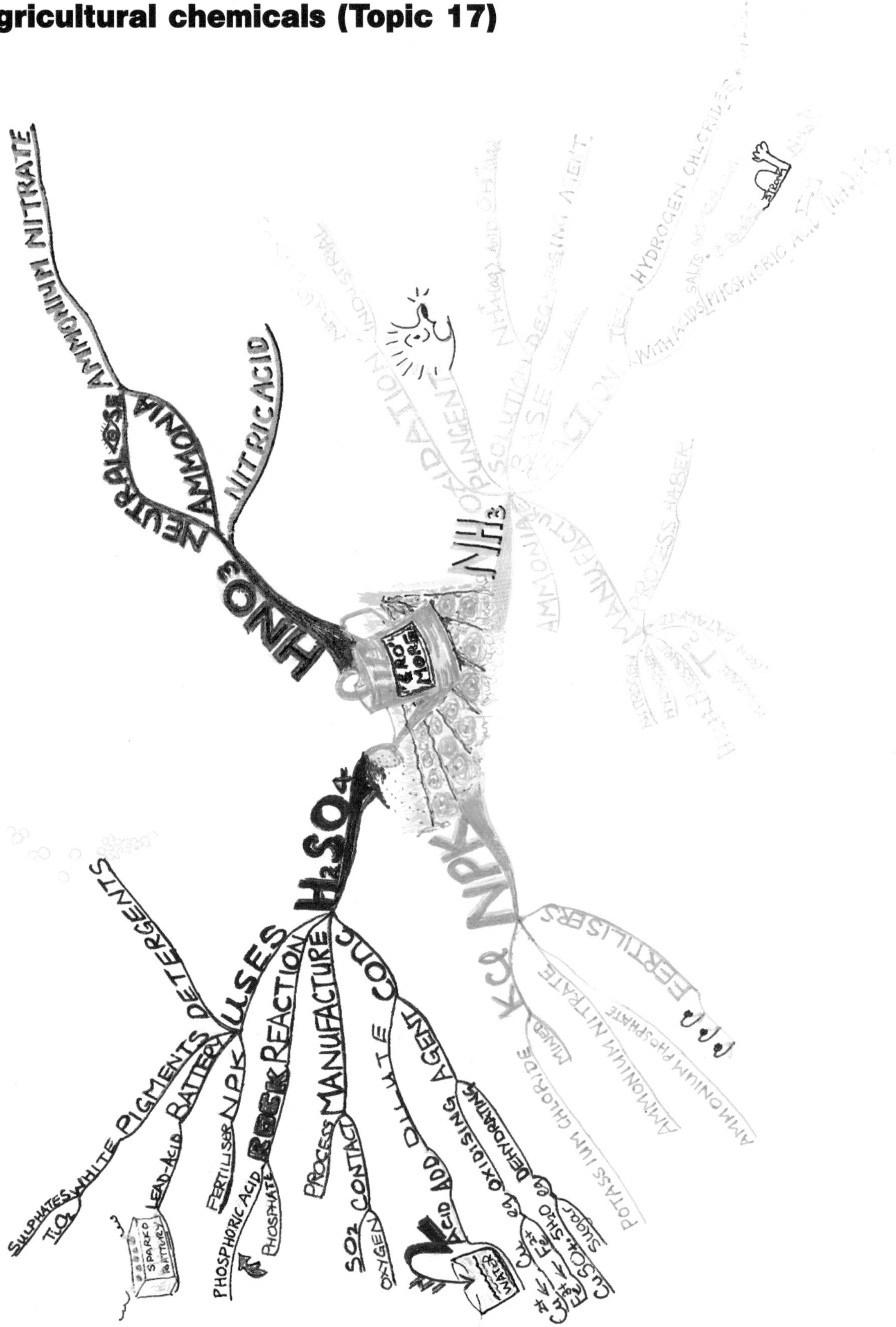

HNO_3
NEUTRALISE
AMMONIA
NITRIC ACID
AMMONIUM NITRATE

H_2SO_4
USES
DETERGENTS
PIGMENTS
WHITE
TiO_2
SULPHATES
BATTERY
LEAD-ACID
NPK
FERTILISER
PHOSPHORIC ACID
ROCK REACTION
PHOSPHATE
MANUFACTURE
PROCESS
CONTACT
SO_2
OXYGEN
DILUTE
ACID ADD
AGENT
OXIDISING
DEHYDRATING
SUGAR

NH_3
OXIDATION
PUNGENT
SOLUTION
BASE
REACTION
MANUFACTURE
AMMONIA
PROCESS HABER

NPK
K
FERTILISERS
MIXED
POTASSIUM CHLORIDE
AMMONIUM NITRATE
AMMONIUM PHOSPHATE

Alcohols, acids and esters (Topic 18)

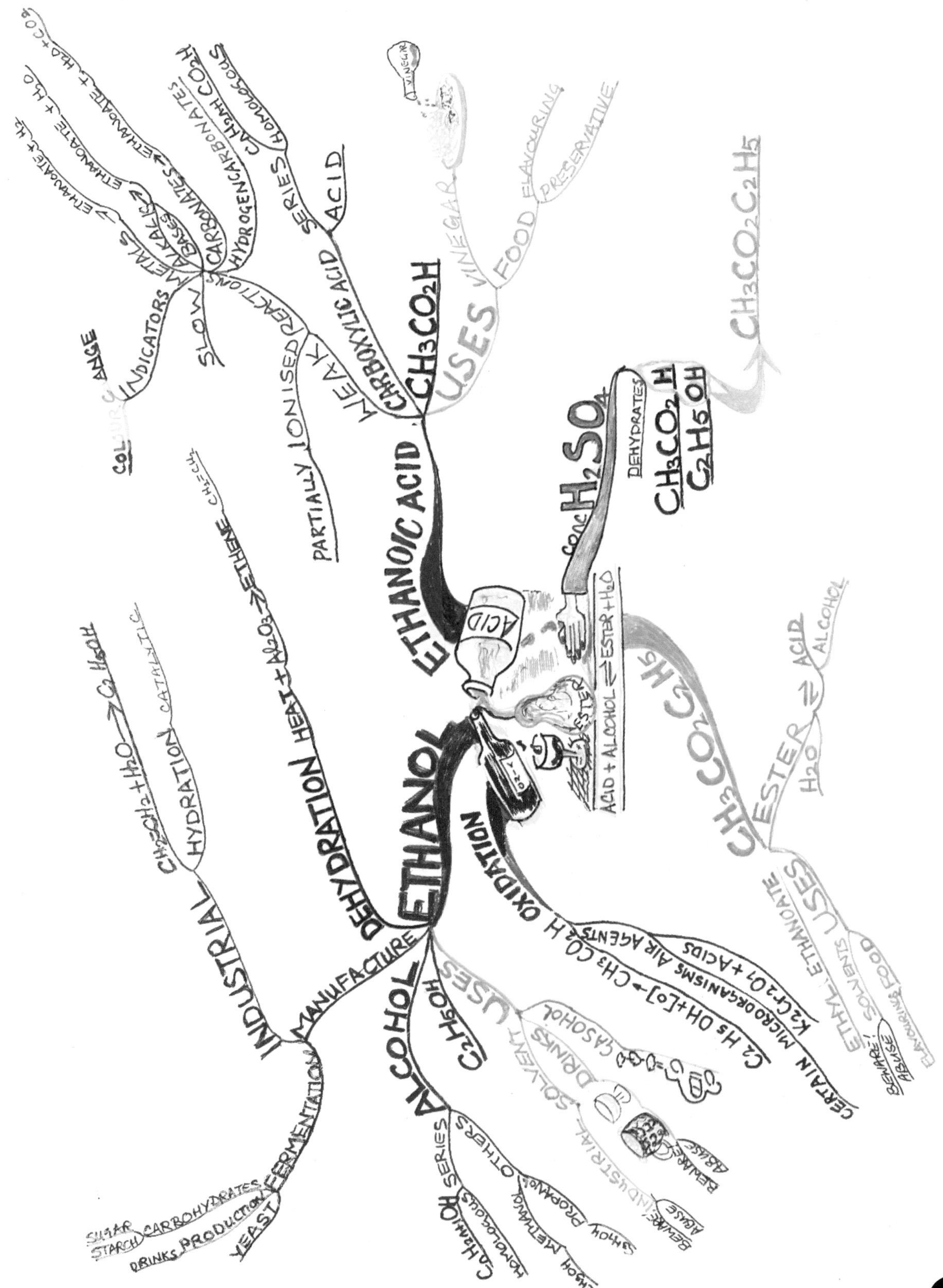

Index

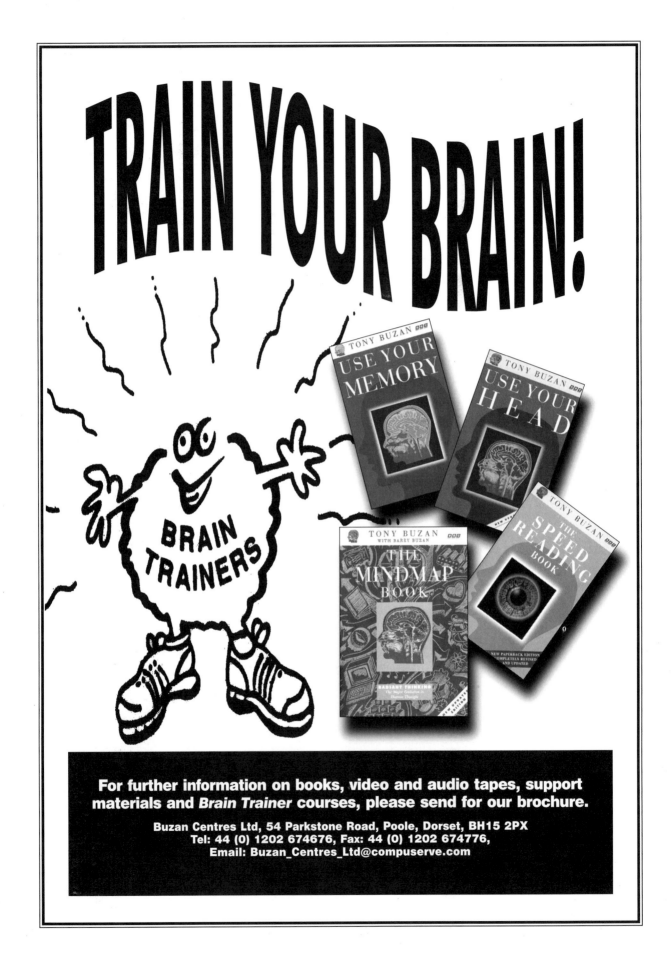